THE CERTIFIED QUALITY
TECHNICIAN HANDBOOK

Also available from ASQ Quality Press:

The Certified Quality Inspector Handbook, Third Edition
H. Fred Walker, Ahmad K. Elshennawy, Bhisham C. Gupta, and Mary McShane-Vaughn

The Certified Quality Engineer Handbook, Fourth Edition
Sarah E. Burke and Rachel T. Silvestrini

The Certified Reliability Engineer Handbook, Third Edition
Mark Allen Durivage

The ASQ CQE Study Guide
Connie M. Borror and Sarah E. Burke

The Certified Manager of Quality/Organizational Excellence Handbook, Fourth Edition
Russell T. Westcott, editor

The Certified Six Sigma Black Belt Handbook, Third Edition
T.M. Kubiak and Donald W. Benbow

The Certified Six Sigma Yellow Belt Handbook
Govindarajan Ramu

The Certified Six Sigma Green Belt Handbook, Second Edition
Roderick A. Munro, Govindarajan Ramu, and Daniel J. Zrymiak

Practical Engineering, Process, and Reliability Statistics
Mark Allen Durivage

Practical Attribute and Variable Measurement Systems Analysis (MSA): A Guide for Conducting Gage R&R Studies and Test Method Validations
Mark Allen Durivage

The Quality Toolbox, Second Edition
Nancy R. Tague

Root Cause Analysis: Simplified Tools and Techniques, Second Edition
Bjørn Andersen and Tom Fagerhaug

To request a complimentary catalog of ASQ Quality Press publications, call 800-248-1946, or visit our Web site at http://www.asq.org/quality-press.

THE CERTIFIED QUALITY TECHNICIAN HANDBOOK

Third Edition

H. Fred Walker, Donald W. Benbow,
and Ahmad K. Elshennawy

ASQ Quality Press
Milwaukee, Wisconsin

American Society for Quality, Quality Press, Milwaukee, WI 53203
© 2019 by ASQ.
All rights reserved. Published 2018.
Printed in the United States of America.

23 22 21 20 19 18   5 4 3 2 1

Library of Congress Cataloging-in-Publication Data

Names: Walker, H. Fred, 1963- author. | Benbow, Donald W., 1936- author. |
  Elshennawy, Ahmad K., author.
Title: The certified quality technician handbook / H. Fred Walker, Donald W.
  Benbow, and Ahmad K. Elshennawy.
Description: Third edition. | Milwaukee, Wisconsin: ASQ Quality Press, 2018.
Identifiers: LCCN 2018043193 | ISBN 9780873899765 (hardcover: alk. paper)
Subjects: LCSH: Production management—Quality control.
Classification: LCC TS156 .W27 2018 | DDC 658.5—dc23
LC record available at https://lccn.loc.gov/2018043193

Director, Quality Press and Programs: Ray Zielke
Managing Editor: Paul Daniel O'Mara
Sr. Creative Services Specialist: Randy L. Benson

ASQ Mission: The American Society for Quality advances individual, organizational,
and community excellence worldwide through learning, quality improvement, and
knowledge exchange.

Attention Bookstores, Wholesalers, Schools, and Corporations: ASQ Quality Press books,
video, audio, and software are available at quantity discounts with bulk purchases for
business, educational, or instructional use. For information, please contact ASQ Quality Press
at 800-248-1946, or write to ASQ Quality Press, P.O. Box 3005, Milwaukee, WI 53201-3005.

To place orders or to request ASQ membership information, call 800-248-1946. Visit our
Web site at www.asq.org/quality-press.

∞ Printed on acid-free paper

Quality Press
600 N. Plankinton Ave.
Milwaukee, WI 53203-2914
E-mail: authors@asq.org
The Global Voice of Quality®

Table of Contents

List of Figures and Tables. . . . . *ix*

Preface . . . . *xv*

Chapter 1 I. Quality Concepts and Tools. 1

A. Quality Concepts. 1

   1. Customers and Suppliers 1

   2. Quality Principles for Products and Processes. 2

   3. Quality Standards, Requirements, and Specifications 5

   4. Cost of Quality (COQ) 6

B. Quality Tools 8

   Cause-and-Effects Diagrams 8

   Flowcharts (Process Maps). 10

   Check Sheets. 11

   Pareto Charts 13

   Scatter Diagrams 15

   Control Charts 16

   Histograms 20

  8. Problem Solving Techniques 22

   Five Whys 22

   8D (Eight Disciplines) 24

  9. Six Sigma 36

   Design of Experiments 39

   Main Effects 42

   Interactions 43

   Fractional Factorial Designs. 44

   DMAIC 46

  10. Lean. 49

   Kanban 51

   Pull Systems 52

   5S 52

   Flow 53

   Value Stream Maps 54

  11. Continuous Improvement Techniques. 54

   The Plan-Do-Check-Act (PDCA) Cycle. 55

   Brainstorming 56

   Benchmarking 57

C. ASQ Code of Ethics for Professional Conduct   57
    The ASQ Code of Ethics   57
    Ethical Dilemmas.   58
Chapter Summary.   59

Chapter 2   II. Statistical Techniques **61**
A. General Concepts   61
    1. Terminology   61
    2. Frequency Distributions.   62
B. Calculations   69
    1. Measures of Central Tendency   69
    2. Measures of Dispersion   71
    3. Confidence Levels   73
    4. Confidence Limits   74
    5. Probability   75
C. Control Charts   82
    1. Control Limits vs. Specification Limits   82
    2. Variables Charts.   83
    3. Attributes Charts.   88
    4. Process Capability Measures.   92
    5. Common and Special Cause Variation.   94
    6. Data Plotting   97

Chapter 3   III. Metrology and Calibration **101**
A. Types of Measurement and Test Equipment (M&TE)   101
    Concepts in Measurements   103
    1. Hand Tools   105
    2. Gauges   112
    3. Optical Tools   123
    4. Coordinate Measuring Machines   124
    5. Electronic Measuring Equipment   133
    6. Weights, Balances, and Scales   137
    7. Hardness Testing Equipment   138
    8. Surface Plate Methods and Equipment   139
    9. Surface Analyzers   142
    Roughness Reference Standards   143
    10. Force Measurement Tools.   146
    11. Angle Measurement Tools   146
    12. Color Measurement Tools   148
    13. Automated in-line inspection methods   148
    Summary of Gauge Uses and Applications   148
B. Control and Maintenance of M&TE   150
    1. M&TE Identification, Control, and Maintenance   150
    2. Customer-Supplied M&TE.   151
C. Calibration of M&TE.   152
    Gauge Repeatability and Reproducibility   152
    Calibration Systems.   153
    1. Calibration Intervals   153
    2. Calibration Results   155

3. Calibration Error 156
4. Hierarchy of Standards. 157

Chapter 4   IV. Inspection and Test. **161**
A. Blueprint Reading and Interpretation 161
1. Blueprint Symbols and Components 161
2. Geometric Dimensioning and Tolerancing (GD&T) Terminology. 162
3. Classification of Product Defect Characteristics 166
B. Inspection Concepts 167
Uses of Inspection 167
1. Types of Measurements 168
2. Gauge Selection 169
3. Measurement Systems Analysis (MSA) 171
4. Rounding Rules 174
5. Conversion of Measurements 175
6. Inspection Points 176
7. Inspection Error 178
8. Product Traceability 179
9. Certificates of Compliance (COC) and Analysis (COA). 179
C. Inspection Techniques and Processes 180
1. Nondestructive Testing (NDT) Techniques. 181
2. Destructive Testing Techniques 182
3. Other Testing Techniques 183
D. Sampling. 184
1. Sampling Characteristics 184
2. Sampling Types 186
3. Selecting Samples from Lots 190
E. Nonconforming Material 194
1. Identifying and Segregating 194
2. Material Review Process 195

Chapter 5   V. Quality Audits. **199**
A. Audit Types and Terminology 199
Source of Auditors. 201
Audit Types. 202
B. Audit Components 202
Purpose/Scope. 203
Preparation 203
Performance 205
Documentation. 207
Closure 207
C. Audit Tools and Techniques 207
Checklists 208
Audit Working Papers. 209
Quantitative Quality Tools. 210
Objective Evidence 211
Forward and Backward Tracing 211
Audit Sampling Plans 211
Procedural Guidelines 212

D. Audit Communication Tools 213
    Interviewing Techniques 213
    Listening Skills... 215

Chapter 6   VI. Risk Management.. 217
A. Risk Assessment and Management 218
    Selecting a Standard for FMEA................................. 219
    Planning for an FMEA 219
    Establishing a Single Point of Responsibility 220
    FMEA Team Members 220
    Inputs to an FMEA 221
    FMEA and Other Quality Tools 221
    Outputs from an FMEA 221
    Basic Steps in an FMEA 222
    Qauntifying the Risk Associated with Each Potential Failure.......... 223
    Risk Components... 223
    Taking Action Based on an RPN................................ 223
    Do We Rate the Failure Mode or the Cause?...................... 224
    Types of FMEAs... 225
    Design and Process FMEA...................................... 226
    A Final Word on Taking Corrective Action........................ 233
    A Caution About Using FMEA 234
    Design and Process FMEA Examples............................. 234
  Investigation of Root Causes...................................... 237
B. Corrective Action 238
C. Preventive Action 242
  Nonconforming Material Identification 245
    Determining Conformance Status 246
    Identifying Nonconforming Materials............................ 246
    Segregating Nonconforming Materials 246
  Nonconforming Material Review Process 246

Appendix A   ASQ Certified Quality Technician (CQT) Body of Knowledge ... 249

Appendix B   Areas under Standard Normal Curve 257

Appendix C   Control Limit Formulas.................................... 259

Appendix D   Constants for Control Charts............................... 260

Appendix E   Standard Normal Distribution for Select Values of Z 261

Glossary... 263
References 279
Index 283

List of Figures and Tables

Table 1.1	Supplier–customer relationship examples.	2
Table 1.2	Examples of standards	6
Figure 1.1a	Cause-and-effects diagram with the six Ms	9
Figure 1.1b	Completed cause-and-effects diagram.	9
Figure 1.2	Flowchart for a steel forming process	10
Figure 1.3	Flowchart for an invoicing process.	10
Figure 1.4	Flowchart for calculating a weekly paycheck	11
Figure 1.5	Defects check sheet	12
Figure 1.6	A time-related check sheet.	12
Figure 1.7	Check sheet showing points of internal porosity	12
Figure 1.8	Pareto chart of power outage causes	13
Figure 1.9	Pareto chart using revised categories.	14
Table 1.3	Data for Injection molding scatter diagram example.	15
Figure 1.10	Scatter diagrams of variables In Injection molding operation.	16
Figure 1.11	Example of a run chart	17
Figure 1.12	Example of an averages chart	17
Figure 1.13	Example of an averages and range chart	18
Figure 1.14	Example of an $\overline{X}$ and R chart	19
Figure 1.15	Making a tally column	20
Figure 1.16	Frequency distribution and frequency histogram	21
Figure 1.17	Frequency distribution and frequency histogram for grouped data	21
Example 1.1	Five Whys analysis	22
Example 1.2	Five Whys analysis for failed error detection	24
Figure 1.18	Example of an 8D document	28

Example 1.3   The use of 8D documentation form   29

Figure 1.19   Example of an 8D form at the beginning of team activity   29

Figure 1.20   Example of a partial 8D form.   31

Figure 1.21   Final report form for the logistics problem   32

Example 1.4   Medical application of 8D.   33

Figure 1.22   Example of a medication list   33

Figure 1.23   First three steps for the medication error team.   34

Figure 1.24   Cause-and-effects diagram for medication errors   34

Figure 1.25   Sections D4 and D5 of the medication team's report   35

Figure 1.26   Map of the entries for the QFD matrix illustrated
in Figure 1.27   37

Figure 1.27   Example of a QFD matrix for an animal trap   38

Figure 1.28   Example of a data collection sheet   39

Figure 1.29   Data collection sheet with data entered   40

Figure 1.30   Data collection sheet with averages   41

Figure 1.31   Graph illustrating experimental error   41

Figure 1.32   Data collected after reducing noise factors   42

Figure 1.33   Displays the experimental error for the data in Figure 1.32   42

Figure 1.34   Illustrations of interactions   44

Figure 1.35   Half fraction of 2^3 (also called a 2^{3-1} design).   45

Figure 1.36   Interactions for the fractional factorial design in Figure 1.35 . . .   46

Example 1.5   Refining a problem definition   47

Figure 1.37   Example of a CTQ flow-down diagram   50

Example 1.6   A simple kanban system.   51

Example 1.7   An idealized pull system   52

Example 1.8   Batch-and-queue process versus one-piece flow   53

Figure 1.38   Example of a small value stream map   54

Figure 1.39   The PDCA cycle   56

Table 2.1   Parameters versus statistics   62

Figure 2.1   Histograms of error values.   63

Figure 2.2   Normal curve   63

Figure 2.3   Area under the standard normal curve between
$z = 0$ and $z = 1$.   65

Figure 2.4   Area under the standard normal curve between
$z = -2$ and $z = 1$ 65

Figure 2.5   Area under a normal curve between 0.750 and 0.754   66

Figure 2.6   Binomial distribution with $n = 10$ and $p = .20$ 67

Figure 2.7   Standard deviation calculation   72

Table 2.2   Confidence levels versus confidence coefficients   74

Figure 2.8   Example of an $\overline{X}$ and R chart   84

Figure 2.9   Control chart indicators of process change   84

Figure 2.10   Example of median control chart   86

Figure 2.11   Example of individuals and moving range (I-MR)
               control chart   87

Figure 2.12   Example of a p control chart   89

Figure 2.13   Example of an np control chart   90

Figure 2.14   Example of a u control chart   91

Figure 2.15   Point outside control limit   95

Figure 2.16   Seven successive points trending downward   96

Figure 2.17   Seven successive points on one side of the process average   96

Figure 2.18   Fewer than 40% of the points in the middle third of the
               chart after plotting at least 25 points   96

Figure 2.19   More than 90% of the points in the middle third of the
               chart after plotting at least 25 points   97

Figure 2.20   Nonrandom pattern.   97

Figure 2.21   Examples of analyzing plots visually   98

Figure 2.22   Two plots of the same data giving different impressions
               of the change   99

Figure 2.23   The effect of histogram group size   99

Figure 3.1   Standard measuring instruments including steel rules (A–D),
               spring caliper (F), micrometer depth gauges (G, H, J), depth
               rule (I), vernier caliper (K), vernier height gauge (L), inside
               micrometer (M), combination set (N), and surface gauge (O) . . .   106

Figure 3.2   Fine-adjustment style vernier caliper   107

Figure 3.3   LCD digital-reading caliper with 0–152 mm (0–6 in) range   108

Figure 3.4   Digital-reading, single-axis height gauge for
               two-dimensional measurements   109

Figure 3.5   A 0–25 mm micrometer caliper.   109

Figure 3.6   Micrometer reading of 10.66 mm.   110

Figure 3.7   Scales of a vernier micrometer showing a reading of
               10.666 mm   111

Figure 3.8   A digital micrometer   111

Figure 3.9   An indicating micrometer   112

Figure 3.10   Examples of typical gauges   114

Figure 3.11   Typical flush pin gauge for gauging the depth of a hole   119

Figure 3.12   Methods of assigning gauge tolerances   120

Figure 3.13   Specifications on working and inspection limit plug gauges . . .   120

Figure 3.14   Simple dial indicator mechanism   121

Figure 3.15   An application of dial indicators for inspecting flatness
by placing the workpiece on gauge blocks and checking full
indicator movement (FIM)   122

Figure 3.16   Optical comparator system   124

Figure 3.17   Horizontal optical comparator with a 356 mm (14 in) viewing
screen, digital readout, and edge-sensing device   125

Figure 3.18   Coordinate measuring machine classifications   128

Figure 3.19   Typical moving bridge coordinate measuring machine
configuration   130

Figure 3.20   Coordinate measuring machine   131

Figure 3.21   Manual indexable probe   132

Figure 3.22   A multisensor coordinate measuring machine with optical,
laser, and touch probes for noncontact and contact
measurements   133

Figure 3.23   Elements of electronic gauges   134

Figure 3.24   Diagrams of air gauge principles   136

Figure 3.25   Application of a granite surface plate for checking the flatness
of a part with a dial indicator and leveling screws   139

Figure 3.26   (A) Typical surface highly magnified; (B) profile of surface
roughness; (C) surface quality specifications   141

Figure 3.27   (A) Skid-type or average surface-finish measuring gauge;
(B) skidless, or profiling, gauge   143

Figure 3.28   (A) Light-wave interference with an optical flat; (B) application
of an optical flat; (C) diagram of an interferometer   145

Figure 3.29   Application of a sine bar   147

Table 3.1   Summary of commonly used gauges and their applications . . .   148

Figure 3.30   The calibration system   154

Figure 3.31   Calibration standards hierarchy   158

Figure 4.1	Some geometric tolerancing symbols	163
Figure 4.2	Illustration of geometric tolerances on a drawing	163
Figure 4.3	Part drawing with and without tolerances of form	164
Figure 4.4	Two parts dimensioned with positional tolerances	164
Example 4.1	Gauge Repeatability and Reproducibility (GR&R)	172
Table 4.1	Guidelines for conversion between metric and English units	175
Figure 4.5	An operating characteristic (OC) curve	185
Figure 4.6	Average outgoing quality curve for $n = 50$, $c = 3$	189
Figure 4.7	Switching rules for normal, tightened, and reduced inspection	192
Figure 4.8	Structure and organization of ANSI/ASQ Z1.9-2008	193
Figure 5.1	Relationships between audit types	201
Figure 5.2	Audit planning checklist	209
Figure 5.3	Audit completion checklist	210
Figure 5.4	Audit guideline and checklist hierarchy	213
Figure 6.1	Blank design FMEA form	227
Figure 6.2	Blank process FMEA form	228
Table 6.1	Design FMEA severity criteria	230
Table 6.2	Process FMEA severity criteria	230
Table 6.3	Design FMEA occurrence criteria	231
Table 6.4	Process FMEA occurrence criteria	232
Table 6.5	Design FMEA detection criteria	232
Table 6.6	Process FMEA detection criteria	233
Figure 6.3	Design FMEA example	235
Figure 6.4	Process FMEA example	236
Figure 6.5	The corrective action process	239
Table 6.7	Tools and techniques used to support the CAP process (non-exhaustive)	240
Figure 6.6	Ketola and Roberts corrective action process (K&R CAP)	241
Figure 6.7	A graphical representation of the preventive action process	243
Table 6.8	Tools and techniques used to support the PAP process (non-exhaustive)	244
Figure 6.8	Ketola and Roberts preventive action process (K&R PAP)	245

Preface

The quality technician is a person responsible for understanding and utilizing quality concepts and tools; statistical techniques; metrology and calibration procedures and protocols; inspection and test techniques; quality auditing; and preventive and corrective action in the context of product/process/service improvement or in correcting problems. Quality technicians frequently work in the quality function of organizations in the various measurement and inspection laboratories, as well as on the shop floor supporting and interacting with quality engineers, mechanical inspectors, and production/service delivery personnel. This book, *The Certified Quality Technician Handbook* (CQTH), was commissioned by the American Society for Quality (ASQ) to support individuals preparing for, or those already performing, this type of work.

The CQTH is intended to serve as a ready reference for quality technicians and quality technicians-in-training, as well as a comprehensive reference for those individuals preparing to take the ASQ Certified Quality Technician (CQT) examination. Examples and problems used throughout the handbook are thoroughly explained, are algebra-based, and are drawn from "real-world" situations encountered in the quality profession.

To assist readers in using the book as a ready reference or as a study aid, the book has been organized to conform closely to the CQT Body of Knowledge (BoK).

Chapter 1

I. Quality Concepts and Tools

A. QUALITY CONCEPTS

1. Customers and Suppliers

> Define internal and external customers,
> identify their expectations, and determine
> their satisfaction levels. Define internal
> and external suppliers and key elements of
> relations with them. (Understand)
>
> **Body of Knowledge I.A.1**

Organizations of all types and sizes have come to realize that their main focus must be to satisfy their customers. This applies to industrial firms, retail and wholesale businesses, governmental bodies, service companies, nonprofit organizations, and every subgroup within an organization. Two important questions arise:

1. Who are the customers?

2. What does it take to satisfy them?

Who Are the Customers and Who Are the Suppliers? *Customers* include anyone to whom the organization supplies products or services. Table 1.1 illustrates some supplier–customer relationships. Note that many organizations are simultaneously customers and suppliers.

It is conventional to think of customers as being outside the organization. These are referred to as *external* customers as illustrated in lines 1–8 of Table 1.1. Lines 9–11 of the table illustrate the concept of *internal* customers and suppliers. Our internal customers are the people within the organization that receive products or services from us. A similar statement can be made regarding internal suppliers.

What Does It Take to Satisfy Customers? It is important that an organization not assume that it knows what the customer wants. There are many examples of errors in this area, such as software that isn't updated to meet current market

1

expectations, and car models that don't sell. Many organizations exert considerable effort determining the "voice" of the customer. Tools such as consumer surveys, focus groups, and polling are often used. Satisfying the customer includes providing what is needed when it is needed. In many situations, it is up to the customer to provide the supplier with requirements. For example, the payroll department, as customer in Table 1.1, should inform other departments as to the exact format for reporting number of hours worked. If the payroll department does not do this job properly, they must bear some responsibility for the variation in reporting that will occur.

There is some merit to more than merely meeting specifications in the purchase order or contract. An example might be a purchase order that specifies 1.000 ± 0.005 being fulfilled with parts that are all within ± 0.002. Another example is a report that is submitted earlier than the contracted due date. The supplier that regularly exceeds customer expectations will be remembered.

Table 1.1   Supplier–customer relationship examples.

Supplier	Customer	Product or Service
1. Automobile manufacturer	Individual consumers	Cars
2. Automobile manufacturer	Car dealer	Sales literature, and so on
3. Bank	Checking account holders	Secure check handling
4. High school	Students and parents	Education
5. County recorder	Residents of county	Maintenance of records
6. Hospital	Patients	Healthcare
7. Hospital	Insurance company	Data on patients
8. Insurance company	Hospital	Payment for services
9. Steel shear department	Punch press department	Steel sheets
10. Punch press department	Spot weld department	Shaped parts
11. All departments	Payroll department	Data on hours worked, and so on

2. Quality Principles for Products and Processes

Identify basic quality principles related to products (such as features, fitness-for-use, freedom from defects) and processes (such as monitoring, measuring, continuous improvement). (Understand)

Body of Knowledge I.A.2

All customers want their needs met consistently. Almost all products or services perform exactly right some of the time. The reason they don't perform exactly right all the time is because things change. What things change? The short answer is that almost everything involving the production and use of the product or service changes. A more elaborate answer might include raw materials, worker morale, process parameters, customer expectations, conditions of use, employee abilities, machine wear, legal restrictions, the economy, the weather, and so on. How does the quality professional cope with this vast amount of variation? Three important steps are:

1. Understand variation and its effect on performance.

2. Reduce variation where possible.

3. Design the product or service to perform consistently in the presence of variation.

Much of the content of this book relates in some way to these three activities.

Features, Fitness-for-Use, Freedom from Defects. The most successful companies are those that have developed a strong communication tie with their customers. For example, this would help a company know how a customer's product is assembled and how their component fits into it. This would permit the supplying company to do a better job of emphasizing the critical features and characteristics that make the product fit for the customer to use. It also helps when the supplier understands the effect of defective products on the customer's operations.

The ideal time to influence the performance of a product or service is the design stage. A system should be in place to assure that consideration is given to the variation that will be present in the production and use of the product or service. For example, if prototypes are built, some should be made from the full range of raw materials that will be specified. The prototypes should be exposed to the temperature, humidity, acidity, vibration, operator usage, and other circumstances that the product will encounter in practice. If a service is being designed, consideration should be given to variation in the service provider, the service recipient, and the environment in which the service is performed.

A thorough study of the impact of all these sources of variation will not happen automatically unless the design phase is carefully planned and controlled. Therefore, any quality policy should include provision for a system to do this. There are several tools available to aid in this effort, including:

1. *Design of experiments* (DOE). A body of organized procedures for generating knowledge about products and processes.

2. *Failure mode and effects analysis* (FMEA). Discussed in Chapter 6.

3. *Design for manufacture and assembly* (DFMA). Techniques that provide for design input from the manufacturing community.

Design changes present additional opportunities to ignore the effects of variation. Businesses are replete with examples of the law of unintended consequences. The automotive recalls that are later "re-recalled," the pharmaceuticals that are removed from the shelves, and the contract revisions that have to be revised are just a few examples. The design system should assure that proposed design changes are subjected to the same scrutiny with regard to variation as the original design.

If components or materials are purchased outside the organization, then the vigilance regarding design should be pushed upstream to the supplier. It is the customer's responsibility to verify that the supplier employs a system to assure that this happens.

Processes. The processes that produce a product are also vulnerable to influence by many sources of variation. These sources are often grouped into categories such as:

- Machines (for example, speed variation, wear-related variation, lubrication schedule, and so on)

- Workers (for example, skills, training, health, attitudes, and so on)

- Methods (for example, procedures and practices for operating the process)

- Materials (for example, variations in raw materials, catalysts, and so on)

- Measurement (for example, since the information about the process often results from measurement activity, variation in the measurement system can be misleading)

- Environment (for example, temperature, humidity, and so on; some authorities include the psychological environment of the workplace)

For a visual scheme for portraying these sources of variation, see the cause-and-effect diagrams in section B of this chapter.

A good product design system considers these sources during the design stage. Minor product design changes may result in significant reductions in process-related variation. For example, if maintaining cylindricity of deep holes is difficult, the product design should avoid specifying deep holes where possible. In addition to product design, the system for process design should include steps for reducing variation and its impact. These steps include understanding the capability of various processes and finding ways of increasing capability. Calculation of capability is discussed in Chapter 2, Section II.C.4.

Once product and process designs have been finalized and the process is running, it may be advisable to monitor it through the use of statistical process control or other quality tools. This technique helps pinpoint the time when the process becomes unstable, increasing the probability that the source of variation can be reduced. Control charts are discussed in detail in Section C of Chapter 2.

Every person in the organization must understand that continuous improvement is a significant part of his or her job. Envision a production line consisting of 40 people arranged along an overhead chain conveyor. Each of the 40 people has a red button that can be pushed when a problem is encountered. When a person pushes the button, the line stops and a response team made up of the group leaders and nearby workers help solve the problem. The clock on the wall is set at 12:00 at the start of each shift and only runs when the line is stopped. The number of minutes on the clock at the end of the shift is the number of minutes the line was stopped and also the number of minutes that problems were being solved. The company's philosophy is that the clock should have accrue at least 30 minutes on it during each shift; when the line is stopped, problems are being solved, and the process or product is better than it was the previous day. If everyone in an organization does something each day better than the way it was done the previous day, then the organization will continuously improve.

Needless to say, continuous improvement requires resources, and it may be necessary to consider several options in order to find those that are most cost-effective. Most authorities in the quality field feel that the typical organization could save dollars by investing more in defect prevention. This will usually save money otherwise spent on costs of failure such as warranty claims, rework, lost customer goodwill, and so on. For example, a company may be unwilling to invest a lot of money in improving a 20¢ brake part until it realizes that the failure of the part can cause thousands of dollars in liability. In other words, the cost accountants may price a good part at 20¢, but a bad one can cost much more than that.

3. Quality Standards, Requirements, and Specifications

Define and distinguish between national or international standards, customer requirements, and product or process specifications. (Understand)

Body of Knowledge I.A.3

The quality of the product or service that an organization provides is dependent on the organization's suppliers. For example, the consumer's satisfaction with an appliance is impacted by the quality of the drive motor. If the appliance manufacturer purchases the drive motors from another company, the appliance manufacturer must have a method of assuring that the motor manufacturer provides a quality product. This requires a good understanding of the entire supply chain.

Specifications. The first thing the appliance manufacturer would do in this situation is to produce specifications for the motor. These might include dimensions, horsepower, resistance to adverse environmental conditions, and so on. If the customer does not communicate appropriate requirements to the supplier, the customer must bear some of the responsibility for poor quality of the products.

Standards. Customer organizations realize that their suppliers must prove that they can produce a good product and that they have some sort of system in place to assure that the product quality and consistency will continue in future orders. For this reason, customers sometimes audit their suppliers' quality management systems. Suppliers often find their quality systems being audited by various customers, sometimes with different and conflicting requirements. The International Organization for Standardization (ISO) attempts to reduce some of the confusion by publishing a series of documents called standards. One of these specifies the elements of a quality management system, for instance. Other organizations, such as the American National Standards Institute (ANSI) and the American Society for Quality (ASQ), have cooperated in producing and publishing these standards. Companies can be certified as having met the standards by third-party registrars. Many customers recognize this certification and do not require further audit of the certified function. Examples of some standards are shown in Table 1.2. Copies of these and other standards are available through the American Society for Quality.

Table 1.2   Examples of standards.

Number	Contents
ANSI/ISO/ASQ 9000:2015	*Quality management systems—Fundamentals and vocabulary*
ANSI/ISO/ASQ 9001:2015	*Quality management systems—Requirements*
ANSI/ISO/ASQ Q9004:2018	*Quality management—Quality of an organization—Guidance to achieve sustained success*
ANSI/ISO/ASQ 14001:2015	*Environmental Management Systems—A Practical Guide for SMEs*
ANSI/ISO/ASQ 3534-1:2006	*Statistic—Vocabulary and symbols—Part 1: General statistical terms and terms used in probability*

4. Cost of Quality (COQ)

> Describe and distinguish between the four classic cost-of-quality categories (prevention, appraisal, internal failure, external failure) and classify activities appropriately. (Apply)
>
> **Body of Knowledge I.A.4**

The discussion in this section is partially excerpted from Principles of Quality Costs: Financial Measures for Strategic Implementation of Quality Management, *Fourth Edition, Douglas C. Wood, ed. Milwaukee: ASQ Quality Press, 2013.*

The four major categories for quality costs are:

1. *Prevention costs.* Those costs of all activities specifically designed to prevent poor quality in products or services. Examples are the costs of:
   - New product review
   - Quality planning

- Supplier capability surveys

- Process capability evaluations

- Quality improvement team meetings

- Quality improvement projects

- Quality education and training

2. *Appraisal costs.* The costs associated with measuring, evaluating, or auditing products or services to assure conformance to quality standards and performance requirements. Examples include:

  - Incoming and source inspection/test of purchased material

  - In-process and final inspection/test

  - Product, process, or service audits

  - Calibration of measuring and test equipment

  - Associated supplies and materials

3. *Internal failure costs.* The costs associated with product failure prior to delivery or shipment of a product, or the furnishing of a service, to the customer. Examples include:

  - Scrap

  - Rework

  - Reinspection

  - Retesting

  - Material review

  - Downgrading

4. *External failure costs.* The costs associated with failure that occurs after delivery to the customer. Examples include:

  - Customer complaints

  - Customer returns

  - Warranty claims

  - Product recalls

Total failure cost is the sum of the internal and external failure costs. There is a tendency to underestimate the true cost of failure because it involves loss of customer goodwill, market reputation, and morale of personnel. Most quality professionals believe that when organizations spend more on prevention, they reduce total quality costs because failure cost and, in most cases, appraisal costs are reduced.

Total Quality Costs. The sum of the four major categories of costs is the total quality cost. This represents the difference between the actual cost of a product or service and what the reduced cost would be if there were no possibility of substandard service, failure of products, or defects in their manufacture.

The ideal place to detect and prevent problems is at their source. Allowing a problem to occur and detecting it internally is perhaps ten times as expensive as the cost of preventing the problem in the first place. Furthermore, another multiple of ten should be added if the problem is detected by external customers.

Pitfalls to watch for when implementing COQ calculation:

- Data are collected but not analyzed and used effectively by management.

- Process and product design decisions do not include consideration of COQ.

- COQ efforts may move costs around between the various categories without reducing total COQ.

B. QUALITY TOOLS

> Select, construct, and interpret: 1) cause-and-effect diagrams, 2) flowcharts (process maps), 3) check sheets, 4) Pareto charts, 5) scatter diagrams, 6) control charts, and 7) histograms. (Evaluate)
>
> **Body of Knowledge I.B.1–7**

Cause-and-Effect Diagrams

Once defects or failures are identified, one of the most difficult and critical tasks in the entire enterprise begins, that of determining the root cause or causes. The fundamental tool for this purpose is the *cause-and-effect diagram*, also called the *fishbone* or *Ishikawa diagram*. This tool helps a team identify, explore, and communicate all the possible causes of the problem. It does this by dividing possible causes into broad categories that help stimulate inquiry as successive steps delve deeper. The general structure of the diagram, shown in Figure 1.1a, illustrates why it is sometimes called the fishbone diagram. Categories shown are sometimes referred to as the six Ms: methods, machines, measurement, material, manpower, and Mother Nature. The choice of categories or names for the main "bones" depends on the situation. Some alternatives might include policies, technology, tradition, legislation, and so on. Figure 1.1b shows a completed cause-and-effect diagram.

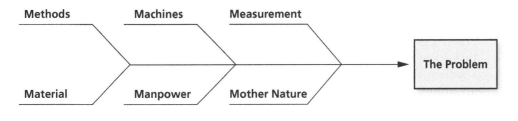

Figure 1.1a Cause-and-effects diagram with the six Ms.

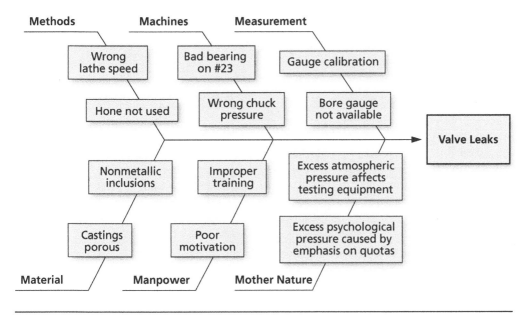

Figure 1.1b Completed cause-and-effects diagram.

A team may use a cause-and-effect diagram to generate a number of potential causes in each category by going around the room and asking each person to suggest one cause and its associated category. As each cause is selected, it is shown as a subtopic of the main category by attaching a smaller line to the main "bone" for that category. This activity continues until the group is satisfied that all possible causes have been listed. Individual team members can then be assigned to collect data on various branches or sub-branches for presentation at a future meeting. Ideally the data collection process should consist of changing the nature of the cause being investigated and observing the result. For example, if voltage variation is a suspected cause, put in a voltage regulator and see whether the number of defects changes. One advantage of this approach is that it forces the team to work on the causes and not symptoms, personal feelings, history, and various other baggage. An alternative to the meeting format is to have an online fishbone to which team members may post possible causes over a set period of time.

Flowcharts (Process Maps)

When a group first begins the job of process improvement, it is important that they have a good understanding of the various process steps and how they fit together. Various pictorial tools have been developed for this purpose, and they are grouped under the general heading of *process maps*. One example of a process map is the flowchart. It may be designed to show the flow of material, information, documentation, custody, cash, or some other quantity. The quality professional will probably encounter flowcharts showing successive steps in a process or service. Three simple examples of flowcharts are shown in Figures 1.2, 1.3, and 1.4. There is no universal set of symbols for flowcharts, but decision points are usually designated with diamond-shaped boxes as shown in Figure 1.4.

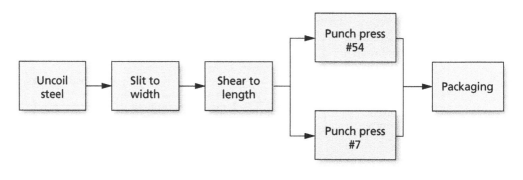

Figure 1.2   Flowchart for a steel forming process.

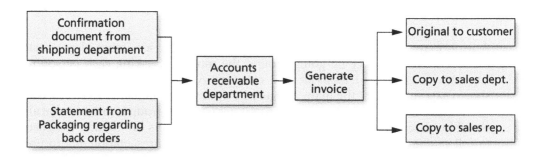

Figure 1.3   Flowchart for an invoicing process.

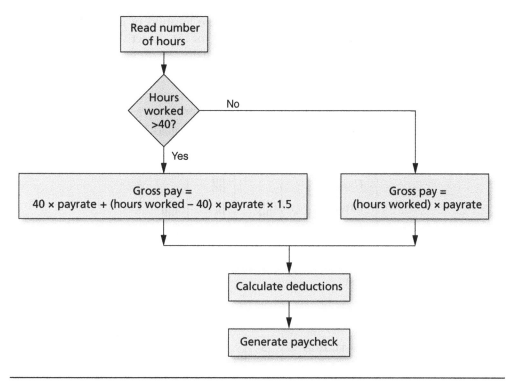

Figure 1.4 Flowchart for calculating a weekly paycheck.

Check Sheets

A *check sheet* is used to record the occurrence of defined events. The user is typically observing the events in real time but may be examining products or data produced earlier. As an event is observed, a tally mark is placed on the appropriate area on the sheet. Suppose a quality technician inspected a batch of finished products and recorded the observed defects as shown in Figure 1.5. The advantages of the check sheet in this case are:

- It emphasizes facts, not opinion. (In this example, it would help dispel the opinion that incomplete lenses are a big problem.)

- It may show groupings to be investigated. (In this case, why are most cracked covers black and all fogged lenses green?)

- Rows and columns can be added to obtain useful subtotals.

- It requires a valid definition of the various defects. (For example, exactly what is a fogged lens?)

Some check sheet categories are time related. An example is shown in Figure 1.6. Time-related check sheets sometimes show trends to be investigated. In this example, an interesting trend occurs in the "TV Guide missing" category. Something worth studying appears to have happened on July 8, also.

Another form of check sheet illustrates the location of items of interest. In Figure 1.7 internal porosity points are located for ten defective castings. This led to the discovery of a plugged coolant line in the die.

Line 12 Dec. 4, 2018	Lens color		
	Red	Green	Black
Cracked cover	||	|	||||||
Fogged		||||	
Pitted	||||	|||	|||||
Incomplete	|		|

Figure 1.5 Defects check sheet.

Deficiencies noted July 5–11, 2018	5	6	7	8	9	10	11
Towels incorrectly stacked				|||||			
Soap or shampoo missing	|||||||	|||||||		|||||			
TV Guide missing			||	|||	|||||	|||||||	|||||||	|
Mint missing from pillow	|			|	|||||		|
Toilet paper not folded into V				|	|||||		

Figure 1.6 A time-related check sheet.

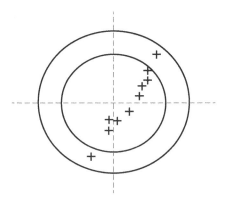

Figure 1.7 Check sheet showing points of internal porosity.

Pareto Charts

Process improvement teams may need help in prioritizing activities. The *Pareto chart* is a useful tool for this purpose. This diagram is based on the theory that the vast majority of problems are caused by a few sources. Suppose the following data have been collected on power outages:

Cause	Number of occurrences	% of occurrences
Human error	5	10
Capacitor failure	2	4
Animals	33	65
Transformer leaks	3	6
Weather	8	16
Total	51	101

A Pareto chart of this data would list the causes on the horizontal axis and the percent of occurrences on the vertical axis. The causes are listed in order of decreasing number of occurrences. The Pareto chart is shown in Figure 1.8.

The Pareto chart shows that the people working to reduce the number of occurrences should put their main efforts into preventing outages caused by animals. If they expended a lot of resources to prevent transformer leakage and were able to eliminate it completely as a cause of power outage, it would still solve only about six percent of the occurrences.

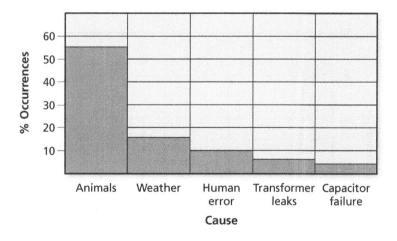

Figure 1.8 Pareto chart of power outage causes.

A Pareto chart often shows one source as the overwhelming cause of defects. However, in some cases it may be necessary to do some creative grouping to obtain a single cause that accounts for the bulk of the problem. Suppose a team is seeking to reduce the number of defective valve stems from a multi-stage machine operation. They gather the following data on the types of defects observed:

Type	%	Type	%
1. Scratched shaft	12	11. Surface finish	6
2. ID undersize	4	12. Porosity	1
3. ID oversize	6	13. Material hardness	2
4. Dented chamfer	7	14. Gouges in knob area	5
5. Length oversize	5	15. Nonconcentricity	3
6. Length undersize	8	16. Bent shaft	5
7. Nicks on shaft	7	17. Tapered shaft	4
8. OD oversize	3	18. Out of round	5
9. OD undersize	4	19. Abrasion on head	6
10. Scratched face	7	**Total**	**100**

The resulting Pareto chart would not exhibit a single defect type as the overwhelming cause. The team might look for grouping schemes that produce a single group with a large percentage. In this case, the team might find that *mishandling* accounts for all the defects in categories 1, 4, 7, 10, 14, and 19. Then, mishandling as a new defect type accounts for 44% of the defects, and the resulting Pareto chart is as illustrated in Figure 1.9.

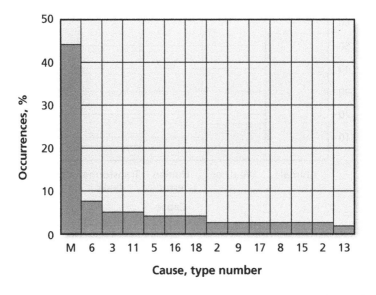

Figure 1.9   Pareto chart using revised categories.

Scatter Diagrams

When several causes for a problem have been proposed, it may be necessary to collect some data to help determine which are potential root causes. One way to view such data is with a *scatter diagram*. In this technique, measurements are taken for various levels of the variables suspected of being a cause. Then each variable is plotted against the measured value of the problem to get a rough idea of correlation or association.

Example: An injection molding machine is producing parts with pitted surfaces, and four possible causes have been suggested: mold pressure, coolant temperature, mold cooldown time, and mold squeeze time. Values of each of these variables as well as the quality of the surface finish were collected on 10 batches. The data are shown in Table 1.3.

Four graphs have been plotted in Figure 1.10. In each graph, *surface finish* is on the vertical axis. The first graph plots *mold pressure* against surface finish. Batch #1 has a mold pressure of 220 and a surface finish of 37. Therefore one dot is plotted at 220 in the horizontal direction and 37 in the vertical direction. On each graph, one point is plotted for each batch. If the points tend to fall along a straight line, this indicates there may be a linear correlation or association between the two variables. If the points tend to closely follow a curve rather than a straight line, there may be a nonlinear relationship. Note that a high correlation does not imply a cause-and-effect relationship. A low correlation, however, does provide evidence that there is no such relationship, at least in the range of values considered. What variables can be eliminated as probable causes based on the above analysis?

Table 1.3   Data for injection molding scatter diagram example.

Batch no.	Variables				Surface finish
	Mold pressure	Coolant temperature	Cooldown time	Squeeze time	
1	220	102.5	14.5	.72	37
2	200	100.8	16.0	.91	30
3	410	102.6	15.0	.90	40
4	350	101.5	16.2	.68	32
5	490	100.8	16.8	.85	27
6	360	101.4	14.8	.76	35
7	370	102.5	14.3	.94	43
8	330	99.8	16.5	.71	23
9	280	100.8	15.0	.65	32
10	400	101.2	16.6	.96	30

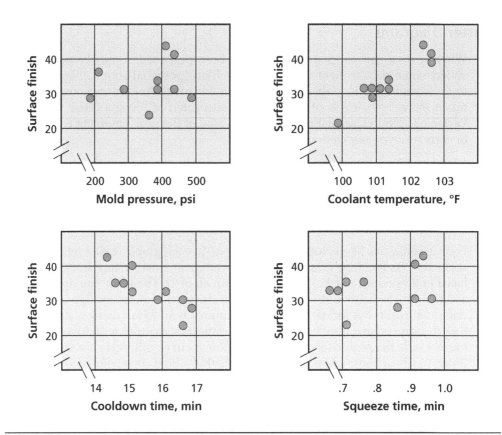

Figure 1.10 Scatter diagrams of variables in injection molding operation.

The closer the points are to forming a straight line, the greater the linear correlation coefficient, denoted by the letter r. A positive correlation is indicated when the line tips up on the right end. A negative correlation is indicated when the line tips down on its right end. If all the points fall exactly on a straight line that tips up on the right end, then $r = 1$. If all the points fall on a straight line that tips down on the right end, $r = -1$. In general, $-1 \leq r \leq 1$.

Control Charts

One of the disadvantages of many of the tools discussed up to this point is that they have no time reference. The chart may clearly demonstrate that a process had a problem but give no clue as to when the problem occurred. This section will illustrate a number of time-related techniques. The discussion will culminate with control charts.

The Run Chart. If a specific measurement is collected on a regular basis, say every 15 minutes, and plotted on a time scale, the resultant diagram is called a *run chart*. An example of a run chart is shown in Figure 1.11.

One of the problems of the run chart is that the natural variation in the process and in the measurement system tends to cause the graph to go up and down when no real change is occurring. One way to smooth out some of this "noise" in the process is to take readings from several consecutive parts and plot the average of the readings. The result is called an *averages chart*. An example is shown in Figure 1.12.

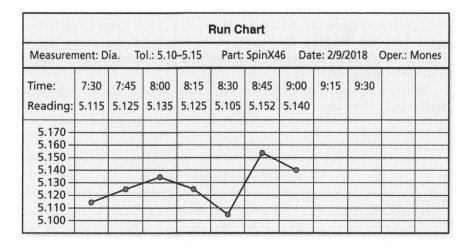

Figure 1.11   Example of a run chart.

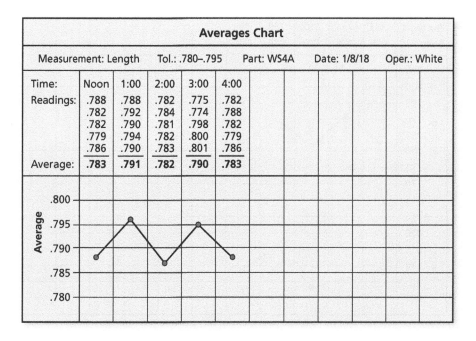

Figure 1.12   Example of an averages chart.

One of the dangers of the averages chart is that it can make the process look better than it really is. For example, note that the average of the five 3:00 p.m. readings is .790, which is well within the tolerance of .780–.795, even though every one of the five readings is outside the tolerance. Therefore, tolerance limits should never be drawn on an averages chart. To help alert the chart user that the readings are widely dispersed, the averages chart usually has a range chart included as part of the same document. The range for each set of points is found by subtracting the smallest number in the set from the largest number in the set. The data from Figure 1.12 are used in the averages and range chart illustrated in Figure 1.13. Note that the sharp jump in the value of the range for the 3:00 p.m. readings would warn the user of this chart that the dispersion of the readings has drastically increased.

None of the charts listed so far is a "control chart." The averages and range chart requires the user to notice when the range is "too high." The control chart that uses averages and ranges differs from this chart in that it has control limits

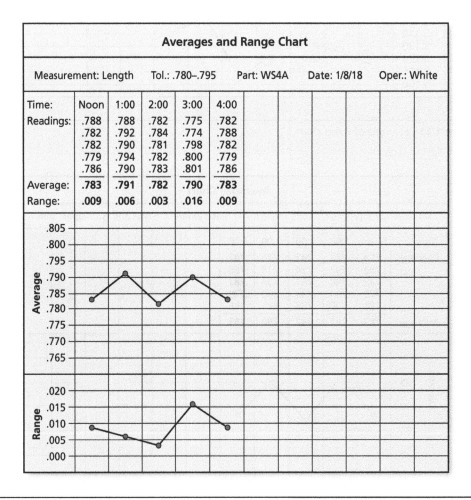

Figure 1.13   Example of an averages and range chart.

drawn on the chart. When a point falls outside these limits, the user is alerted that the process has changed and appropriate action should be taken.

The control chart using averages and ranges is called the X-bar and R ($\overline{X}$ and R) chart and is illustrated in Figure 1.14. The data used in Figure 1.14 are taken from Figure 1.13. It is conventional to draw the control limits with dashed lines or in a contrasting color. The average value is usually drawn with a solid line. Control limits help the user of the chart make statistically sound decisions about the process. This is because the limits are drawn so that a very high percentage of the points should fall between them. In the case of the averages chart, about 99.7% of the points from a stable process should fall between the upper and lower control limits. This means that when a point falls outside the limits, there is approximately 0.3% probability that this could have happened if the process hasn't changed. Therefore, points outside the control limits are very strong indicators that the process has changed. Control charts, then, can be used by process operators as real-time monitoring tools.

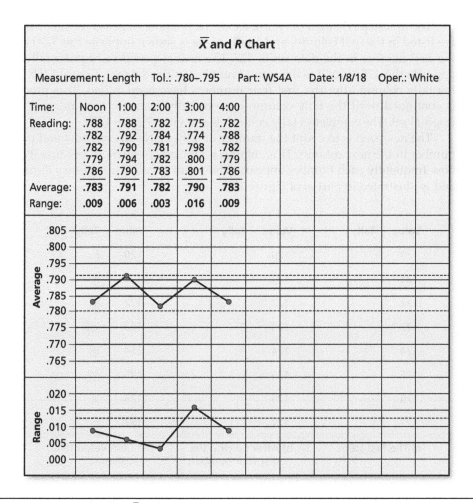

Figure 1.14 Example of an $\overline{X}$ and R chart.

Further details on the construction and use of various control charts are provided in Section C of Chapter 2.

Histograms

The following numbers were obtained by measuring the diameters of 27 drilled holes:

.127 .125 .123 .123 .120 .124 .126 .122 .123 .125 .121 .123 .122 .125
.124 .122 .123 .123 .126 .121 .124 .121 .124 .122 .126 .125 .123

What is known about the drilling process just by looking at the data? For one thing, the smallest diameter is .120 and the largest is .127. This gives an idea of the spread or "dispersion" of the data. The values seem to be centered around .123 or .124, which is related to the "central tendency" of the data. Sometimes it helps to make a diagram from the data. A good first step is to list the possible values from smallest to largest in a column. In the adjacent column a tally mark is made for each number in the original data set.

The first step is shown in Figure 1.15a. The possible values of the hole diameter are listed in the first column, and a tally mark is shown opposite the .127 because the first number in the data set is .127. The next step will be to put a tally mark opposite the .125 since it is the second number in the data set. Figure 1.15b shows the tally column after the first four numbers have been tallied. This procedure is continued until the tally column has one tally mark for each number in the original set. The completed tally column is shown in Figure 1.15c.

The next step is to count the number of tally marks in each row and put this number in the next column. This column is labeled "frequency" because it shows how frequently each number appears. The result is called a *frequency distribution* and is illustrated in part a) of Figure 1.16.

Value	Tally	Value	Tally	Value	Tally
.120		.120		.120	|
.121		.121		.121	|||
.122		.122		.122	||||
.123		.123	||	.123	|||||||
.124		.124		.124	||||
.125		.125	|	.125	||||
.126		.126		.126	|||
.127	|	.127	|	.127	|
a) The first step		b) After tallying the first four numbers		c) Completed tally column	

Figure 1.15   Making a tally column.

If a bar graph such as that shown in part b) of Figure 1.16 is drawn, the result is called a *histogram*, or more precisely, a *frequency histogram*. In this text, the vertical axis of a histogram displays the frequency and the horizontal axis represents measured values.

Suppose these data are to be displayed on a frequency histogram:

46, 65, 72, 108, 33, 70, 68, 51, 44, 110, 84, 52, 75, 106, 62, 90, 71, 86, 54, 98, 80, 73, 39, 101, 64, 59, 82, 87, 94, 57, 32, 61, 78, 38, 63, 49, 87, 63

If each bar represents just one value, most bars would have a frequency of zero or one, and there would be a very large number of bars. An alternative approach would be to group the data. One grouping scheme would have 10 possible values in each group. The first group could be 30–39 and the following groups 40–49, 50–59, and so on. The tally sheet, frequency distribution, and frequency histogram are shown in Figure 1.17.

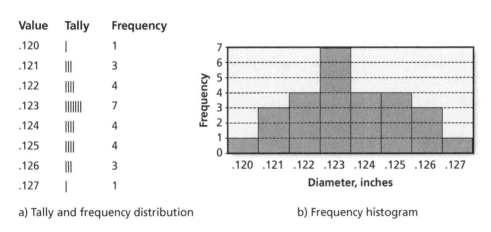

Value	Tally	Frequency
.120	|	1
.121	|||	3
.122	||||	4
.123	|||||||	7
.124	||||	4
.125	||||	4
.126	|||	3
.127	|	1

a) Tally and frequency distribution   b) Frequency histogram

Figure 1.16 Frequency distribution and frequency histogram.

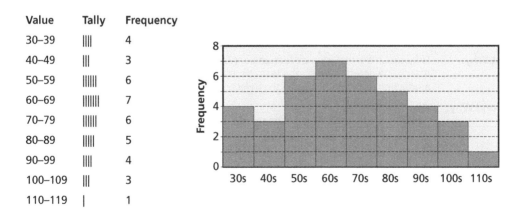

Value	Tally	Frequency
30–39	||||	4
40–49	|||	3
50–59	||||||	6
60–69	|||||||	7
70–79	||||||	6
80–89	|||||	5
90–99	||||	4
100–109	|||	3
110–119	|	1

Figure 1.17 Frequency distribution and frequency histogram for grouped data.

8. PROBLEM SOLVING TECHNIQUES

> Define, describe, and apply problem
> solving techniques such as Five Whys and
> 8D. (Apply)
>
> **Body of Knowledge I.B.8**

Problem solvers are a very important resource in any organization. These are the people who are able to creatively identify and remove barriers that keep the organization from accomplishing its mission. All personnel should understand that part of their job is to solve problems, to identify and overcome barriers to improvement. Some organizations find it useful to require periodic written reports detailing problems identified and progress toward their resolution.

Many problems can be solved by an individual working alone. Other problems require a group effort involving people with various skills and knowledge bases. The purpose of this section is to provide some methods for use in the problem solving process.

Five Whys

One of the hazards of team problem solving is the tendency to quit too soon. When the immediate cause of a problem is found it is tempting to terminate the search for underlying causes. The five whys tool helps the team dig deeper. Once an immediate cause is found, the team is challenged to consider that cause as an effect and ask why it occurred. When this cause is found, the team determines why this cause occurred, and so forth. Example 1.1 illustrates this process.

Example 1.1 Five Whys analysis.

Problem: Machine 209 produced a defective part.

First Why: *Why did 209 produce a defective part?*
After some detective work, the team discovers that the machine stopped during the production of the part, causing the defect.

Second Why: *Why did 209 stop?*
The team uses a fishbone diagram to help with this investigation and discovers that an internal thermal-switch cut off power to the drive motor.

Possible fixes:
1. Provide better ventilation for the switch
2. Re-wire the machine by-passing the switch
3. Reset the switch and keep rolling

This is, in fact, what is usually done, perhaps as part of a short-term containment measure. But obviously the team should not stop here. They should ask why a third time.

Example 1.1 Five Whys analysis *(continued).*

Third Why:	*Why did the thermal switch cut off power?*

Possible causes:
1. Faulty thermal switch
2. Incorrect setting on the thermal switch
3. Over-heating machine

The switch is found to be functional and properly set, so the team is ready to ask the fourth why.

Fourth Why:	*Why is the machine over-heating?*

Possible causes:
1. Fan not running correctly
2. Amperage exceeds rating
3. Filter clogged

The team finds that the amount of current to a motor exceeds the manufacturer's specification.

Fifth Why:	*Why is the machine drawing too much current?* The team reviews the machine specifications and discovers that the machine is being overloaded. This brings up the sixth why.
Sixth Why:	*Why is the machine being overloaded?* Further investigation shows that machine specifications are not consulted when determining machine loading.

The team reports that is has found the root cause and recommends that machine 209 specifications be consulted when determining its loading.

But the team should probe further. A new Five Whys analysis could be initiated where this one left off, digging into company policy.

The problem-solving team's principle mission is to determine the root cause and devise a corrective action so that the problem never re-occurs. However, if the error or defect gets to a customer, an additional task is to answer this question. "Why did our detection system fail to protect our customer from this problem?" A five whys approach is helpful, as shown in Example 1.2.

Example 1.1 Five Whys analysis *(continued).*

First Why:	*Why aren't machine specifications consulted when determining loading?* The team finds that the company has no policy on this matter.
Second Why:	*Why hasn't the company developed a policy on this?* Because machine overloading was not considered a failure mode when possible process failures were studied.
Third Why:	*Why wasn't machine overloading considered?*
Lesson Learned:	Machine overloading should be considered on all process failure mode and effects analysis studies.

Example 1.2   Five Whys analysis for failed error detection.

A farmer has returned a bag of seed corn because the label location for the hybrid number is blank.

First Why:	*Why did the blank label go undetected?*
	Because the sensor on the printing machine didn't catch it.
Second Why:	*Why didn't the sensor catch it?*
	Because it only looks for company name and date, it does not look for number.
Third Why:	*Why doesn't the sensor look for a number?*
	Because it wasn't programmed to look for the number.
Lesson Learned:	All printer error sensors should be re-programmed to look for a hybrid number.

8D (Eight Disciplines)

[Some of the following is excerpted from Introduction to 8D Problem Solving, *Ali Zarghami and Don Benbow, ASQ Quality Press, 2017.]*

8D analysis is used in much of the automotive industry. As has been observed in the past, automotive industry initiatives often migrate to other fields. The eight disciplines constitute an eight-step problem solving process. They are:

1. Use a team

2. Define and describe the problem

3. Develop interim containment plan; implement and verify interim actions

4. Determine, identify, and verify root causes and escape points

5. Choose and verify permanent corrections (PCs) for problem/nonconformity

6. Implement and validate corrective actions

7. Take preventative measures

8. Congratulate your team

There is some parallelism between the 8D steps and the DMAIC steps used by Six Sigma practitioners in that D2 is essentially the DMAIC Define step, D4 is similar to the DMAIC Analyze step, D5 and D6 are like the DMAIC Improve step, and D7 parallels the DMAIC Control step. The 8D objective is to define the problem, implement containment, correct and eliminate the concern, improve quality control systems, and document and report findings. It is important to note that the problem could be product or process related and the 8D process is well equipped to address both. The 8D approach to problem solving is highly structured and scientific. It should be noted that 8D does not offer much that is brand new as a problem solving tool. In practice, one thing that is new is the tendency for 8D activities to be initiated by a customer. Typically, a supplier receives a request for 8D action on a quality problem. The customer may require a report on Interim

Containment Action (D3) within a stated time interval. The supplier typically responds with information on how it will handle these scenarios:

- shipments already received by the customer (for example, the supplier will hire a third party to inspect material at the customer's site)

- shipments that are on the way to the customer (for example, the supplier will intercept the shipments and inspect them)

- product that is in-house at the supplier's site (for example, the supplier will quarantine product at its site and institute 100% inspection)

Individual steps of the 8D methodology are discussed in the following paragraphs.

D0 *Plan.* Of course, this is not one of the formal eight disciplines but it is an understood preceding requirement.

In this phase, a customer or internal management indicates they have a specific problem that needs to be addressed. At this time a Quality Alert is generated and vigorous containment effort is started to isolate the problem from the customer(s). Management will decide whether this problem is simple and can be handled by an individual, or whether it is significant enough to require an 8D problem-solving team.

The 8D effort requires significant time and resources, management support and time allocation, and team authorization, all of which are essential for the success of the team.

D1 *Use A Team.* Management is responsible for assembling a team that has the relevant knowledge and experience needed to address the issue. Management needs to allow time for the team to go through the four phases of team development—forming, norming, storming, and performing—to be effective. In some organizations a senior manager is assigned as champion for the team, to provide additional support and remove barriers.

It is very important that management assign a team leader for the project. It is recommended that the team leader be an experienced subject matter expert who has completed a few 8D projects. The team leader must have the authority to allocate time and acquire other resources needed for the team.

In manufacturing, the team members could be from production, industrial engineering, design engineering, purchasing, programming, human resources, or quality. In retail, the team members could be retail associates, shift supervisors, marketing partners, maintenance workers, or delivery people. In healthcare, the team members could be nurses, nurse supervisors, programmers, or doctors. In the food industry, team members could include hostesses, servers, bus people, cooks, bartenders, shift supervisors, dieticians, and accountants.

Based on team experience, the team leader might facilitate some root cause analysis training (which we discuss in the next chapter) with the team members. It is the team leader's responsibility to keep the team on track and provide an open line of communication between all stakeholders. It is also the team leader's responsibility to ensure that all team meeting minutes are kept—including team progress, action plans, and individual assignments and dates.

Documentation of learning is a very important part of the 8D process. An 8D documentation form is provided on the Iowa Quality Systems website. It is suggested that as each step is completed, every attempt be made to complete and update this form.

D2 *Define and Describe the Problem.* The team will precisely detail the problem. It is extremely important that the problem be described in measurable terms because it is difficult to improve something that can't be measured. A nice tool available to define the problem is called 5W & 2H. It is defined as follows:

- Who? Who is complaining?

- What? What are they are complaining about?

- When? When did the problem start?

- Where? Where is the problem occurring?

- Why? Why is this problem occurring? (an educated guess)

- How? How did this problem occur? (an educated guess)

- How? How many problems are there? (frequency and magnitude)

Document your learning on the 8D documentation form.

D3 *Develop Interim Containment Plan; Implement and Verify Interim Actions.* All nonconforming material must be isolated from the customer. This step is typically already in progress as discussed in step D0. An open and honest line of communication is required in this step between producer and recipient of the problem.

Every effort is made to isolate the problem from the customer. It may involve 100% inspection of the product in house and in the customer's warehouse and additional steps in the process to maintain the integrity of the product being produced. It is the team's responsibility to review whether the containment action taken already is appropriate and to modify the action plan if needed.

Containment action is not a substitute for a permanent solution. Most containment actions are inspection in nature, are temporary band aids, add cost, and are no substitute for a permanent solution. The containment action plan must be documented on the 8D form and reviewed periodically.

D4 *Determine, Identify, and Verify Root Causes and Escape Points.* This is the most difficult part of the 8D process. If this problem were simple and easily solved, we would not be here in the first place and the problem would be resolved already. Two types of variability exist that should be considered—special cause and random cause. Naturally, we are interested in finding the special cause that is deeply hidden in the process. The main reason to form teams with subject matter experts is to find the special cause.

Problem solving tools are sometimes categorized as *soft* or *hard*. Here the term *hard* refers to those using statistical analysis. In this book we concentrate on the following soft tools:

- Team brainstorming events

- Five Whys process

- Flow charts

- Check sheets

- Fishbone diagrams

Fortunately, these simple tools are easy to learn and very effective in solving the majority of problems. It may happen that a problem the team is working on is complex and more sophisticated statistical tools are needed, such as hypothesis testing, ANOVA, DOE, and so on. In this case, a statistical expert should be engaged with the team. In many situations, sophisticated statistical tools will not to be needed to solve the problem. The key is to have all team members engaged and contributing.

The root cause solution must be documented on the 8D form and reviewed periodically.

D5 *Choose and Verify Permanent Corrections (PCs) for Problem/nonconformity.* Once the root cause of the problem has been identified, a number of corrections may be discovered. Scientific methods should be utilized to screen for the best solution.

It is essential that the correction(s) be realistic, practical, cost effective, and robust against process variability. Error proofing the process is a preferred method.

The team must ensure that the correction does not create unintended consequences. At this stage, the correction should be implemented on a small scale to verify its effectiveness.

Permanent corrective action should be documented on the 8D form.

D6 *Implement and Validate Permanent Corrective Actions.* At this stage a permanent correction has been verified. The next step is to validate the correction on a large production scale. Again, the team needs to ensure the correction does not create other issues. All changes need to be documented and all procedures updated. As the team implements the permanent solution, other people will be affected and will need to be made aware and trained.

An environment needs to be created so that the user(s) of the new method will have an opportunity to participate and should be encouraged to do so. All suggestions from other groups need to be reviewed and, if valid, should be incorporated into the total change process.

Implementation of permanent corrective action should be documented on the 8D form.

D7 *Take Preventive Measures.* For a reasonable time, the team should monitor whether the improved process is meeting all team goals set at the onset. It should verify that ongoing performance metrics are not negatively affected and that they meet all requirements. The lessons learned from this effort should now be leveraged on similar processes. All quality control systems should now be in place and validated.

Permanent future re-occurrence effort should be documented on the 8D form.

D8 *Congratulate Your Team*
Once the team task is completed and results meet all customer requirements, the team should be formally recognized and thanked by the management. The team should also thank all others who helped them to succeed. The team should

complete all relevant paperwork and publish their work for future use. Team focus should especially be on lessons learned and application to similar processes.

At this time, the team is dissolved and members wait for another opportunity to serve.

Documentation of the problem and its resolution is an important part of the 8D process. An example of an 8D working document is shown in Figure 1.18. The actual document will often have more pages because the individual D items may require extensive explanation.

Team 8D Working Document	Concern No._____	Date Initiated_____

D1: Team Members

D2: Problem Statement/Description

D3: Interim Containment Action(s):

D4: Root Cause(s):

D5: Choose and verify permanent corrections(s):

D6: Implement and validate corrective actions:

D7: Take preventative actions:

D8: Congratulate your team: Date/Notes:

Figure 1.18 Example of an 8D document.

The use of the 8D documentation form is shown in Example 1.3. When customers initiate the 8D process, they may require that the supplier use their 8D form. These forms may require a Five Whys section or a process flowchart. The lack of a standard form complicates the job of quality teams

---

Example 1.3

The problem-solving team at a trucking company is charged with reducing customer complaints. They immediately install a small department for handling customer complaints with the authority to resolve the problem expeditiously. The D8 form at this point looks like Figure 1.19.

Team 8D Working Document	Concern No.__*278*____	Date Initiated__*7/10/18*_

D1: Team Members
John Jones (4887), Jane Smith (4872), Lynn Doe (4811), Jill Brown (4866), Bill Howard (4888)

D2: Problem Statement/Description
Find a cost effective way to reduce customer complaints. Last fiscal year we had 238 customer complaints. The team is charged with reducing this number by 25% for next year.

D3: Interim Containment Action(s):
Establish a customer support department with authority to rapidly respond to complaints. Activated 7/20/18.

D4: Root Cause(s):

Figure 1.19   Example of an 8D form at the beginning of team activity.

The team decides to look at the complaint data for the last year and uses a check sheet to determine the frequency of the causes. The resulting check sheet:

Customer Complaint	Frequency
Damaged goods	28
Missing goods	18
Delivered to wrong address	22
Late delivery	152
Wet goods	11
Incomplete shipment	3
Attempt to deliver after hours	4
Total	238

The team decides to investigate the causes for late delivery. The following check list shows the results.

Reasons for Late Delivery	Frequency
Delayed departure	6
Driver illness	2
Wrong address on paperwork	7
Truck mechanical problem	127
Traffic accident	2
Flooding/storms	4
GPS failure	4
Total	152

The team looks further at the "mechanical problem" events and produces the following check list:

Mechanical Problems	Frequency
Engine failure	5
Drive train failure	4
Electrical system failure	76
Exhaust system failure	11
Tire failure	18
Total	127

Further analysis of the electrical systems failures:

Reasons for Electrical System Failure	Frequency
Battery failure	1
Headlight failure	63
Tail/brake light failure	10
Alternator failure	2
Total	76

To recapitulate, 41% of late deliveries are caused by a failed headlight. The team finds that the headlight repair procedure consists of having the driver pull off the road, call the nearest company depot, and wait for a mechanic to arrive. Depending on the weather and location, the headlight may be repaired on site or the truck may be towed to the nearest depot. Either way, enough time often elapses to cause a late delivery. At this time the report form would look like Figure 1.20.

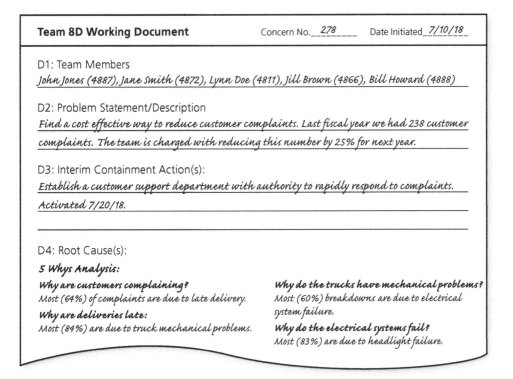

Team 8D Working Document   Concern No.__*278*____   Date Initiated__*7/10/18*__

D1: Team Members
John Jones (4887), Jane Smith (4872), Lynn Doe (4811), Jill Brown (4866), Bill Howard (4888)

D2: Problem Statement/Description
Find a cost effective way to reduce customer complaints. Last fiscal year we had 238 customer complaints. The team is charged with reducing this number by 25% for next year.

D3: Interim Containment Action(s):
Establish a customer support department with authority to rapidly respond to complaints. Activated 7/20/18.

D4: Root Cause(s):
5 Whys Analysis:
Why are customers complaining?
Most (64%) of complaints are due to late delivery.
Why are deliveries late:
Most (84%) are due to truck mechanical problems.

Why do the trucks have mechanical problems?
Most (60%) breakdowns are due to electrical system failure.
Why do the electrical systems fail?
Most (83%) are due to headlight failure.

Figure 1.20 Example of a partial 8D form.

The team brainstormed several corrective action alternatives:

1. Train operators to change headlights.
2. Provide a spare headlight that could be switched on when one fails.
3. Establish a non-depot repair network to greatly increase the availability of repair people.
4. Install a different type of headlight.

As the team discusses option 4 they decide to study the current headlight's life cycle. They find that after 1800 hours of service there is a 50–50 chance that the bulb will fail. A team member locates a more expensive headlight system that will run 20,000 hours before reaching the 50–50 failure point. In addition to longer life, these bulbs cast a reddish light when they have fewer than 200 hours of useful remaining life; they can usually be changed prior to departure and without delaying delivery. Unfortunately, the new headlight requires a step-up transformer to supply the voltage needed. The team decides to recommend that all trucks in the system be fitted with the new transformer and headlights. Management agrees to retrofit 100 vehicles (10% of the fleet) with the new system for a one year trial. At the end of the year, none of the 100 vehicles had a failed headlight. Management then decided to retrofit the entire fleet and to specify to their tractor supplier that all new units be equipped with the new headlight system. Customer complaints decreased by 22% during the following year. The team had a restrained celebration because they had not met the 25% decrease that had been their original goal. They set about analyzing the complaint types for further improvement. Their final report cover form is shown as Figure 1.21.

Team 8D Working Document   Concern No._____278_____   Date Initiated___7/10/18_

D1: Team Members
John Jones (4887), Jane Smith (4872), Lynn Doe (4811), Jill Brown (4866), Bill Howard (4888)

D2: Problem Statement/Description
Find a cost effective way to reduce customer complaints. Last fiscal year we had 238 customer complaints. The team is charged with reducing this number by 25% for next year.

D3: Interim Containment Action(s):
Establish a customer support department with authority to rapidly respond to complaints. Activated 7/20/18.

D4: Root Cause(s):
5 Whys Analysis:

Why are customers complaining?
Most (64%) of complaints are due to late delivery.

Why are deliveries late:
Most (84%) are due to truck mechanical problems.

Why do the trucks have mechanical problems?
Most (60%) breakdowns are due to electrical system failure.

Why do the electrical systems fail?
Most (83%) are due to headlight failure.

D5: Choose and verify permanent corrections(s):
Management agreed to install a new headlight system on 100 vehicles to verify the predicted improvement. These were tested for one year.

D6: Implement and validate corrective actions:
At the end of the one year verification period, none of the test vehicles had failed headlights. Management then decided to retrofit all vehicles with the new headlight system. A 22% reduction in customer complaints occurred.

D7: Take preventative actions:
Management decided not to buy any new tractors that didn't have the new headlight system.

D8: Congratulate your team: Date/Notes:
Lunch together 10/5/18

Figure 1.21   Final report form for the logistics problem.

End of Example 1.3

Example 1.4 is from the health field but is similar to problems in complex environments.

Example 1.4

A corporation that operates a chain of nursing homes is concerned about the possibility of medication errors. A problem-solving team is assigned to study this issue and produce recommendations. The team finds that there are no data on medication errors in the corporation's institutions, but national studies indicate that this is a significant problem. The team decides to observe the medication process in detail.

The current procedure is for the practical nurse (PN) to use an alphabetized list of patients with their medications scheduled as indicated in Figure 1.22.

Mary Ames Room 418	
8:00 AM	40 mg sybeterol 20 mg aboid
10:00 AM	20 mg aboid 20 cc borsil
John Armstead Room 403	
8:00 AM	100 mg Wazlort
10:00 AM	83 mg aspirin

Figure 1.22   Example of a medication list.

The PN unlocks the medication drawer and locates the section reserved for Mary Ames. The appropriate medicine containers are found, the amounts are counted out and given to the patient. The PN then initials the entry on the medication list. The list itself is generated for each shift by the office of the Director of Nursing and incorporates any changes from patient's physician.

While going through the medication list, the PN is frequently interrupted with questions from patients, families, and certified nursing assistants (CNAs). "Did I miss my 4 PM pill?" "Can Mr. Jones have fruit juice with his renitiun?" "Can Mr. Smith in 408 have another pain pill?"

After collecting data and discussing the process, the team agrees that there are multiple opportunities for errors. They determine that the situation justifies providing a CNA to work with each PN during medication rounds as an interim containment strategy. These CNAs and the PNs are made aware of the corporation's concern and are asked for suggestions. At this point the team's 8D form is that shown in Figure 1.23.

The team—together with the PN staff, the CNAs assigned to help them, and other stakeholders—is asked to list possible causes for medication errors. The team places responses on a cause-and-effects fishbone diagram. A part of the diagram is shown in Figure 1.24.

Team 8D Working Document   Concern No.___15_____   Date Initiated__6/20/18_

D1: Team Members
J. Rainy, MD, J. Wasn, RN, J. Veldu, LPN, U. Smith, CNA

D2: Problem Statement/Description
Study current medication process and determine ways to reduce errors.

D3: Interim Containment Action(s):
1. Assign a CNA to work with each PN during
2. The CNAs and PNs are solicited for suggestions for process

---

Figure 1.23   First three steps for the medication error team.

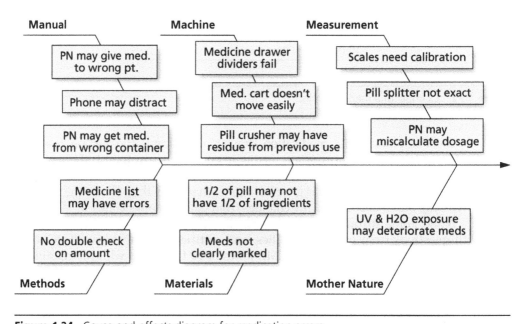

Figure 1.24   Cause-and-effects diagram for medication errors.

After further discussion, the team agrees that one weak point in the process is the step where the PN locates the medicine container in the drawer and counts out the dosage. Errors could include picking up the wrong bottle (Mr. Jones' qualibe rather than that for Mr. Doe, or Mr. Doe's qualibe rather than his theiop) or counting the wrong dosage (is 20 mg two pills or four?). The issue is broached with the supplying pharmacy, which explains that for an extra fee it can prepackage the medicines. The package will have a label with the patient's name, the date, and the time for use. It will contain all the meds for that patient for that time. The PN will be able to rip open the sealed envelope at the labeled time, double check the contents, and provide the medicine to the patient. The team decides to recommend that as a solution to improve the accuracy of the dosage.

The next weak point identified by the team is the point at which the PN may give the medicine to patient A thinking that the person is patient B. This is more likely when the PN is not familiar with the names and faces involved. After some study and consultation with the IT department, the team comes up with a recommendation that requires the pharmacy to barcode the medicine packets with the patient name, medication, and date/time when the medicine is due. Each patient would be provided with a bar coded wrist band. The PN would scan the patient's wrist band and the screen would display the medicine, if any, due at that time. The PN would pull and scan the medicine packet. If any discrepancy occurs, the computer will give a visual and audible alert. Even if no discrepancy is found, the PN is still required to double check the contents of the medicine packet against the daily list and initial that list. The team decides to recommend this procedure. The next two sections of the 8D form now look like that shown in Figure 1.25.

In this situation, the partial D8 form is provided to the parent corporation for consideration. The team agrees to work with implementation of their recommendations, should the corporate office decide to accept either or both.

D4: Root Cause

The Root Cause is the general chaos that surrounds the PN as medications are dispensed. Patients and families interrupt, phone calls from doctors and pharmacies must be answered, emergencies occur, etc. This environment can cause medication errors in two ways:

1. In the process of locating the appropriate medicine and determining the dosage.
2. In the process of providing the medicine to the correct patient.

D5: Choose and verify permanent correction(s)

1. The team recommends institutions contract with a pharmacy that will prepackage the medicines for each patient for each time of day that tey are due.

2. The team recommends that each patient be fitted with a wrist band that can be scanned and that software be updated to provide the PN with guidance for the administration of medications.

Figure 1.25 Sections D4 and D5 of the medication team's report.

Note on Root Causes. The 8D protocol puts a great deal of emphasis on identification and elimination of the root cause of a problem. While this is always desirable, it is sometimes not practical. In the previous example, the root cause of medication error is the tendency of concerned patients, family members, and doctors to interrupt the nurse with medication related questions. These interruptions could be eliminated by refusing access to the PN or providing additional staff to answer questions. In this case, neither of these options was deemed viable and the best solution was to find ways to pass meds accurately in a somewhat chaotic environment.

Nurses have been known to mutter "We could get a lot more work done if it weren't for all the patients." In the manufacturing field they say, "…if it weren't for all these cars we have to build."

9. SIX SIGMA

Identify key Six Sigma concepts and tools such as quality function deployment (QFD), design of experiments (DOE), and design, measure, analyze, improve, control (DMAIC). (Remember)

Body of Knowledge I.B.9

A tool that is especially designed to study the voice of the customer and links it to product and service design is called *quality function deployment* (QFD). The QFD matrix helps illustrate the linkage between the needs of the customer and the technical requirements of the product or service. A QFD matrix consists of several parts. There is no standard format matrix or key for the symbols, but the example shown in Figure 1.26 is typical.

A map of the various parts of Figure 1.27 is shown in Figure 1.26.

The matrix is formed by first filling in the customer requirements ①, which are developed from analysis of the voice of the customer (VOC). This section often includes a scale reflecting the importance of the individual entries. The technical requirements are established in response to the customer requirements and placed in area ②. The symbols on the top line in this section indicate whether lower (↓) or higher (↑) is better. A circle indicates that target is better. The relationship area ③ displays the connection between the technical requirements and the customer requirements. Various symbols can be used here. Area ④ is not shown on all QFD matrices. It plots comparison with competition for the customer requirements. Area ⑤ provides an index to documentation concerning improvement activities. Area ⑥ is not shown on all QFD matrices. It plots comparison with competition for the technical requirements. Area ⑦ lists the target values for the technical requirements. Area ⑧ shows the co-relationships between the technical requirements. A positive co-relationship indicates that both technical requirements can be improved at the same time. A negative co-relationship indicates that improving one of the technical requirements will make the other one worse. The column weights shown at the bottom of the figure are optional. They indicate the importance of the technical requirements in meeting customer requirements. The values in the column weights row are obtained by multiplying the value in the *importance* column in the customer requirements section by values assigned to the symbols in the relationship matrix. These assigned values are arbitrary, and in this example a strong relationship was assigned a 9, moderate 3, and weak 1.

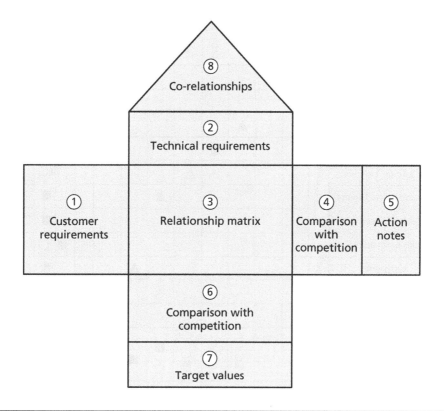

Figure 1.26   Map of the entries for the QFD matrix illustrated in Figure I.27.

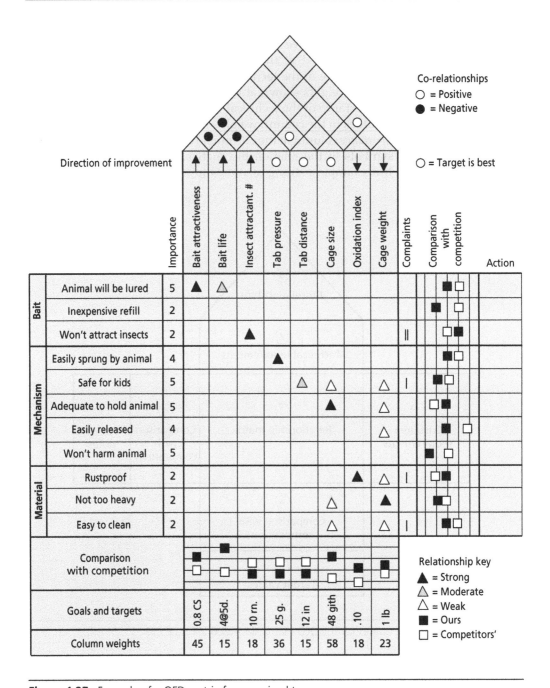

Figure 1.27   Example of a QFD matrix for an animal trap.

Design of Experiments

This section provides an introduction to some of the basic concepts in experimental design.

The objective of a designed experiment is to generate knowledge about a product or process. The experiment seeks to find the effect a set of independent variables has on a set of dependent variables. For example, suppose a machine operator who can adjust the feed, speed, and coolant temperature wished to find the settings that will produce the best surface finish. The feed, speed, and coolant temperature are called independent variables. The surface finish is called the dependent variable because its value depends on the values of the independent variables. There may be additional independent variables, such as hardness of the material or ambient temperature, that have an effect on the dependent variable. The independent variables that the experimenter controls are called *control factors* or just *factors*. The independent variables that the experimenter does not control are called *noise factors*. The following example will be used throughout this section. In this example, the experimental design may specify that the speed will be set at 1300 rev/min for part of the experiment and at 1800 rev/min for the remainder. These values are referred to as the *levels* of the speed factor. The experimenting team decides to test each factor at two levels, as follows:

Feed (F): 0.01 and 0.04 in/rev

Speed (S): 1300 and 1800 rev/min

Coolant temperature (C): 100° and 140° F

The team further decides to test all possible combinations of these factors. They want to test each combination five times. So they set up the worksheet shown in Figure 1.28.

Run #	Feed	Speed	Coolnt	1	2	3	4	5
1	0.01	1300	100					
2	0.01	1300	140					
3	0.01	1800	100					
4	0.01	1800	140					
5	0.04	1300	100					
6	0.04	1300	140					
7	0.04	1800	100					
8	0.04	1800	140					

Figure 1.28   Example of a data collection sheet.

Each run represents a unique combination of the factors and each combination is tested five times, resulting in forty tests. These tests should be conducted in random order. One way to randomize is to put eight slips of paper, numbered 1 to 8, in a box. The numbers are drawn out one at a time and dictate the first eight tests to be set up. For instance, if the number drawn is 6, the machine would be set up with values for run number six: F = 0.04, S = 1300, and C = 140. A part would be produced and its surface finish measured and entered in the first column of row six. The next number drawn would dictate the next combination of F, S, and C and the resultant surface finish would be entered in column one for that run. In the same way the remaining six slips of paper would show the values to be entered in the remaining six blanks of column one. The slips would then be replaced in the box and redrawn to dictate the order of the eight tests to be run for column two. The slips are replaced in the box and redrawn for each of the five columns. The five duplications of each run are called replicates. The number of replicates is somewhat arbitrary and depends on the resources available. In the example, the measured values are those shown in Figure 1.29.

Note that the five values for a particular run are not all the same. This may be due to drift in the factor levels, variation in the measurement system, and/or the influence of other noise factors. The variation observed in the readings for a particular run is referred to as *experimental error*. If the number of replications is decreased, the calculation of experimental error is less accurate although the experiment has a lower total cost. Thus the accurate determination of experimental error and cost are competing design properties.

The next step is analyzing the collected data. A typical first step is to calculate the average for each run as shown in Figure 1.30.

Run #	Feed	Speed	Coolnt	1	2	3	4	5
1	0.01	1300	100	10.3	9.5	11.5	8.3	10.0
2	0.01	1300	140	4.6	2.8	2.4	5.1	4.7
3	0.01	1800	100	4.9	6.3	6.7	5.1	7.2
4	0.01	1800	140	0.6	2.3	1.5	3.4	2.1
5	0.04	1300	100	7.6	8.6	5.2	5.8	8.1
6	0.04	1300	140	3.2	5.8	4.9	8.2	7.1
7	0.04	1800	100	4.6	6.0	4.8	7.3	8.0
8	0.04	1800	140	0.8	1.9	4.1	6.2	1.8

Figure 1.29 Data collection sheet with data entered.

Assuming that a lower reading means a better surface finish, the team might choose run number four as having the settings that provide the best finish, with run number eight coming in a close second. In fact, the team might conclude that number eight is preferable because it runs four times as fast at the sacrifice of little in surface quality.

The team decides to visualize the experimental error by plotting the original forty measurements. The resulting graph is shown in Figure 1.31.

Figure 1.31 is a little difficult to interpret but it shows that each run has considerable experimental error. Comparing the averages misses that fact. This graph raises doubts about recommending the settings for run 8 because several parts made using settings from other runs have lower scores than some of those made using the settings for run 8. The team might decide that the experiment does not provide support for any setting due to the large amount of experimental error. They seek to reduce experimental error by improving measurements and using more consistent materials and methods. They then repeat the entire experiment with the results shown in Figure 1.32.

Run #	Feed	Speed	Coolnt	1	2	3	4	5	Run Average
1	0.01	1300	100	10.3	9.5	11.5	8.3	10.0	9.9
2	0.01	1300	140	4.6	2.8	2.4	5.1	4.7	3.9
3	0.01	1800	100	4.9	6.3	6.7	5.1	7.2	6.0
4	0.01	1800	140	0.6	2.3	1.5	3.4	2.1	2.0
5	0.04	1300	100	7.6	8.6	5.2	5.8	8.1	7.1
6	0.04	1300	140	3.2	5.8	4.9	8.2	7.1	5.8
7	0.04	1800	100	4.6	6.0	4.8	7.3	8.0	6.1
8	0.04	1800	140	0.8	1.9	4.1	6.2	1.8	3.0

Figure 1.30 Data collection sheet with averages.

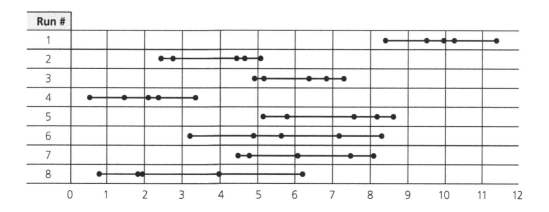

Figure 1.31 Graph illustrating experimental error.

Run #	Feed	Speed	Coolnt	1	2	3	4	5	Run Average
1	0.01	1300	100	10.1	10.0	10.2	9.8	9.9	10.0
2	0.01	1300	140	4.0	4.2	4.0	4.0	3.8	4.0
3	0.01	1800	100	6.1	6.0	6.3	5.7	6.0	6.0
4	0.01	1800	140	2.0	2.0	2.2	1.9	1.9	2.0
5	0.04	1300	100	6.7	7.0	7.2	7.1	7.0	7.0
6	0.04	1300	140	5.8	6.1	6.2	6.0	6.0	6.0
7	0.04	1800	100	5.8	6.0	6.1	6.2	5.9	6.0
8	0.04	1800	140	3.1	2.9	3.0	2.9	3.1	3.0

Figure 1.32 Data collected after reducing noise factors.

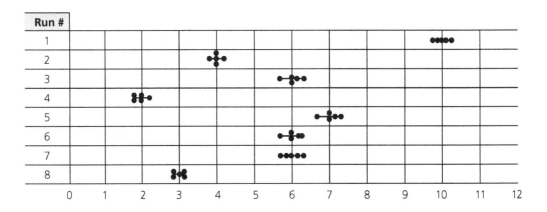

Figure 1.33 Displays the experimental error for the data in Figure 1.32.

When comparing Figure 1.33 to Figure 1.31, the team feels more confidence in their results. The settings for a particular run is sometimes called a *treatment*. In this experiment there were eight treatments. The length of the horizontal bars in Figures 1.33 and 1.31 provides a measure for the *in-treatment variation*. The difference between the run averages in Figures 1.30 and 1.32 is called the *between-treatment variation*. An essential question is this. "Is the between-treatment variation enough larger than the within-treatment variation to be significant?" In this example the issue was approached graphically. There are statistical answers that are beyond the scope of this book.

Main Effects

The symbol $A+$ denotes the average of the run averages that used factor A at its high level. The symbol $A-$ denotes the average of the run averages that used factor A at its low level. In the example the high level for factor F is 0.04. The four runs with F at 0.04 are runs 5, 6, 7, and 8. These four runs have average values of 7, 6, 6, and 3. Therefore

$$F_+ = \frac{7+6+6+3}{4} = 5.5 \quad \text{similarly,} \quad F_- = \frac{10+4+6+2}{4} = 5.5$$

The main effect of a factor A is defined as $A = \frac{A_+ - A_-}{2}$.

For the example, $F = \frac{5.5-5.5}{2} = 0$

Similarly, $S_+ = \frac{6+2+6+3}{4} = 4.25$ because factor S is at its high level in

runs 3, 4, 7, and 8 with values 6, 2, 6, and 3.

And $S_- = \frac{10+4+7+6}{4} = 6.75$ because factor S is at its low level in

runs 1, 2, 5, and 6 with values 10, 4, 7, and 6.

So the main effect $S = \frac{4.25-6.75}{2} = -2.50$

Similarly, $C+ = \frac{4+2+6+3}{4} = 3.75$ because factor C is at its high level in

runs 2, 4, 6, and 8 with values 4, 2, 6, and 3.

And $C_- = \frac{10+6+7+6}{4} = 7.25$ because factor C is at its low level in

runs 1, 3, 5, and 7 with values 10, 6, 7, and 6.

So the main effect $C = \frac{3.75-7.25}{2} = -1.75$

The larger the absolute value of the main effect, the more influence that factor has on the quality characteristic. It is possible that the perceived difference between high and low results is not statistically significant. This would occur if the experimental error were so large that it would be impossible to determine whether the difference between the high and low values is due to a real difference in the dependent variable or due to experimental error. In other words, if the ratio of between treatment variation to within treatment variation is too low. Statistics texts discuss this using a procedure known as analysis of variance (ANOVA).

Interactions

Interactions may occur between two or more factors. For example, two medicines taken individually may be harmless but when taken together, serious side effects may occur. Interactions between experimental factors can occur. To assess the interaction effects, return to the original design matrix, replacing each high level by "+" and each low level by "–" as shown in Figure 1.34. This table has new columns for the interaction of various factors. The interaction between factor F and factor C is labeled F x C. This is referred to as a two-way interaction. The last column is labeled F x S x C to represent the three-way interaction between the three factors.

Run #	F	S	C	F x S	F x C	S x C	F x S x C	Run Average
1	–	–	–	+	+	+	–	10
2	–	–	+	+	–	–	+	4
3	–	+	–	–	+	–	+	6
4	–	+	+	–	–	+	–	2
5	+	–	–	–	–	+	+	7
6	+	–	+	–	+	–	–	6
7	+	+	–	+	–	–	–	6
8	+	+	+	+	+	+	+	3

Figure 1.34 Illustration of interactions.

The entry on each line of the F x S column is obtained by multiplying the signs in the that line of the F and S columns. The multiplication rule is this: "If the signs are the same the result is a plus; if the signs are opposite the result is a negative." The remainder of the columns are calculated the same way. For the three-way column the rule is this: "If there is an even number of negatives, the result is plus; if there is an odd number of negatives, the result is a negative."

To calculate the effect of the interaction between factors F and S, first find F x S+ by averaging the results of the runs that have a + in the F x S column:

$$F \times S+ = \frac{10 + 4 + 6 + 3}{4} = 5.75 \quad \text{Similarly} \quad F \times S- = \frac{6 + 2 + 7 + 6}{4} = 5.25$$

The effect of the F x S interaction is $\frac{5.75 - 5.25}{2} = 0.50$

Similar calculations show that $F \times C = 0.75$ $S \times C = 0$ $F \times S \times C = -0.50$

When interaction effects are large, more careful analysis is required.

Fractional Factorial Designs

In the example there are three factors and each is tested at two levels. The formula for calculating the number of possible runs is

$$n = L^F$$

where n = number of possible runs

L = number of levels

and   F = number of factors

For the example $n = 2^3 = 8$ runs as was shown in the earlier tables. The expression 2^3 is sometimes used to denote the design in this example. If the number of factors is large, the number of runs tends to get out of hand. A two level experiment with seven factors has $2^7 = 128$ runs. If each run is replicated five times, 640 tests are required. In many situations the resources required for this number of tests are not available. Several options are possible:

- Omit some factors (deciding which factors to omit is a guessing game).

- Decrease the number of replications per run (this decreases the ability to account for experimental error).

- Don't include all possible combinations (the design is called a fractional factorial and is discussed next).

Returning to the earlier example, a fractional factorial design for three factors with two levels each is shown in Figure 1.35.

Comparing this design to the earlier eight-run design, it is clear that this design uses runs 2, 3, 5, and 8 from the eight-run experiment. This design has the advantage of requiring half the runs and therefore much less in the way of time, material, etc. As might be expected, less data results in a lower quality result. There is another disadvantage to the fractional factorial designs (also called Taguchi designs). Figure 1.36 shows the interactions for the experimental design in Figure 1.35.

Notice the list of +/- signs in columns A and B x C. They are identical (both are - - + +). This means that the same formula is used when calculating the main effect of factor A and finding the interaction effect B x C. The result is some combination of the two. It is said that factor A and the interaction B x C are *confounded*. It is not possible to calculate the main effect for factor A or the effect of the interaction B x C. Examining Figure 1.36 further shows that factor B is confounded with the interaction A x C. Also, factor C is confounded with the interaction A x B. Confounding occurs when using fractional factorial designs. It is one of the costs of using these designs. Fractional factorial designs should only be used when the interaction effects are known to be very small.

Some notes on design of experiments. This section has provided an introduction to DOE and laid out some techniques for data collection and analysis. It has also covered some caveats that should be kept in mind. It is intended as a background for those who work with trained DOE professionals.

Run #	A	B	C
1	−	−	+
2	−	+	−
3	+	−	−
4	+	+	+

Figure 1.35 Half fraction of 2^3 (also called a 2^{3-1} design).

Run #	A	B	C	A x B	A x C	B x C	A x B x C
1	–	–	+	+	–	–	+
2	–	+	–	–	+	–	+
3	+	–	–	–	–	+	+
4	+	+	+	+	+	+	+

Figure 1.36 Interactions for the fractional factorial design in Figure 1.35.

DMAIC

(Portions of this section are excerpted from the Certified Six Sigma Black Belt Handbook, *3rd Edition, T. M. Kubiak and Donald W. Benbow, Milwaukee: ASQ Quality Press, 2017).*

DMAIC is an acronym using the first letters of five important problem-solving steps—define, measure, analyze, improve, and control. These steps provide a structured approach to problem solving. When Six Sigma is implemented as part of an organization's approach to quality improvement, individuals are trained in the DMAIC approach. This may involve some or all of the following positions.

Master Black Belts. Master Black Belts have advanced knowledge in statistics and other fields. They provide mentoring and technical support to Black Belts. They also ensure that improvement projects are the right fit strategically for the organization.

Black Belts. Black Belts work full time on Six Sigma projects. These projects are usually prioritized on the basis of their potential financial impact on the enterprise. Individuals designated as Black Belts must be thoroughly trained in statistical methods and be proficient at working with teams to facilitate project success. They train and mentor Green Belts as well as lead improvement projects using specified methodologies such as DMAIC (define, measure, analyze, improve, and control), DMADV (define, measure, analyze, design, and verify), and DFSS (Design for Six Sigma).

Green Belts. A Green Belt works under the direction of a Black Belt, assisting with all phases of a project. This person typically retains his or her regular position within the firm but is trained in the tools, methods, and skills necessary to conduct Six Sigma improvement projects.

Six Sigma Projects. A project selection group, including Master Black Belts, Black Belts, and key executive supporters, establishes a set of criteria for project selection and team assignments. These criteria have the furthering of organization goals as a key element. One key to gauging both the performance and the health of an organization and its processes lies with its selection and use of metrics. These are usually converted to financial terms such as return on investment, cost reduction, increases in sales, and/or profit. Other things being equal, projects with the greatest contributions to the bottom line receive the highest priority. The following sections explain the DAMIC steps in detail and an example problem will illustrate their use.

Define. A problem definition should include:

- Statement of the problem
- Quality cost
- Criteria for solution

The problem definition should indicate how systems and processes have failed. The quality cost involved with the problem can be an approximation, but is helpful in prioritizing projects. A part of the definition of the problem is an explanation of just how an observer will know when the problem is solved. The problem definition should be stated in a way that places limits on the project to help avoid "scope creep," the tendency for a team to expand the problem definition.

Example 1.5

Problem: Department PE5 is responsible for machine maintenance. The department has been asked to expand their coverage to a newly-opened building without using any additional staff. After some deliberation the following definition is agreed to:

DEFINITION:
Find ways to increase productivity so that the new facility can be covered without a decrease in average down-time. This will result in a 16% decrease in cost per ft² for maintenance coverage.

Measure. Metrics should be related to financial performance. Baseline data are collected to shed light on the extent of the problem and to provide a comparison with later performance.

Example 1.5 (continued)

The facility has seven basic machine types designated A through G. Maintenance activity is divided into three types:

1. Scheduled preventative maintenance actions

2. Non-emergency requests that don't require immediate maintenance activity

3. Breakdowns that require maintenance activity before production can be continued

Types 1 and 2 are currently handled by routing and scheduling procedures. The average down-time for Type 3 is 2.7 hours. The down-time is broken down as follows:

a. Delay between receipt of call and arrival of maintenance personnel: 20%

b. Diagnosis: 42%

c. Wait for replacement parts: 26%

d. Installation and testing: 12%

Analyze. The baseline data are analyzed for possible correlation with other variables. The team generates potential causes and corrective actions. The corrective actions are discussed and prioritized. Possible corrections are installed and tested. This step consists of trial and error, and it is important to approach failed attempts at correction as learning experiences rather than mistakes. After thorough testing, the team agrees on the best corrective action.

Example 1.5 *(continued)*

A discussion with a team from the department produces consensus on the following:

- It is anticipated that 16% more machines to be tended by the same number of people will cause delay time to increase.
- Regarding diagnosis time:
  - The same problem is solved several times on different machines by different people.
- Wait time for replacement parts is sometimes due to stockroom delays.

Proposed corrective actions:

- Delay time can be reduced if people can be pulled from non-emergency jobs. Schedule 25% longer times for preventative maintenance so people can leave them for emergency jobs.
- Diagnosis time can be improved.
  - Designate several specialists for each of the machine types.
  - Maintain a searchable database of maintenance activity on each machine and machine type so that symptoms can link to possible causes.
- A historical study has identified 27 frequently needed replacement parts to be added to the maintenance stockroom. Stockroom storage should be reorganized.

Improve. The corrective action is installed and documented. Appropriate changes are made to shop prints, work instructions, routing sheets, and other documents.

Example 1.5 *(continued)*

The proposed corrections are made.

Control. Control is an essential step that is often underrated. There is a tendency for solved problems to "unsolve" themselves, that is, for things to return to the way they've always been done. Therefore, there is a need for mechanisms to monitor the revised process to verify that the corrective action continues to work as designed. These mechanisms might include control charts, check sheets, and various auditing techniques. These tools are especially important during the critical first few weeks when new habits are being formed.

Example 1.5 (*continued*)

A one-year schedule is established to assign auditing responsibilities to individuals by name and position. The individuals indicate with their initials that they have verified that the corrections are in operation as designed or improved. The schedule requires weekly audits for eight weeks, then monthly monitoring for the following year.

End of Example 1.5

There are a number of variations on the DMAIC approach, including:

- DMADV: design, measure, analyze, design, and verify

- DFSS: Design for Six Sigma, which emphasizes achieving six sigma quality levels from the earliest design phases of products and services

- IDOV: identify, design, optimize, and validate

A Six Sigma team does not restrict itself to tools that have been developed within the Six Sigma framework, but shamelessly adopts any tool that aids problem solution. One technique found to be helpful is called the *critical-to-quality flow-down*. It focuses on identifying needs from a customer's viewpoint. This technique is illustrated in the following example.

Example: High on Mid America Landscaping's list of strategic goals is customer satisfaction. A survey of past customers raised the need to establish a project team to ensure that customers understand the nature of the plants and trees they are purchasing. The team identifies a number of constituent parts to the problem. These constituents will guide the team. The CTQ flow-down diagram is shown in Figure 1.37.

10. LEAN

Identify key lean concepts and tools such as 5S, value-stream mapping, flow, and pull system. (Remember)

Body of Knowledge I.B.10

Over the years a great deal of effort has gone into improving value-added activities—those activities that impact the form or function of the product. Machines and materials that perform more efficiently have been developed. Lean thinking puts more emphasis on *non-value-added* activities—those activities that occur in every enterprise but do not add value for the customer. Some of these

Strategic goal

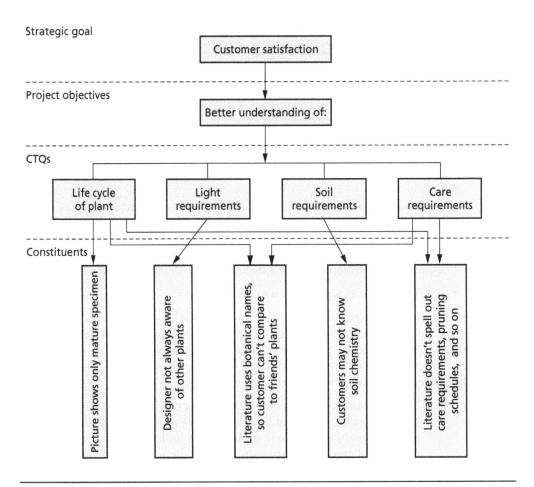

Figure 1.37   Example of a CTQ flow-down diagram.

activities can be eliminated, and some can be simplified, improved, combined, and so forth. Waste falls into seven categories:

1. Transportation—Moving products around does not add to their form or function.

2. Inventory—Some accounting procedures count inventory as an asset. It really is a liability. It has to be counted and recounted, located and relocated, housed under specified temperature/humidity ranges, and so forth.

3. Motion—This refers to excess motion by personnel. Examples include a person moving 30 feet to get paper for the copier or a machine operator walking back and forth to a workbench each time a tool is used.

4. Waiting—Refers to idle time for persons and/or equipment because of upstream delays.

5. Overproduction—Producing more than is currently required. This may include inventory or it may generate product that needs to be disposed of, perhaps at a reduced price or with extra effort.

6. Over processing—Refers to unnecessary steps or duplication of effort. An example would be a punch-press that is forming parts to be painted. To keep the parts from rusting while they wait to be painted, they are oiled. Prep for the paint line requires a degreasing process. The customer would not happy about paying for these two processes.

7. Defects—Whether they require re-work, inspection, or scrap, these cause waste.

Tools for identifying and reducing waste of all kinds are a prime emphasis of lean thinking. Some of these tools are discussed in this section.

Kanban

A *kanban* is a system that signals the need to replenish stock or materials or to produce more of an item. Kanban systems need not be elaborate to be effective. The original inspiration came from observing stock replacement at a supermarket where the authorization to add a box of canned peas to a shelf was the occurrence of the previous box being emptied. In a typical two-bin kanban arrangement, as the first bin is emptied, the user signals resupply personnel. The signal is usually visual and may involve displaying a card that came with the bin, turning on a light, or just showing the empty bin. Example 1.6 illustrates a kanban system.

Example 1.6   A simple kanban system.

In this assembly line example each of four workers removes items from a table and adds them to the product moving on the conveyor. As the supply of items on the various tables becomes depleted, it is replenished by the traveling stocker (also called "the stalker"). The kanban is the technique used to signal the stocker. It may be a light, a card, or simply an open space on the table. The stocker is responsible for assuring that the items on the table correspond to the product mix moving down the conveyor (i.e., if the next product on the conveyor is type B, the next item on each table must be the appropriate item to add to type B).

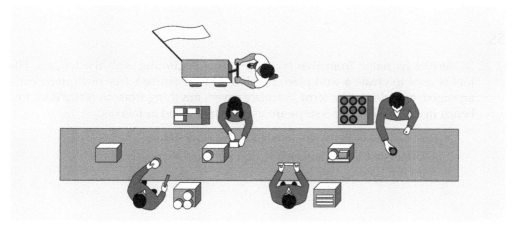

Pull Systems

In a *pull system*, the customer order process withdraws the needed items from a location, and the supplying process produces to replenish what was withdrawn. Manufacturing operations have traditionally operated on a push system in which the decision as to which products are to be produced is based on a forecast. A pull system tends to decrease inventory, reduce obsolescence, and eliminate expediting. Example 1.7 illustrates an idealized pull system.

Example 1.7   An idealized pull system.

Step 1   Warehouse is full. Customer (internal or external) orders product D.

Step 2   Product D is shipped. Production processes are activated to replenish product D.

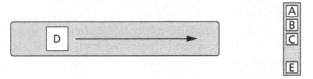

The production processes can use internal pull systems. Removal of an item from the warehouse initiates a ripple of activity through the production system.

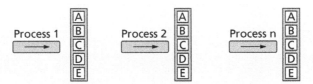

5S

5S derives its name from five Japanese terms beginning with the letter s. The tool is used to create a workplace that is visibly organized, free of clutter, neatly arranged, and clean. The term *workplace* covers anything from an office desk to a bench in a shop. The five S steps are usually translated as follows:

- *Sort.* Get rid of items not needed at the workstation.
  - Unneeded tools, paperwork, and personal items sometimes accumulate.

- *Set in order.* Neatly arrange parts and tools for ease of use.
  - Labels and signs may be needed. Shadow boards are useful here. If people from more than one shift use the area, all should be involved in the arrangement process.

- *Scrub.* Conduct a cleanup operation.

- *Standardize.* Establish a system whereby the above steps are repeated frequently.
  - A check list of activities to be taken at the end of each shift and the end of each week can be helpful. If several people are involved, rotating task assignments are appropriate.

- *Sustain.* Form the habit of always following the above steps.
  - This is the most difficult S. The 5S tool is too often treated as a spring cleaning operation. Maintaining the effort takes discipline and management support. Some organizations require regular reporting using the checklists developed in the previous step. This step should also include revisiting and modifying activities developed on other S steps.

A sixth S, for *safety*, is sometimes added to produce a 6S system.

Flow

Traditional manufacturing has operated on a *batch-and-queue* process in which a set of parts is processed through one operation and put into a waiting line (queue) for the next operation. Lean thinking includes transforming toward a *flow* process in which an individual item is moved to the next operation as soon as it completes a previous operation. In other words, the batch size is one as shown in Example 1.8. Many processes can not immediately change to a batch size of one but in general a reduction in batch size is desirable. This may require finding ways to reduce change-over time, transit time between operations, and other relatively sacred parameters.

Example 1.8   Batch-and-queue process versus one-piece flow.

Batch and Queue: Products may wait in line for the next process.

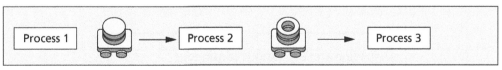

One-piece flow: May be able to slide or roll between close processes. More agile with less inventory.

Value Stream Maps

A *value stream map* is a visual representation of the path followed by a product or service from supplier to customer. The map begins with a traditional flowchart but shows inventories at each step, and usually includes notes for cycle time and changeover time. Value stream maps are often very large, requiring a team hours or days to produce. A common technique is to use sticky notes on a strip of paper that may stretch around a room. A very small value stream map is illustrated in Figure 1.38. The broken line graph along the bottom shows the value-added time versus non-value-added. The value stream map will highlight excess inventories and waiting times. It also shows the gap between value added and non-value added time. In the example, the part is in the plant for several days and receives three minutes of value added time.

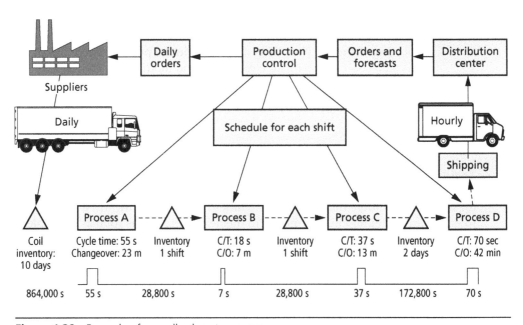

Figure 1.38   Example of a small value stream map.

11. CONTINUOUS IMPROVEMENT TECHNIQUES

Define and use various continuous improvement techniques including the Plan Do Check Act (PDCA) cycle, brainstorming, and benchmarking. (Apply)

Body of Knowledge I.B.11

The Plan–Do–Check–Act (PDCA) Cycle

Dr. Walter Shewhart, the inventor of control charts, is credited with providing a road map for continuous improvement. Sometimes referred to as the Shewhart Cycle (or the Deming Cycle), PDCA has come to be recognized as a critical tool in the problem solver's toolbox. A brief discussion of each element follows, but it is important to recognize that the elements must be incorporated into a cycle that is completed and then repeated endlessly.

Plan. Once a problem has been clearly defined, the first steps in solving it are to collect and analyze data, consider and analyze alternative solutions, and choose the best solution. These steps, although easy to state, can be extremely difficult and time-consuming to execute. Jointly, these steps constitute the plan phase in the PDCA cycle. One approach to this phase is to use a *force field analysis*, which lists the goals, the barriers to reaching those goals, and a strategy for coping with those barriers. This approach provides guidance for the next steps. In most situations, a cross-functional team representing everyone impacted by the problem and its solution should be formed and assigned the problem-solving task. There is a great tendency to jump to the *do* phase of the cycle rather than taking the time to adequately execute the plan phase. Before moving to the do phase, however, careful plans should be made regarding the collection of information during that phase. In some situations it may be useful to apply a "quick and dirty" (or "band-aid") solution to allow time to focus on the permanent solution. Of course, this approach risks the tendency to move on to the next problem because this one is "solved."

Do. Once a solution to the problem has been decided on, and a data collection scheme determined, the next phase is to try it. If possible, this should be done on a small scale and/or off-line. Sometimes, the proposed solution can be tried in a lab setting or outside the regular production process. During the *do* phase, as much data as possible should be collected. In some situations, videotaping a process permits further data collection upon replay.

Check. The *check* phase is used to analyze the information collected during the do phase. The data must be studied carefully, using valid mathematical and statistical techniques. For this reason, some authors, including Dr. W. Edwards Deming, began calling this the *study* phase, and refer to the cycle as PDSA.

Act. In this phase, action is taken based on the conclusions reached in the check phase. If the data show that the proposed correction is a good solution for the problem, the *act* phase consists of integrating the solution into the standard way of doing things. If the data show that another proposed solution is needed, the act phase consists of initiating the search for another solution. As the word "cycle" implies, the act phase is followed by the plan phase of the next cycle; quality improvement is a continuous journey as shown in Figure 1.39

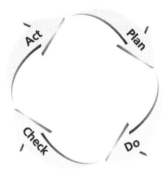

Figure 1.39 The PDCA cycle.

Many organizations are pretty good at the *do* and *check* phases, but fall down on the plan and act phases. Perhaps this is partly due to the impulse to "Don't just stand there, do something." There is a tendency, for instance, to provide a service, process, or product to customers without adequate care in the design (plan) phase. The strategy is that customers will provide feedback and a lot will be learned from the design mistakes. Automotive industries have attempted to combat this with such programs as advanced product quality planning (APQP), potential failure mode and effects analysis (PFMEA), and production part approval process (PPAP).

Brainstorming

In the early stages of problem solving it is useful to collect a large number of ideas. *Brainstorming* is a way to do that. There are several ways to conduct a brainstorming session. One approach starts with asking each person to express just one idea. This idea is written so all can see it, and the next person expresses one thought. After all group members have had a turn, each is asked for a second idea, and so on. One of the rules of a brainstorming session is that no idea is to be criticized or judged. Often, members will "piggyback" on a previous idea and come up with a new or modified thought. The theory of brainstorming is that if all ideas are documented, it is likely that the best idea or solution is on the list somewhere. A brainstorming session benefits from using a diverse group of participants. Some members should be familiar with the process or similar processes. Others should be outsiders who can see with fresh eyes.

The next step is to compress the list somehow. It may be possible to combine two or more ideas into one. Sometimes the ideas can be grouped into categories such as machining problems, supplier problems, painting problems, and so on. This approach is known as *affinity diagramming*. The group may elect to prioritize the items on the list, agreeing to study the highest-priority items first. Individuals may be assigned the task of pursuing individual ideas further and reporting to the next group meeting.

Benchmarking

Benchmarking is another tool for process/product improvement. Its purpose is to learn better techniques by watching others. For example, a quality improvement team could study how other organizations are handling a particular problem and find ways to incorporate those ideas. The team might study other operations within their own organization or they might seek outside opportunities. If a company is known as a leader in handling a particular process, the team might benchmark the process through study and data collection. If a competitor has a better way of solving a particular problem, the team might study the product for non-proprietary opportunities for improvement. Benchmarking can be used to help solve specific process problems or more generic processes such as payroll preparation. A benchmarking initiative requires that a team try to locate a "best practices" organization and then seek ways to collect data that illustrates gaps between the studied process and their own. The team then has the responsibility to propose changes that will close the gap. In many cases there may not be a best practices example to study and the team may study several cases and select the best ideas from each.

C. ASQ CODE OF ETHICS FOR PROFESSIONAL CONDUCT

> Determine and apply appropriate behaviors and action that comply with this ethical code. (Evaluate)
>
> **Body of Knowledge I.C**

The ASQ Code of Ethics

Fundamental Principles
ASQ requires its representatives to be honest and transparent. Avoid conflicts of interest and plagiarism. Do not harm others. Treat them with respect, dignity, and fairness. Be professional and socially responsible. Advance the role and perception of the Quality professional.

Expectations of a Quality Professional

A. *Act with Integrity and Honesty*
1. Strive to uphold and advance the integrity, honor, and dignity of the Quality profession.
2. Be truthful and transparent in all professional interactions and activities.
3. Execute professional responsibilities and make decisions in an objective, factual, and fully informed manner.

4. Accurately represent and do not mislead others regarding professional qualifications, including education, titles, affiliations, and certifications.

5. Offer services, provide advice, and undertake assignments only in your areas of competence, expertise, and training.

B. *Demonstrate Responsibility, Respect, and Fairness*

1. Hold paramount the safety, health, and welfare of individuals, the public, and the environment.

2. Avoid conduct that unjustly harms or threatens the reputation of the Society, its members, or the Quality profession.

3. Do not intentionally cause harm to others through words or deeds. Treat others fairly, courteously, with dignity, and without prejudice or discrimination.

4. Act and conduct business in a professional and socially responsible manner.

5. Allow diversity in the opinions and personal lives of others.

C. *Safeguard Proprietary Information and Avoid Conflicts of Interest*

1. Ensure the protection and integrity of confidential information.

2. Do not use confidential information for personal gain.

3. Fully disclose and avoid any real or perceived conflicts of interest that could reasonably impair objectivity or independence in the service of clients, customers, employers, or the Society.

4. Give credit where it is due.

5. Do not plagiarize. Do not use the intellectual property of others without permission. Document the permission as it is obtained.

Ethical Dilemmas

The world presents many opportunities to rationalize decisions because "no-one will be harmed." The Code of Ethics provides guidelines for use in the business and social environment. Here are some examples where one might draw on those guidelines. Each of these examples is designed to be covered by one of the items in the Code. It is suggested that the reader attempt to identify the particular item.

1. You have been pressured to reduce the scrap rate on a particular process. The scrap rate is determined by daily weighing the amount of scrap. You have not come up with a significant improvement by the deadline. As a temporary fix, a team member suggests a method to avoid weighing part of the scrap.

2. When interviewing for a new position you are asked whether you have had experience measuring a certain type of weld. You have had extensive experience with a similar weld type and you think that a yes answer is needed in order to get the position.

3. A team is being congratulated for a series of process improvements. You have been singled out for a particular upgrade. Although no-one else knows it, a former team mate who is no longer with the company was actually responsible for the upgrade.

4. You have been asked to make a presentation at a conference. The presentation will include reference to an ongoing internal project. A large amount of time would be required to code and disguise the data. The Code of Ethics requires that one should "Ensure the protection and integrity of confidential information."

5. You are working on a project involving a robot. It is necessary to adjust the robot, allow the robot to execute a sequence, and then make further adjustments. This cycle must be repeated many times. The robot cage door has an interlock that cuts power to the enclosure. It has been suggested that you wire the interlock circuit closed, permitting personnel to work more efficiently by staying inside the enclosure while the equipment is energized.

The Code of Ethics emphasizes that we are professionals and should act accordingly. Further information about ethics can be found at ethics.org.

CHAPTER SUMMARY

The first part of this chapter outlined the basic ideas needed by the quality technician for success in the field.

- Recognition of the dynamics of the supplier-customer relationship and implications for the definition of quality is essential.

- It is also important to recognize the operating environment. This includes understanding of regulations and standards that impact processes and products. Finance is another aspect of the operating environment, so the quality technician must be aware of the way quality costs are assigned.

Every quality technician must also be able to decide where and how to apply a number of tools.

- The seven basic quality tools (cause-and-effect diagrams, flowcharts, check sheets, Pareto charts, scatter diagrams, control charts, and histograms).

- Problem solving techniques such as Five Whys and 8D.

This chapter also discussed the larger picture of quality technology.

- Six Sigma concepts

- Lean concepts

- PDCA, brainstorming, and benchmarking

The next chapter will provide methods for more extensive data analysis.

Chapter 2

II. Statistical Techniques

A. GENERAL CONCEPTS

1. Terminology

Identify and differentiate between statistical terms such as population, sample, parameter, statistic, statistical process control (SPC). (Understand)

Body of Knowledge II.A.1

The *probability* that a particular event will occur is a number between 0 and 1 inclusive. For example, if a lot consisting of 100 parts has four defectives, we would say the probability of randomly drawing a defective is .04 or 4%. The word *random* implies that each part has an equal chance of being drawn, and the procedure is called *random sampling*. If the lot had no defectives, the probability would be 0 or 0%. If the lot had 100 defectives, the probability would be 1 or 100%.

In a statistical study, the *population* is defined as the collection of all individuals, items, or data under consideration. The population is also referred to as the *universe*. The part of the population from which information is collected is called the *sample*. For example, if a lot of 1000 items is received and receiving inspection protocol requires measuring 25 randomly selected items, the population is 1000 and the sample is 25.

Statisticians use the word *mean* in place of the word *average*. In the case of discrete values, the mean is also called *expected value* or *expectation*. For example, if 1500 citizens are randomly selected from the United States and their heights are measured, the population would be all U.S. citizens, and the sample, in this case a random sample, would be the 1500 who were selected.

If the mean of those 1500 heights is 64.29 inches, the conclusion is that the sample mean is 64.29. The value 64.29 is called a *statistic*, which is defined as a descriptive measure of a sample. The next step is to infer the mean height of the population, which is likely to be around 64.29. The actual population mean is

61

called a *parameter*, which is defined as a descriptive measure of a population. So, it can be said that a statistic is an estimated value of a parameter.

To ensure that anyone using or referring to sample or population data correctly communicates the origin of the data, it is standard practice to make that distinction as follows:

- *Parameter.* A quantity describing a given population

- *Statistic.* A quantity describing a given sample

Additionally, parameters and statistics are differentiated in the way they are labeled wherein parameters are identified with letters from the Greek alphabet and statistics are identified with the English letters, as defined in Table 2.1.

It is often helpful to plot sequential data on a time-based graph. In the early twentieth century, manufacturers discovered that control limits could be statistically calculated in such a way that a very high percentage of the plotted points fell within those limits. The technique of using a time-based graph with these control limits is called *statistical process control* (SPC). This technique will be studied in detail in Section C of this chapter.

Table 2.1   Parameters versus statistics.

	Parameter	**Statistic**
Data come from a:	Population	Sample
Denoted/identified by:	Greek alphabet	English alphabet
Examples:		
Size	N	n
Mean	μ	$\bar{x}$
Standard deviation	σ	s

2. Frequency Distributions

Define and compute normal, Poisson, and binomial frequency distributions. (Understand)

Body of Knowledge II.A.2

Histograms and Frequency Distributions. The following example illustrates the concepts histograms and frequency distributions.

Example: A 1.00000 inch gauge block is measured 10 times with a micrometer, and the readings are 1.0008, 1.0000, 1.0000, 0.9996, 1.0005, 1.0001, 0.9990, 1.0003, 0.9999, and 1.0000.

The slightly different values were obtained due to variation in the micrometer, the technique used, and so on. The errors for these measurements can be found by subtracting 1.00000 from each. The errors are: 0.0008, 0, 0, −0.0004, 0.0005, 0.0001, −0.0010, 0.0003, −0.0001, and 0. These error values have been placed on a histogram in Figure 2.1a. If 500 measurements had been made and their errors plotted on a histogram, it would look something like Figure 2.1b.

The histogram in Figure 2.1b approximates the normal distribution. This distribution occurs frequently in various applications in the quality sciences. The normal curve is illustrated in Figure 2.2.

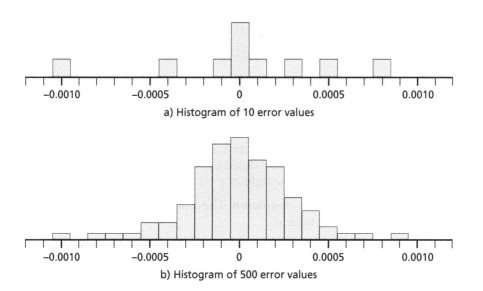

a) Histogram of 10 error values

b) Histogram of 500 error values

Figure 2.1   Histograms of error values.

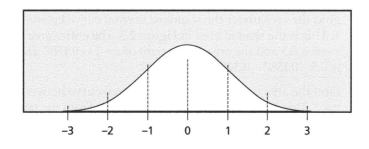

Figure 2.2   Normal curve.

If a very large number of values are plotted on a histogram, it approaches a frequency distribution. The shape of the histogram curve depends on the type of data being plotted. In Figure 2.1b the histogram seems to be approaching a curve known as the normal distribution. This distribution is illustrated in Figure 2.2.

The Normal Distribution. There are several applications in the quality field for the area under a normal curve. This section discusses the basic concepts so the individual applications will be simpler to understand when introduced later in the book.

The normal curve has a fairly complex formula, so locations on the curve are seldom calculated directly. Instead, a "standard normal table," such as the one in Appendix B, is used. Some properties of the "standard normal curve" are:

- The mean is zero and the curve is symmetric about zero.

- The data have a standard deviation of one. The units on the horizontal axis in Figure 2.2 are standard deviations.

- The total area under the normal curve is one square unit.

- The curve doesn't touch the horizontal axis; it extends infinitely far in each direction.

Example: Use the standard normal table (Appendix B) to find the area under the standard normal curve to the right of one standard deviation. The values on the horizontal axis are often referred to as z-values, so this problem is sometimes stated as "Find the area under the standard normal curve to the right of $z = 1$."

In Appendix B find 1 in the z-column. The associated area is 0.1587, which is the correct answer to this problem.

Example: Find the area under the standard normal curve to the right of $z = 0$.

Intuitively, since the curve is symmetric about 0, we would feel that the answer is 0.5. Verify this by finding 0 in the z-column in Appendix B.

Example: Find the area under the standard normal curve to the right of $z = -1$. The area to the right of $z = 1$ is 0.1587, and because of the symmetry of the curve, the area to the *left* of $z = -1$ is also 0.1587. Since the total area under the curve is 1, the area to the right of $z = -1$ is $1 - .1587 = 0.8413$.

Example: Find the area under the standard normal curve between $z = 0$ and $z = 1$. This is the shaded area in Figure 2.3. The entire area to the right of $z = 0$ is 0.5 and the area to the right of $z = 1$ is 0.1587. The shaded area is $0.5 - 0.1587 = 0.3413$.

Example: Find the area under the standard normal curve between $z = -2$ and $z = 1$. This is the shaded area in Figure 2.4. From the table in Appendix B, the area to the right of $z = 2$ is 0.0228, so the area to the *left* of $z = -2$ is also 0.0228. Consequently, the area to the right of $z = -2$ is $1 - 0.0228 = 0.9772$, and the area to the right of $z = 1$ is 0.1587. The shaded area is $0.9772 - 0.1587 = 0.8185$.

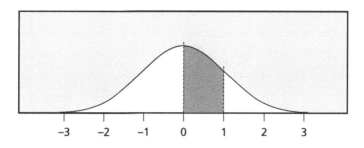

Figure 2.3 Area under the standard normal curve between *z* = 0 and *z* = 1.

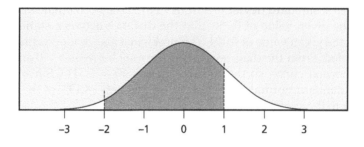

Figure 2.4 Area under the standard normal curve between *z* = –2 and *z* = 1.

Example: Find the area under the standard normal curve between z = –2 and z = 1. This is the shaded area in Figure 2.4. From the table in Appendix B, the area to the right of z = 2 is 0.0228, so the area to the left of z = –2 is also 0.0228. Consequently, the area to the right of z = –2 is 1 – 0.0228 = 0.9772, and the area to the right of z = 1 is 0.1587. The shaded area is 0.9772 – 0.1587 = 0.8185.

Some normal distributions are not the standard normal distribution. The next example shows how the standard normal table in Appendix B can be used to find areas for these cases.

Example: An automatic bar machine produces parts whose diameters are normally distributed with a mean of 0.750 and standard deviation of 0.004. What percentage of the parts has diameters between 0.750 and 0.754?

Figure 2.5 illustrates the problem. This is not the standard normal distribution because the mean is not 0 and the standard deviation is not 1.

> **The standard normal distribution has mean = 0 and standard deviation = 1. There are other normal distributions and this example uses one of them.**

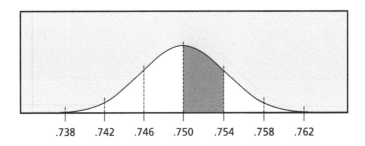

Figure 2.5   Area under a normal curve between 0.750 and 0.754.

It is possible to use Appendix B to find the area. Figure 2.5 shows vertical dashed lines at standard deviations from –3 to 3. The horizontal axis has the mean scaled at the given value of 0.750, and the distance between standard deviation markers is the given value of 0.004. The problem asks what percentage of the total area is shaded. From the diagram, this is the area between $z = 0$ and $z = 1$ on the standard normal curve, so the area is $0.5 - 0.1587 = 0.3413$. Since the total area under the standard normal curve is 1, this represents 34.13% of the area, which is the answer to the problem.

The standard normal curve can be related to probability in the previous example by asking the question, "If a part is selected at random from the output of the automatic bar machine, what is the probability that it will have a diameter between .750 and .754?" Since 34.13% of the parts have diameters in this range, the probability is 0.3413.

How accurate are the answers to the above examples? Suppose that 10,000 parts are produced. If the distribution is exactly normal and the population mean and standard deviation are exactly .750 and .004, then the number with diameters between .750 and .754 would be 3413. But since exactly normal distributions exist only in textbooks, and sample data are typically used to estimate the population mean and standard deviation, the actual number will vary somewhat.

Discrete Distributions. The other two distributions discussed here, the binomial distribution and the Poisson distribution, are called *discrete distributions*. In quality applications these distributions typically are based on count data rather than data measured on a continuous scale such as the normal distribution. The items being counted are often defective products or products that have defects. The word *defective* is used when all products are divided into two categories such as good and bad. The word *defect* is used when a particular product may have several defects or flaws, none of which may cause the product to be defective. The word *defective* would be used for light bulbs that failed to light up. The word *defect* would be used to describe minor scratches, paint runs, and so on, that would not cause the product to be rejected. To add to the confusion, a defective product is sometimes referred to as a *nonconforming* product while a defect is sometimes called a *nonconformity*. This latter terminology has been recommended by legal experts who feel that "nonconformity" sounds better than "defect" in a courtroom. This book uses the terms *defect* and *defective* because they seem less awkward.

The Binomial Distribution. The prefix "bi-" implies the number two, as in *bi*cycle (two wheels) and *bi*partisan (two political parties). The binomial distribution is used when every object fits in one of two categories. The most frequent application in the quality field is when every part is classified as either good or defective, such as in valve leak tests or circuit continuity tests. In these cases there are two possibilities: the valve either leaks or it doesn't; the circuit either passes current or it doesn't. If data on the amount of leakage or the amount of resistance were collected, the binomial distribution would not be appropriate. The word *defective* is often used in binomial distribution applications. A typical example might consider the number of defectives in a random sample of size 10. Notice that the number of defectives is not a continuous variable because, for instance, between two defectives and three defectives there are not an infinite number of other values, that is, there can't be 2.3 defectives. That is why this distribution is called *discrete*.

Example: Suppose 20% of the parts in a batch of 100,000 are defective, and a sample of 10 parts is randomly selected. What is the probability that exactly one of the 10 is defective? The correct answer, stated in the usual notation, is $P(X = 1) \approx .27$. This reads, "The probability that the number of defectives equals 1 is approximately .27." The formula for finding this answer will be given later. It can be used to find the probability that exactly two of the 10 are defective, exactly three are defective, and so on. The results of applying the formula 11 times for the 11 possible answers are shown in Figure 2.6. Figure 2.6 also displays a histogram of the 11 results.

As the title line of Figure 2.6 indicates, the histogram depicts the binomial distribution for sample size = 10 when the rate of defectives is 20%. Statistics books sometimes refer to this as "ten trials with probability of success = .20 on each trial." *Success* in this example refers to selection of a defective part.

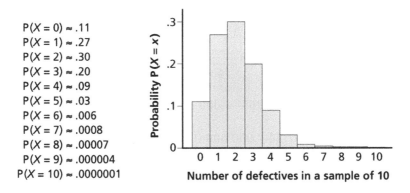

$P(X = 0) \approx .11$
$P(X = 1) \approx .27$
$P(X = 2) \approx .30$
$P(X = 3) \approx .20$
$P(X = 4) \approx .09$
$P(X = 5) \approx .03$
$P(X = 6) \approx .006$
$P(X = 7) \approx .0008$
$P(X = 8) \approx .00007$
$P(X = 9) \approx .000004$
$P(X = 10) \approx .0000001$

Figure 2.6 Binomial distribution with $n = 10$ and $p = .20$.

The formula for calculating the binomial probabilities is called the binomial formula:

$$P(X = x) = \binom{n}{x} p^x (1-p)^{n-x} \text{ Binomial formula}$$

where

n = Number of trials or sample size

x = Number of successes (or defectives in this example)

p = Probability of success for each trial (the probability of a part being defective)

and $\binom{n}{x}$ = Number of combinations of x objects from a collection of n objects

$$= \frac{n!}{(n-x)!\,x!}$$

This formula is discussed in section B.5 of this chapter.

To calculate $P(X = 3)$ in the example shown in Figure 2.6:

$$P(X = 3) = \binom{10}{3}.2^3 \times .8^7 \approx \frac{10!}{3!7!}.008 \times .21 \approx .20$$

The probability of finding at most three defectives:

$$P(X \le 3) = P(X = 0) + P(X = 1) + P(X = 2) + P(X = 3)$$

Each of these terms may be calculated using the binomial formula.

Example: A large batch of parts is 3.5% defective. A random sample of five is selected. What is the probability that this sample has at least four defective parts?

Solution: Calculate two probabilities and add them together:

$$P(X \ge 4) = P(X = 4) + P(X = 5)$$

$$P(X = 4) = \binom{5}{4}.035^4 \times .965^1 \approx \frac{5!}{4! \times 1!}.000\,001\,5 \times .965 \approx .000\,007\,24$$

$$P(X = 5) = \binom{5}{5}.035^5 \times .965^0 \approx .000\,000\,05$$

$$P(X \ge 4) \approx .000\,007\,24 + .000\,000\,05 = .000\,007\,29$$

The mean and standard deviation of a binomial distribution are given by the formulas

$$\mu = np \qquad \sigma = \sqrt{p(1-p)}$$

In this example

$$\mu = .5 \times .035 = .175 \qquad \sigma = \sqrt{.035 \times .965} \approx .184$$

The Poisson Distribution. When counting defects rather than defectives, the Poisson distribution is used rather than the binomial distribution. For example, a process for making sheet goods has an upper specification of eight bubbles per square foot. Every 30 minutes, the number of bubbles in a sample square foot is counted and recorded. If the average of these values is $\bar{c}$, the Poisson distribution is

$$P(X = x) = \frac{e^{-\bar{c}}\bar{c}^x}{x!}$$

where

    x = Number of defects

    $\bar{c}$ = Mean number of defects

    e = Natural log base (use the e^x key on the calculator)

In the example, if the average number of defects (bubbles) per square foot is 2.53, the probability of finding exactly four bubbles is:

$$P(X = 4)\frac{e^{-2.53}2.53^4}{4!} \approx \frac{.0797 \times 40.972}{24} \approx 0.136$$

Consult a calculator instruction manual to evaluate $e^{-2.53}$.

The symbol in the position of the $\bar{c}$ in the above formula varies from book to book; some authors use the Greek letter λ (lambda). The use of $\bar{c}$ in this formula is more consistent with the control limit formulas for the c-chart to be discussed later in this chapter. The formulas for the mean and standard deviation of the Poisson distribution are:

$$\mu = \bar{c} \qquad \sigma = \sqrt{\bar{c}}$$

The variance is defined as the square of the standard deviation, so for the Poisson distribution, the mean is equal to the variance.

B. CALCULATIONS

1. Measures of Central Tendency

> Define, compute, and interpret mean, median, and mode. (Analyze)
>
> **Body of Knowledge II.B.1**

The values that represent the center of a data set are called, rather awkwardly, *measures of central tendency*. There are three commonly used measures of central tendency: mean, median, and mode.

Mean. *Mean* is statistical jargon for the more common word "average." It is calculated by finding the total of the values in the data set and dividing by the number of values. The symbol used for "total" is the Greek capital sigma, Σ. The values of the data set are symbolized by x's and the number of values is usually referred to as *n*. The symbol for mean is an x with a bar above it ($\bar{x}$). This symbol is pronounced "x bar." The formula for mean is

$$\bar{x} = \frac{\Sigma x}{n}$$

This formula tells the user to obtain $\bar{x}$ by adding all the *x*'s and dividing the sum by *n*, the number of values. In other words, what is commonly known as "finding the average."

Example: Find the mean of this data set: 4 7 8 2 3 3 2 1 6 7 4 3 9

There are 13 members in the data set, so the mean is the total divided by 13:

$$\bar{x} = \frac{4+7+8+2+3+3+2+1+6+7+4+3+9}{13} \approx 4.5$$

The ≈ symbol is used to indicate "approximately equal" because the value has been rounded to 4.5. It is common practice to calculate the mean to one more digit of accuracy than that of the original data.

Median. The *median* is the value that has approximately 50% of the values above it and 50% below. To find the median, first sort the data in ascending order. If there is an odd number of values, the median is the middle value of the sorted list. If there is an even number of values, the median is the mean of the two middle values. The common symbol for median is $\tilde{x}$, pronounced "x wiggle."

Example: The list in the previous example is first sorted into ascending order: 1 2 2 3 3 3 4 4 6 7 7 8 9

Since there are 13 values, the median is the seventh value in the sorted list, in this case

$$\tilde{x} = 4$$

Example: Find the median of the six-element set 12.7 12.9 13.5 15.0 15.0 17.2

Since the list is already sorted and has an even number of values, the median is the mean of the two middle values, in this case the mean of 13.5 and 15.0, or $\tilde{x} = 14.25$.

Mode. The *mode* is the value that occurs most often in a data set. If no value occurs more than once, the set has no mode. If there is a tie for the value that occurs most often, the set will have more than one mode.

Example: For the data set 1 2 2 3 3 3 3 4 4 6 7 7 8 9, the mode is 3 because this value occurs most often, four times in this example.

Example: For the data set 1 2 2 3 3 4 4 6 7 7 8 9, there are four modes because four values each occur twice. The four modes are 2, 3, 4, and 7.

Modes appear as high points or peaks on histograms. If a histogram has two peaks, it is referred to as *bimodal* even if the peaks aren't exactly the same height.

A bimodal histogram usually indicates that a process variable had two different distributions. For example, the data might include values collected when two different raw materials were used. A bimodal histogram often presents an opportunity to reduce variation by using more consistent raw materials, for instance.

2. Measures of Dispersion

> Define, compute, and interpret standard deviation, range, and variance. (Analyze)
>
> **Body of Knowledge II.B.2**

The *spread*, also called the *dispersion* or the *variation*, may be measured using the *range*, which is defined as the largest value minus the smallest value:

$$\text{Range} = (\text{largest value}) - (\text{smallest value})$$

Example: For the data set 15.7 12.9 13.5 15.0 15.0 13.2, the range $= 15.7 - 12.9 = 2.8$.

The range is often plotted on control charts as discussed in Section C of this chapter.

One of the disadvantages of using the range as a measure of dispersion is that it uses only two of the values from the data set: the largest and the smallest. If the data set is large, the range does not make use of much of the information contained in the data. For this and other reasons, the *standard deviation* is frequently used to measure dispersion. The value of the standard deviation may be approximated using numbers from the control chart. This method is explained in Part 4, "Process Capability," of Section C of this chapter. The standard deviation can also be found by entering the values of the data set into a calculator that has a standard deviation key. See the calculator manual for appropriate steps.

Although the standard deviation is seldom calculated by hand, the following discussion provides some insight into its meaning. Suppose it is necessary to estimate the standard deviation of a very large data set. One approach would be to randomly select a sample from that set. Suppose the randomly selected sample consists of the values 2, 7, 9, and 2. It would be better to use a larger sample, but this will illustrate the steps involved. It is customary to refer to the sample values as "x-values" and list them in a column headed by the letter x. The first step, as illustrated in Figure 2.7a, is to calculate the sum of that column, $\sum x$ and the mean of the column $\bar{x}$. Recall that

$$\bar{x} = \frac{\sum x}{n}$$

where n is the sample size, 4 in this case. The next step, as illustrated in Figure 2.7b, is to calculate the deviation of each of the sample values from the mean. This is done by subtracting $\bar{x}$ from each of the sample values. In this example, the value of $\bar{x}$ is 5, so 5 is subtracted from each of the sample values. The values in this column are called the deviations from the mean. The total of the $x - \bar{x}$ column will typically be zero, so this total is not of much use. In Figure 2.7c a third column labeled $(x - \bar{x})^2$ has been added. The values in this column are obtained by squaring each of the four values in the previous column. Recall that the square of a negative number is positive. The values in this column are called the squares of the deviations from the mean, and the sum of this column is the sum of the squares of the deviations from the mean. The next step is to divide this sum by $n - 1$. Recall that $n = 4$ in this example, so the result is

$$\frac{38}{3} \approx 12.7$$

x
2
7
9
2

Σ 20

a) Step 1: Find Σx and $\bar{x}$

x	$x - \bar{x}$
2	$2 - 5 = -3$
7	$7 - 5 = 2$
9	$9 - 5 = 4$
2	$2 - 5 = -3$

Σ 20   0

b) Step 2: Form $x - \bar{x}$ column by subtracting $\bar{x}$ from each x-value

x	$x - \bar{x}$	$(x - \bar{x})^2$
2	-3	9
7	2	4
9	4	16
2	-3	9

Σ 20   0   38

c) Step 3: Form the $(x - \bar{x})^2$ column by squaring the values in the $(x - \bar{x})^2$ column

Figure 2.7 Standard deviation calculation.

This quantity is called the *variance,* and its formula is

$$\text{Sample variance} = s^2 = \frac{\Sigma(x - \bar{x})^2}{n - 1}$$

One disadvantage of the variance is that, as the formula indicates, it is measured in units that are the square of the units of the original data set. That is, if the x-values are in inches, the variance is in square inches. If the x-values are in degrees Celsius, the variance is in square degrees Celsius, whatever that may be. For many applications, quality professionals need to use a measure of dispersion that is expressed in the same units as the original data. For this reason, the preferred measure of dispersion is the square root of the variance, which is called the *standard deviation*. Its formula is

$$\text{Sample standard deviation} = s = \sqrt{\frac{\Sigma(x - \bar{x})^2}{n - 1}}$$

As indicated at the beginning of this example, the sample standard deviation is used to estimate the standard deviation of a data set by using a sample from that data set. In some situations it may be possible to use the entire data set rather than a sample. Statisticians refer to the entire data set as the *population,* and the standard deviation as the *population standard deviation,* symbolized by the lowercase Greek sigma, σ. It is common to use capital N to refer to the number of values in the population. The differences in the formula are that the divisor in the fraction is N rather than n – 1, and $\bar{x}$ has been replaced by μ, the population mean:

$$\text{Population standard deviation} = \sigma = \sqrt{\frac{\Sigma(x-\mu)^2}{N}}$$

When using the standard deviation function on a calculator, care should be taken to use the appropriate key. Unfortunately, there is not a universal labeling agreement among calculator manufacturers. Some label the sample standard deviation key s_{n-1} and the population standard deviation key s_n, while others use S_x and s_x. Consult the calculator manual for details. Try entering the values 2, 7, 9, 2 in a calculator and verify that the sample standard deviation rounds to 3.6 and the population standard deviation is 3.1.

Of just what use is the standard deviation? One application is the comparison of two data sets. Suppose two machines can produce a certain shaft diameter. Sample parts from the two machines are collected, the diameters are measured, and their sample standard deviations are calculated. Suppose the sample standard deviation of the parts from machine A is much smaller than the sample standard deviation of the parts from machine B. This means that the diameters from machine A have less variation, or smaller dispersion, than those produced by machine B, and, other things being equal, machine A would be the preferred machine for these parts. The sample standard deviation is used rather than the population standard deviation because the population would be all the parts of this type that the machine would ever produce. In most practical applications the sample standard deviation is the appropriate choice. In fact, some calculators do not have a population standard deviation key.

The standard deviation also has applications to statistical inference, control charts, and process capability, which will be discussed later in this chapter.

3. Confidence Levels

> Explain confidence levels in various situations. (Understand)
>
> **Body of Knowledge II.B.3**

Confidence Level. When making inferences based on statistical data, it is common practice to quantify the level of confidence one has with respect to the inferences. By specifying the level of a term called a *confidence coefficient* it is possible to identify a probability that describes the risk associated with making any given inference. This probability also describes the area in one or both tails of a normal distribution wherein we would expect to see data or observations that fall outside a selected confidence interval.

In normal use, the confidence coefficient (which is stated as a decimal value indicating a probability) is converted to a percent. When a confidence coefficient is converted to a percent it is referred to as a *confidence level*. Confidence levels are normally set as one of the following: 90%, 95%, or 99%. Table 2.2 indicates the relationship between confidence levels and confidence coefficients at the most commonly used levels.

Table 2.2 Confidence levels versus confidence coefficients.

Confidence level $100(1 - \alpha)$	One-tailed: Confidence coefficient (α)	Two-tailed: Confidence coefficient $(\alpha / 2)$	Normalized: $(Z_{\alpha/2})$
99%	.01	.005	2.575
95%	.05	.025	1.96
90%	.10	.05	1.645

4. Confidence Limits

> Explain confidence limits in various situations. (Understand)
>
> **Body of Knowledge II.B.4**

A *confidence interval* is a quantity used when making inferences about a sample statistic. When using sample data as an estimate of a population parameter, such as mean or proportion, it is not known with certainty whether or not the sample data accurately identify the population parameter. Since sample data may not accurately identify any given population parameter, it is necessary to specify at some level of confidence the upper and lower boundaries of where a true population parameter would be located.

A confidence limit has two components as follows:

Point estimate ± Margin of error

The interval defined by the confidence limits is called the confidence interval. As was mentioned above, a point estimate is obtained from a sample statistic and generally involves a measure of location such as a mean or a proportion, or a measure of dispersion such as the standard deviation. The margin of error involves a simple calculation and is the component of the formula that determines the width of the confidence interval. As the level of confidence increases, the width of the interval increases to reflect the uncertainty for making inferences.

When the parameter is normally distributed, the margin of error is calculated for a given level of confidence using the following formula:

$$\text{Margin of error} = \frac{Z_{\alpha/2}s}{\sqrt{n}}$$

where

$Z_{\alpha/2}$ = Confidence level (normalized)

s = Sample standard deviation

n = Sample size

The following example is provided to illustrate application of the concept:

Example: Let $\bar{x}$ = the sample average particulate count as the byproduct of a production process that was sampled once daily for 30 days.

In this case $\bar{x}$ = 5250 with s (sample standard deviation) = 1445.

Wanted: A 95% confidence interval. $\dfrac{1445}{\sqrt{30}}$

In this example, α = .05 and $\alpha/2$ = .025.

Confidence limit	=	Point estimate	±	Margin of error	
	=	$\bar{x}$	±	$z_{\alpha/2} * \dfrac{s}{\sqrt{n}}$	
	=	5250	±	$196 \dfrac{1445}{\sqrt{30}}$	
	=	5250	±	517	
	=				4733, 5767

Interpretation: Based on our 30 days of observations, we are confident that the limit or interval specified by 4733 and 5767 will contain the true population value for mean particulate count 95% of the time. Another way to describe the confidence limit or interval is as follows: based on our 30 days of observations we are 95% confident that the true population mean is contained in the interval (4733, 5767).

5. Probability

> Explain probability using basic concepts of combinations, permutations, and area under the normal curve. (Understand)
>
> **Body of Knowledge II.B.5**

The probability that a particular event occurs is a number between 0 and 1 inclusive. For example, if a lot consisting of 100 parts has four defectives, we would say the probability of randomly drawing a defective is .04 or 4%. Symbolically, this is written P(defective) = .04. The word "random" implies that each part has an equal chance of being drawn. If the lot had no defectives, the probability would be 0 or 0%. If the lot had 100 defectives, the probability would be 1 or 100%.

Basic Probability Rules. *Complementation rule.* The probability that an event A will not occur is 1 – (the probability that A does occur). Stated symbolically, P(not A) = 1 – P(A). Some texts use symbols for "not A" including –A, ~A, and $\overline{A}$.

Special addition rule. Suppose a card is randomly selected from a standard 52-card deck. What is the probability that the card is a club? Since there are 13 clubs, P(♣) = 13/52 = .25. What is the probability that the card is either a club or a spade? Since there are 26 cards that are either clubs or spades, P(♣ or ♠) = 26/52 = .5. Therefore, it appears that P(♣ or ♠) = P(♣) + P(♠), which, generalized, becomes the *special addition rule:*

$$P(A \text{ or } B) = P(A) + P(B)$$

Warning: Use only if A and B can not occur simultaneously

The general addition rule. What is the probability of selecting either a king or a club? Using the special addition rule, P(K or ♣) = P(K) + P(♣) = 4/52 + 13/52 = 17/52. This is incorrect because there are only sixteen cards that are either kings or clubs (the thirteen clubs plus K♦, K♥, and K♠). The reason that the special addition rule doesn't work here is that the two events (drawing a king and drawing a club) can occur simultaneously. We'll denote the probability that A and B both occur as P(A & B). This leads to the *general addition rule:*

$$P(A \text{ or } B) = P(A) + P(B) - P(A \& B)$$

The special addition rule has the advantage of being somewhat simpler, but its disadvantage is that it is not valid when A and B can occur simultaneously. The general addition rule, although more complex, is always valid. For the above example,

$$P(K \& ♣) = 1/52$$

since only one card is both a K and a club. To complete the example,

$$P(K \text{ or } ♣) = P(K) + P(♣) - P(K \& ♣) = 4/52 + 13/52 - 1/52 = 16/52$$

Two events that can't occur simultaneously are called *mutually exclusive.* So, the warning for the special addition rule is sometimes stated as follows: "Use only if events A and B are mutually exclusive."

Contingency Tables. Suppose each part in a lot is one of four colors (red, yellow, green, blue) and one of three sizes (small, medium, large). A tool that displays these attributes is the contingency table:

	Red	Yellow	Green	Blue
Small	16	21	14	19
Medium	12	11	19	15
Large	18	12	21	14

Each part belongs in exactly one column and each part belongs in exactly one row. So each part belongs in exactly one of the 12 cells. When columns and rows are totaled, the table becomes:

	Red	Yellow	Green	Blue	Totals
Small	16	21	14	19	70
Medium	12	11	19	15	57
Large	18	12	21	14	65
Totals	46	44	54	48	192

Note that 192 can be computed in two ways. If one of the 192 parts is randomly selected, find the probability that the part is red.

Solution: $P(red) = 46/192 \approx .240$.

Example: Find the probability that the part is small.

Solution: $P(small) = 70/192 \approx .365$.

Example: Find the probability that the part is red and small.

Solution: Since there are 16 parts that are both red and small, $P(red \& small) = 16/192 \approx .083$.

Example: Find the probability that the part is red or small.

Solution: Since it is possible for a part to be both red and small simultaneously, the general addition rule must be used:

$P(red \text{ or } small) = P(red) + P(small) - P(red \& small) = 46/192 + 70/192 - 16/192 \approx .521$

Example: Find the probability that the part is red or yellow.

Solution: Since no part can be both red and yellow simultaneously, the special addition rule can be used: $P(red \text{ or } yellow) = P(red) + P(yellow) = 46/192 + 44/192 \approx .469$

Notice that the general addition rule also could have been used:

$P(red \text{ or } yellow) = P(red) + P(yellow) - P(red \& yellow) = 46/192 + 44/192 - 0 \approx .469$

Conditional probability. Continuing with the above example, suppose the selected part is known to be green. With this knowledge, what is the probability that the part is large?

Solution: Since the part is located in the green column of the table, it is one of the 54 green parts. So, the lower number in the probability fraction is 54. Since 21 of those 54 parts are large, $P(large$, given that it is green$) = 21/54 \approx .389$.

This is referred to as *conditional probability*. It is denoted: P(large | green) and pronounced "The probability that the part is large given that it is green." It is useful to remember that the category to the right of the | in the conditional probability symbol points to the lower number in the probability fraction.

Find the following probabilities:

P(small | red)	*Solution:* P(small | red) = 16/46 ≈ .348
P(red | small)	*Solution:* P(red | small) = 16/70 ≈ .229
P(red | green)	*Solution:* P(red | green) = 0/54 = 0

A formal definition for conditional probability is:

$$P(B|A) = P(A \ \& \ B) \div P(A)$$

Verifying that this formula is valid in each of the above examples will aid in understanding this concept.

General Multiplication Rule. Multiplying both sides of the conditional probability formula by $P(A)$:

$$P(A \ \& \ B) = P(A) \times P(B \mid A)$$

This is called as the *general multiplication rule*. It is useful to verify that this formula is valid using examples from the contingency table.

Independence and the Special Multiplication Rule. Consider the contingency table.

	X	Y	Z	Totals
F	17	18	14	49
G	18	11	16	45
H	25	13	18	56
Totals	60	42	48	150

$$P(G \mid X) = 18/60 = .300 \text{ and } P(G) = 45/150 = .300 \text{ so } P(G \mid X) = P(G)$$

When this occurs, the events G and X are called *statistically independent* or just independent. Knowing that a part is of type X does not affect the probability that it is of type G. Intuitively, two events are called independent if the occurrence of one does not affect the probability that the other occurs. The formal definition of independence is P(B | A) = P(B). Making this substitution in the general multiplication rule produces the *special multiplication rule*:

$$P(A \ \& \ B) = P(A) \times P(B)$$

Caveat: Use only if A and B are independent.

Example: A box holds 129 parts, of which six are defective. A part is randomly drawn from the box and placed in a fixture. A second part is then drawn from the box. What is the probability that the second part is defective?

The probability can't be determined directly unless the outcome of the first draw is known. In other words, the probabilities associated with successive draws depend on the outcome of previous draws. Using the symbol D_1 to denote the event that the first part is defective and G_1 to denote the event that the first part is good, and so on, following is one way to solve the problem.

There are two mutually exclusive events that can result in a defective part for the second draw: good on first draw and defective on second, or else defective on first and defective on second. Symbolically, these two events are (G_1 & D_2) or else (D_1 & D_2). The first step is to find the probability for each of these events. By the general multiplication rule:

$$P(G_1 \text{ \& } D_2) = P(G_1) \times P(D_2 \mid G_1) = 123/129 \times 6/128 = 0.045$$

Also, by the general multiplication rule:

$$P(D_1 \text{ \& } D_2) = P(D_1) \times P(D_2 \mid D_1) = 6/129 \times 5/128 \approx 0.002$$

Using the special addition rule:

$$P(D_2) = 0.045 + 0.002 = 0.047$$

When drawing two parts, what is the probability that one will be good and one defective? Drawing one good and one defective can occur in two mutually exclusive ways:

$$P(\text{one good and one defective}) = P(G1 \text{ \& } D_2 \text{ or } G_2 \text{ \& } D_1) = P(G1 \text{ \& } D_2) + P(G_2 \text{ \& } D_1)$$

$$P(G1 \text{ \& } D_2) = P(G_1) \times P(D_2 \mid G_1) = 123/129 \times 6/128 \approx 0.045$$

$$P(G_2 \text{ \& } D_1) = P(D_1) \times P(G_2 \mid D_1) = 6/129 \times 123/128 \approx 0.045$$

$$\text{So } P(\text{one good and one defective}) = 0.045 + 0.045 \approx 0.090$$

Combinations

Example: A box of 20 parts has two defectives. The quality technician inspects the box by randomly selecting two parts. What is the probability that both parts selected are defective? The general formula for this type of problem is:

$$P = \frac{\text{Number of ways an event can occur}}{\text{Number of possible outcomes}}$$

The "event" in this case is selecting two defectives, so "number of ways an event can occur" refers to the number of ways two defective parts could be selected. There is only one way to do this since there are only two defective parts. Therefore, the top number in the fraction is 1. The lower number in the fraction is the "number of possible outcomes." This refers to the number of different ways of selecting two parts from the box. This is also called the "number of combinations of two objects from a collection of 20 objects." The formula is:

Number of combinations of r objects from a collection of n objects =

$$nCr = \frac{n!}{r!(n-r)!}$$

Note: Another symbol for number of combinations is $\binom{n}{x}$

In this formula the exclamation mark is pronounced "factorial," so *n!* is pronounced "*n* factorial." The value of 6! is $6 \times 5 \times 4 \times 3 \times 2 \times 1 = 720$. The value of *n!* is the result of multiplying the first *n* positive whole numbers. Most scientific calculators have a factorial key, typically labeled *x!*. To calculate 6! using this key, press 6 followed by the *x!* key. Returning to the previous example, the lower number in the fraction is the number of possible combinations of two objects from a collection of 20 objects. Substituting into this formula:

$$_{20}C_2 = \binom{20}{2} = \frac{20!}{2!(20-2)!} = \frac{20!}{2!18!} = 190$$

The answer to the problem posed in the example:

$$\text{Probability is } \frac{1}{190} \approx .005$$

How might this be useful in the inspection process? Suppose a supplier has shipped this box with the specification that it have no more than two defective parts. What is the probability that the supplier has met this specification? Answer ≈ .005.

Example: A box of 20 parts has three defectives. The quality technician inspects the box by randomly selecting two parts. What is the probability that both parts selected are defective?

The bottom term of the fraction remains the same as in the previous example. The top term is the number of combinations of two objects from a collection of three objects:

$$\binom{n}{r} = \frac{n!}{r!(n-r)!} = \binom{3}{2} = \frac{3!}{2!(3-2)!} = \frac{6}{2!1!} = \frac{6}{2} = 3$$

To see that this makes sense, name the three defectives A, B, and C. The number of different two-letter combinations of these three letters is AB, AC, BC. Note that AB is not a different combination from BA because it is the same two letters. If two defectives are selected, the order in which they are selected is not significant. The answer to the probability problem has a 3 as its top term: $P = 3/190 \approx .016$.

An important thing to remember: *combinations are used when order is not significant.*

Note: Calculators have an upper limit to the value that can use the x! key. If a problem requires a higher factorial, use the statistical function in a spreadsheet program such as Excel. It is interesting to observe that a human can calculate the value of some factorial problems that a calculator can't.

Example: Find $\dfrac{1000!}{997!}$

Solution: Most calculators can't handle 1000! But humans know that the terms of this fraction can be written:

$$\frac{1000!}{997!} = \frac{1000 \times 999 \times 998 \times 997 \times 996 \times 995 \times 994...}{997 \times 996 \times 995 \times 994 \times...}$$

The factors on the bottom term cancel out all but the first three factors in the top term, so the answer is $1000 \times 999 \times 998$, which, unfortunately, most of us need a calculator to calculate.

Permutations. With combinations, the order of the objects doesn't matter. Permutations are very similar except that the order does matter.

Example: A box has 20 parts labeled A through T. Two parts are randomly selected. What is the probability that the two parts are A and T in that order? The general formula applies:

$$P = \frac{\text{Number of ways an event can occur}}{\text{Number of possible outcomes}}$$

The bottom term of the fraction is the number of orderings or permutations of two objects from a collection of 20 objects. The general formula:

Number of permutations of r objects from a collection of n objects =

$$nPr = \frac{n!}{(n-r)!}$$

In this case $n = 20$ and $r = 2$: $_{20}P_2 = \frac{20!}{(20-2)!} = \frac{20!}{18!} = 380$

Of these 380 possible permutations, only one is AT, so the top term in the fraction is one. The answer to the probability problem is

$$P = \frac{1}{380} \approx .003$$

Example: A team with seven members wants to select a task force of three people to collect data for the next team meeting. How many different three-person task forces could be formed? This is not a permutations problem because the order in which people are selected doesn't matter. In other words, the task force consisting of Barb, Bill, and Bob is the same task force as the one consisting of Bill, Barb, and Bob. Therefore the combinations formula will be used to calculate the number of combinations of three objects from a collection of seven objects:

$$_7C_3 = \frac{7!}{(7-3)!3!} = 35$$

Thirty-five different task forces could be formed.

Example: A team with seven members wants to select a cabinet consisting of a chairman, facilitator, and scribe. How many ways can the three-person cabinet be formed? Here, the order is important because the cabinet consisting of Barb, Bill, and Bob will have Barb as chairman, Bill as facilitator, and Bob as scribe, while the cabinet consisting of Bill, Barb, and Bob has Bill as chairman, Barb as facilitator, and Bob as scribe. The appropriate formula is the one for permutations of three objects from a collection of seven objects:

$$P = \frac{7!}{(7-3)!} = 210$$

Two hundred ten different cabinets could be formed.

Normal Distribution. Use of area under the normal curve to calculate probability is discussed in Section A of this chapter.

C. CONTROL CHARTS

1. Control Limits vs. Specification Limits

> Identify and describe the different uses of control limits and specification limits. (Understand)
>
> **Body of Knowledge II.C.1**

Control limits are used to detect process changes. These limits are calculated using statistical formulas that imply that, for a stable process, a high percentage of the points will fall between the upper and lower control limits. In other words, the probability that a point from a stable process falls outside the control limits is very small, and the user of the chart is almost certainly correct to assume that such a point indicates that the process has changed. When the chart is correctly used, the user will take appropriate action when a point occurs outside the control limits. The action that is appropriate varies with the situation. In some cases it may be that the wisest course is to increase vigilance through more frequent sampling. Sometimes an immediate process adjustment is called for. In other cases, the process must be stopped immediately.

One of the most common mistakes in using control charts is to use the specification limits as control limits. Since the specification limits have no statistical basis, the user of the chart has no statistical basis for assuming that the process has changed when a point occurs outside them.

> **When control charts are introduced there is a temptation to draw specification limits on the chart. This temptation must be resisted. In the case of the $\bar{x}$ chart, it is possible that all points in a sample can be outside the specification limits but the plotted mean is inside, leading the casual observer to think everything is ok.**

The statement "I just plotted a point outside the control limits but it is well within specification limits, so I don't have to worry about it" represents a misunderstanding of the chart. The main purpose of the control chart is to signal the user that the process has changed. If the signal is ignored, the control chart loses much of its value as an early warning tool. This misunderstanding of the significance of the control limits is especially dangerous in the case of the averages portion of the $\overline{X}$ and R or the $\overline{X}$ and s chart. Recall that the points on this portion of the chart are calculated by averaging several measurements. It is possible for the average (or mean) to fall within the specification limits even though none of the actual measurements are within these limits. For example, suppose the specification limits for a dimension are 7.350 to 7.360, and a sample of five parts yields the following measurements: 7.346, 7.344, 7.362, 7.365, 7.366. The mean of these values is 7.357, well within the specification limits. In this case the range chart would likely have shown the point above its upper control limit. Should the user take comfort in the fact that the plotted point, located at the mean, is well inside the specification limits?

2. Variables Charts

> Identify, select, construct, and interpret variables charts such as $\overline{X} - R$, $\overline{X} - s$. (Analyze)
>
> **Body of Knowledge II.C.2**

In Section B of Chapter 1 the $(\overline{X})$ and R control chart was introduced. That chart is copied here as Figure 2.8.

As explained in Chapter 1, values are calculated by averaging the sample of readings taken at a particular time, and the range values are found by subtracting the low value from the high value for each sample. The discussion in Chapter 1 indicated that the locations of the control limits are statistically based. The following paragraphs provide more guidance on this concept.

There are a number of events that are very unlikely to occur unless the process has changed and thus serve as statistical indicators of process change. The lists vary somewhat from textbook to textbook but usually include something like those shown in Figure 2.9. When one of these events occurs on a control chart, the process operator needs to take appropriate action. Sometimes this may entail a process adjustment. Sometimes the appropriate action is to stop the process. In some situations the operator should increase watchfulness, perhaps taking readings every few minutes instead of every hour, for instance. The important issue is that the chart has provided a statistical signal that there is a high probability that the process has changed.

Control limits are typically set at three standard deviations above and below the average. The standard deviation is messy to calculate, so the standard way to locate control limits is to use formulas using control limit constants. These formulas are summarized in Appendix C, and the constants are listed in Appendix D.

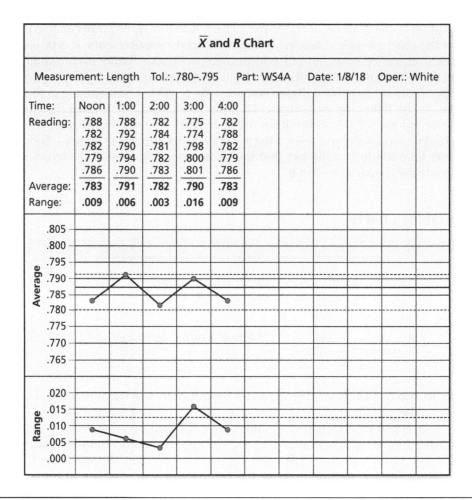

Figure 2.8 Example of an $\bar{X}$ and R chart.

1. A point above the upper control limit or below the lower control limit.

2. Seven successive points above (or below) the average line.

3. Seven successive points trending up (or down).

4. Middle one-third of the chart includes more than 90% or fewer than 40% of the points after at least 25 points have been plotted.

5. Nonrandom patterns.

Figure 2.9 Control chart indicators of process change.

For the $\bar{X}$ and R chart Appendix C shows the following formulas:

$$\text{Averages chart: } \tilde{\bar{x}} \pm A_2\bar{R}$$

$$\text{Range chart: LCL} = D_3\bar{R} \quad \text{UCL} = D_4\bar{R}$$

For these formulas,

$\tilde{\bar{x}}$ = The average of all the average values (that is, the process mean)

$\bar{R}$ = the average of all the range values

A_2, D_3, and D_4 are constants from Appendix D and are dependent on sample size.

Example: Suppose that data have been collected from the process depicted in Figure 2.8 using samples of size five. The averages and ranges of these samples are calculated with the following results: $\tilde{\bar{x}}$ = .786, $\bar{R}$ = .010.

From Appendix D, using sample size n = 5: A_2 = .577, D_3 is undefined, D_4 = 2.114.

Using the formulas shown above, the control limits would be

$$\text{Averages chart: } .786 \pm .577 \times .010 \approx .786 \pm .006 = .792 \text{ and } .780$$

$$\text{Range chart: LCL isn't defined, UCL} = 2.114 \times .010 = .021$$

These control limits have been drawn on the chart shown in Figure 2.8.

An important issue here is that the control limits are not arbitrary, but rather are calculated using data from the process. How much data is needed? The more, the better. Some textbooks say that at least 25 samples should be used. The sample size used when collecting the data dictates the sample size used on the control chart.

The $\bar{X}$ and R control chart is called a *variables* chart. Variables charts use data from a continuous scale, that is, a scale on which between any two points there are in infinite number of other points. The $\bar{X}$ and S chart is another variables control chart. It works a lot like the $\bar{X}$ and R, but instead of calculating and plotting the range of each sample, the standard deviation of each sample is calculated and plotted. Not surprisingly, different control limit formulas and constants are used:

$$\text{Averages chart: } \tilde{\bar{x}} \pm A_3\bar{s}$$

$$\text{Standard deviation chart: LCL} = B_3\bar{R} \quad \text{UCL} = B_4\bar{R}$$

For these formulas,

$\tilde{\bar{x}}$ = The average of all the average values (that is, the process mean)

$\bar{s}$ = The average of all the sample standard deviation values

A_3, B_3, and B_4 are constants from Appendix D and are dependent on sample size

The charts are constructed and interpreted in the same manner as the $\bar{X}$ and R charts.

The *median chart* is another variables control chart. An example of the median chart is shown in Figure 2.10. In this chart all the readings in the sample are plotted and the medians of the samples are connected with a broken line.

One advantage of this chart is that no calculation by the operator is required. The control limit formulas:

$$\tilde{\tilde{x}} \pm \tilde{\tilde{A}}_2 \bar{R}$$

where

$\tilde{\tilde{x}}$ = the average of the medians

$\tilde{\tilde{A}}_2$ = is a constant found in Appendix D

One disadvantage of this chart is that it does not capture the signal when a range is too high. Some authors suggest constructing a paper or plastic mask with width equal to the UCL for the range. If this mask can't cover all the plotted points for a particular sample, the range is above the UCL for range. An example of this sort of mask is shown as a shaded rectangle in Figure 2.10. The formula for UCL of the range is the same as that for the $\overline{X}$ and R chart.

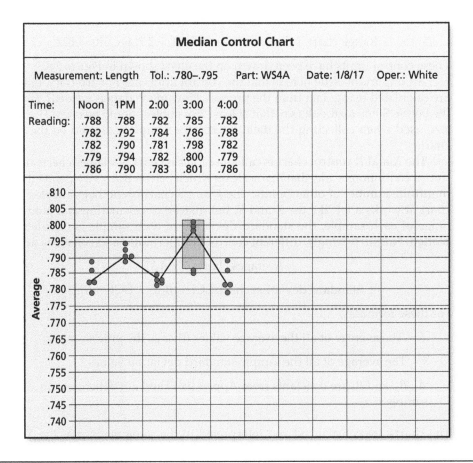

Figure 2.10 Example of median control chart.

The individuals and moving range (I-MR) chart is another variables control chart. It is used when the sample size is 1. An example of this chart is shown in Figure 2.11. Note that the moving range is the absolute value of the difference between the current reading and the previous reading. This means that the first reading will have no moving range.

The control limit formulas for the I-MR (also called the X-MR) chart:

$$\text{Individuals: } \bar{x} \pm E_2\bar{R}$$

$$\text{Moving range: UCL} = D_4\bar{R} \quad \text{LCL} = D_3\bar{R}$$

The sample size is the width of the moving window. In the example, the moving window is two readings wide. *Note:* The moving range points are what statisticians call *correlated*. This means that the only points on the MR chart that signal a process change are those outside the control limits.

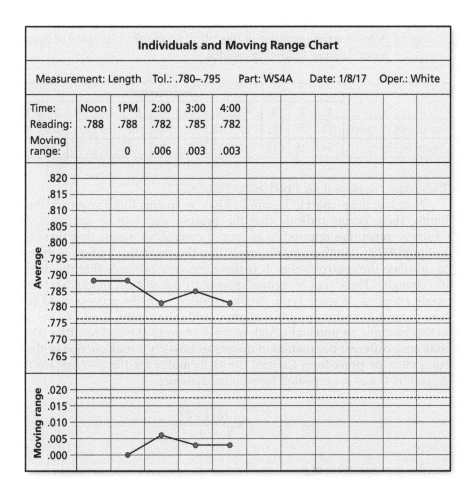

Figure 2.11 Example of individuals and moving range (I–MR) control chart.

3. Attributes Charts

Identify, select, construct, and interpret
attributes charts such as p, np, c, u.
(Analyze)

Body of Knowledge II.C.3

Attributes charts are used for count data. If every item is in one of two categories such as good or bad, "defectives" are counted. If each item may have several flaws, "defects" are counted.

Charting Defectives. If defectives are being counted, the p-chart can be used.

Example: A test for the presence of the "Rh-" factor in 13 samples of donated blood has the following results:

	Test number												
	1	**2**	**3**	**4**	**5**	**6**	**7**	**8**	**9**	**10**	**11**	**12**	**13**
No. of units of blood	125	111	133	120	118	137	108	110	124	128	144	138	132
No. of Rh− units	14	18	13	17	15	15	16	11	14	13	14	17	16

These data are plotted on a p-chart in Figure 2.12.

Note that the p-chart in Figure 2.12 has two points that are outside the control limits. These points indicate that the process was "out of statistical control," which is sometimes referred to as "out of control." It means that there is a very low probability that these points came from the same distribution as the one used to calculate the control limits. It is therefore very probable that the distribution has changed. These "out of control" points are a statistical signal that the process needs attention of some type. People familiar with the process need to decide how to react to various points that are outside the control limits. In the situation in this example an unusually high number of units of blood test Rh−. This could indicate a different population of donors or possibly a malfunction of the testing equipment or procedure. Control limits formulas for the p-chart are listed in Appendix C and are repeated here for convenience:

$$\bar{p} \pm \sqrt{\frac{\bar{p}(1-\bar{p})}{\bar{n}}}$$

where

$\bar{p}$ = average value of p

$\bar{n}$ = average sample size

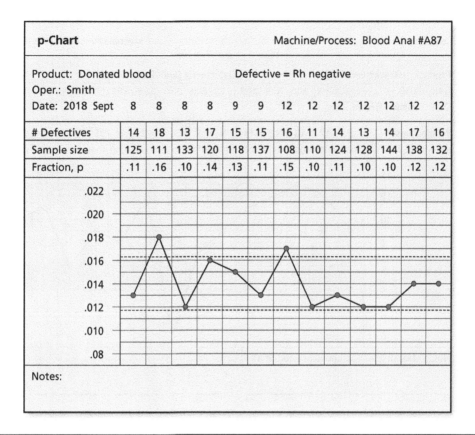

p-Chart													Machine/Process: Blood Anal #A87

Product: Donated blood   Defective = Rh negative
Oper.: Smith

Date: 2018 Sept	8	8	8	8	9	9	12	12	12	12	12	12	12
# Defectives	14	18	13	17	15	15	16	11	14	13	14	17	16
Sample size	125	111	133	120	118	137	108	110	124	128	144	138	132
Fraction, p	.11	.16	.10	.14	.13	.11	.15	.10	.11	.10	.10	.12	.12

Notes:

Figure 2.12   Example of a p control chart.

If defectives are being counted and the sample size remains constant, the np-chart can be used.

Example: Packages containing 1000 light bulbs are randomly selected, and all 1000 bulbs are light-tested. The np-chart is shown in Figure 2.13. Note that on March 25 the point is outside the control limits. This means there is a high probability that the process was different on that day than on the days that were used to construct the control limits. In this case the process was different in a good way. It would be advisable to pay attention to the process to see what went right and to see if the conditions could be incorporated into the standard way of running the process. Notice the operator note at the bottom of the chart.

The control limits for the np chart are given by the formulas:

$$n\bar{p} \pm 3\sqrt{n\bar{p}(1-\bar{p})}$$

where

n = Sample size

$\bar{p}$ = Average number of defectives per sample

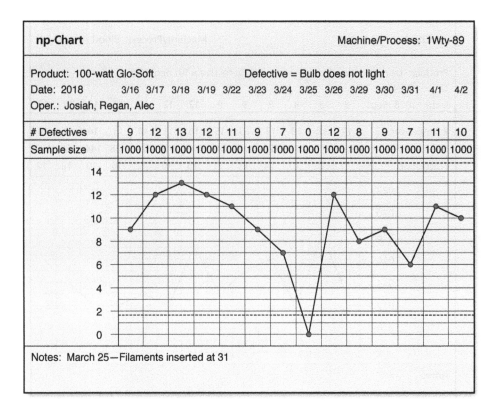

Figure 2.13 Example of an np control chart.

In the example shown in Figure 2.12, $n = 1000$ and $\bar{p} = \dfrac{130}{14\,000} \approx .0093$

So the control limits are:

$$\text{UCL} = 1000 \times .0093 + 3\sqrt{1000 \times .0093(1-.0093)} \approx 12.3$$

$$\text{LCL} = 1000 \times .0093 - 3\sqrt{1000 \times .0093(1-.0093)} \approx 6.3$$

The u- and c-charts are used when defects rather than defectives are being counted. If the sample size varies, the u-chart is used. If the sample size is constant, the c-chart may be used. An example of a u-chart is shown in Figure 2.14. A c-chart would look much like the np-chart illustrated in Figure 2.13 and is not shown here.

To decide which attribute chart to use:

- For defectives, use p or np:
  - Use p for varying sample size.
  - Use np for constant sample size.

- For defects, use u or c:
  - Use u for varying sample size.
  - Use c for constant sample size.

The control limit formulas for the u-chart: $\bar{u} \pm 3\sqrt{\dfrac{\bar{u}}{\bar{n}}}$

where

$\bar{u}$ = average defect fraction = $\dfrac{\Sigma \text{ number of defects}}{\Sigma \text{ sample sizes}}$

$\bar{n}$ = average sample size

Using the data in Figure 2.14, $\bar{u} \approx .518$ and $\bar{n} \approx 9.786$, the control limits would be:

$\text{UCL} = .518 + 3\sqrt{.053} \approx 1.21$

$\text{LCL} = .518 - 3\sqrt{.053}$ Since this value is negative, there is no LCL

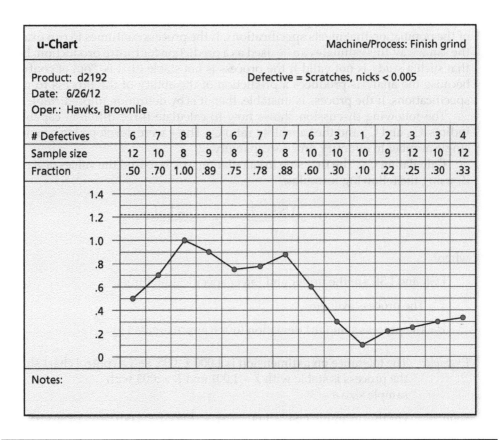

u-Chart											Machine/Process: Finish grind		
Product: d2192						Defective = Scratches, nicks < 0.005							
Date: 6/26/12													
Oper.: Hawks, Brownlie													
# Defectives	6	7	8	8	6	7	7	6	3	1	2	3	3	4
Sample size	12	10	8	9	8	9	8	10	10	10	9	12	10	12
Fraction	.50	.70	1.00	.89	.75	.78	.88	.60	.30	.10	.22	.25	.30	.33

Notes:

Figure 2.14 Example of a u control chart.

4. Process Capability Measures

> Define the prerequisites for capability, and
> calculate and interpret capability indices
> (e.g., C_p, C_{pk}, P_p, P_{pk}) and capability ratio
> (C_R) in various situations. (Analyze)
>
> **Body of Knowledge II.C.4**

If the control chart does not exhibit any of the indicators of instability, it is assumed that the process is stable. If the process is stable, it is appropriate to do a process capability analysis. The purpose of a capability analysis is to estimate the percent of the population that meets specifications. If the process continues to run exactly the same way, this estimate can be used as a prediction for future production. Note that such a study is not valid if the process is not stable (that is, "out of control") because the analysis produces a prediction of the ability of the process to meet specifications. If the process is unstable, then it is by definition unpredictable.

The following discussion shows how to calculate three different capability indices: C_{pk} and C_p, and the capability ratio C_R. These were developed to provide a single number to quantify process capability.

Calculating C_{pk}. The first step in calculating Cpk is to find the values of Z_U and Z_L using the following formulas:

$$Z_U = \frac{\text{USL} - \bar{\bar{x}}}{\sigma} \qquad Z_L = \frac{\bar{\bar{x}} - \text{LSL}}{\sigma}$$

where

USL and LSL are the upper and lower specification limits

$\bar{\bar{x}}$ = The process average

σ = the process standard deviation (often approximated by $\frac{\bar{R}}{d_2}$)

Example: The tolerance on a dimension is $1.000 \pm .005$, and a control chart shows the process is stable with $\bar{\bar{x}} = 1.001$ and $\bar{R} = .003$ with sample size $n = 3$.

Solution: For this example USL = 1.005, LSL = 0.995, $\bar{\bar{x}} = 1.001$, $\bar{R} = 0.003$ and the estimated value of σ is

$$\sigma \approx \frac{.003}{1.693} \approx .0018$$

(Some books use $\hat{s}$ to symbolize the estimated value of σ.)

Substituting these values into the Z formulas:

$$Z_U = \frac{1.005 - 1.001}{.0018} \approx 2.22 \text{ and } Z_U = \frac{1.001 - 0.995}{.0018} \approx 3.33$$

The formula for C_{pk}:

$$C_{pk} = \frac{Min(Z_U, Z_L)}{3}$$

Where Min means select the smallest of the values in the parenthesis.

In this example,

$$C_{pk} = \frac{Min(2.22, 3.33)}{3} = \frac{2.22}{3} \approx 0.74$$

The higher the value of C_{pk}, the more capable the process. A few years ago, a C_{pk} value of 1 or more was considered satisfactory. This would imply that there is at least 3s between the process mean $(\bar{x})$ and the nearest specification limit. More recently, many industries require four, five, or even six standard deviations between the process mean and the nearest specification limit. This would correspond to a C_{pk} of 1.33, 1.67, and 2, respectively. The push for six standard deviations was the origin of the "Six Sigma" program.

If the process data are normally distributed, the Z-values may be used in a standard normal table (Appendix B) to find approximate values for the percent of production that lies outside the specification. In this example, the upper Z of 2.22 corresponds to 0.0132 in Appendix B. This means that approximately 1.32% of the production of this process violates the upper specification limit. Similarly, the lower Z of 3.33 corresponds to 0.0004 in Appendix B. This means that approximately 0.04% of the production of this process violates the lower specification limit. Note that the use of the standard normal table in Appendix B is only appropriate if the process data are normally distributed. Since no real-world process data are exactly normally distributed, it is best to state these percentages as estimates. The percentages can be useful in estimating return on investment for quality improvement projects.

When the two Z-values are not equal, this means that the process average is not centered within the specification limits, and some improvement to the percentages can be made by centering. Suppose, in the above example, that a process adjustment can be made that would move $\bar{x}$ to a value of 1.000. Then Z_U and Z_L would each be 2.77, and from the table in Appendix B, the two percentages would be 0.28%. The total percentage outside specification limits would be .56% compared to 1.36% before the change. Centering a process can be the most cost-effective way to make an improvement.

Calculating C_p. The formula for the capability index C_p is:

$$C_p = \frac{USL - LSL}{6\sigma}$$

Using the values from the previous example:

$$C_p = \frac{1.005 - 0.995}{6(0.0018)} \approx 0.93$$

Note that the formula for this index does not make use of the process average, $\bar{\bar{x}}$. Therefore, the C_p index does not consider whether the process average is centered within the specification limits or, indeed, whether it is even between the two limits. In reality, C_p tells what the process could potentially do if it were centered.

> **The Cpk calculation uses the process average $\bar{\bar{x}}$ and therefore it takes into consideration whether the process is centered. The Cp calculation does not use $\bar{\bar{x}}$ and so does not reflect whether the process is centered.**

For centered processes, C_p and C_{pk} have the same value. For processes that aren't centered, C_p is larger than C_{pk}.

Calculating CR. This index is also referred to as the *capability ratio*. It is the reciprocal of C_p. The formula:

$$CR = \frac{6\sigma}{USL - LSL}$$

Using the data form the previous example,

$$CR = \frac{6(0.0018)}{1.005 - 0.995} \approx 1.08$$

which, not surprisingly, is approximately

$$\frac{1}{0.93}$$

Of course, *lower* values of CR imply more capable processes.

5. Common and Special Cause Variation

> Interpret various control chart patterns (e.g., runs, hugging, trends) and use rules for determining statistical control to distinguish between common cause and special cause variation. (Analyze)
>
> **Body of Knowledge II.C.5**

The variation of a process that is in statistical control is called *common cause variation*. This variation is inherent in the process and can only be reduced through changes in the process itself. Therefore, it is important that process operators not respond to changes attributed to common cause variation.

When additional variation occurs, it is referred to as *special cause variation*. This variation can be assigned to some outside change that affects the process output. It is important that the process operator respond to this variation. The purpose of a control chart is to distinguish between these two types of variation. It does this by providing a statistical signal that a special cause is impacting the process. This permits the operator to have immediate process feedback and to take timely and appropriate action.

The statistical signal consists of the occurrence of an event that is on the list of indicators of process change. That list is repeated here for convenience:

1. A point above the upper control limit or below the lower control limit.

2. Seven successive points above (or below) the average line.

3. Seven successive points trending up (or down).

4. Middle one-third of the chart includes more than 90% or fewer than 40% of the points after at least 25 points have been plotted.

5. Nonrandom patterns.

The action that is appropriate for the operator to take depends on the event and process. The action that is needed should be spelled out in the operating instructions for the process. These instructions should provide for logging of the event and actions taken. Figures 2.15 through 2.20 illustrate the use of the indicators of process change to distinguish between special cause and common cause variation. Control limits are shown as dashed lines on each chart. The caption for each figure explains the indicator involved.

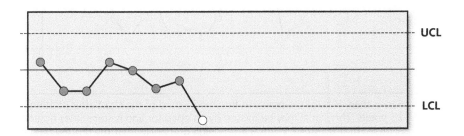

Figure 2.15   Point outside control limit. When the open dot is plotted, the operator is signaled that there is a very high probability that the process has changed.

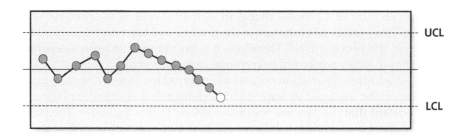

Figure 2.16 Seven successive points trending downward. When the open dot is plotted, the operator is signaled that there is a very high probability that the process has changed.

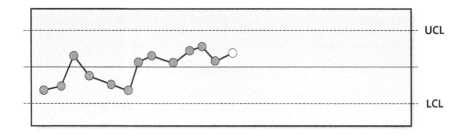

Figure 2.17 Seven successive points on one side of the process average. When the open dot is plotted, the operator is signaled that there is a very high probability that the process has changed.

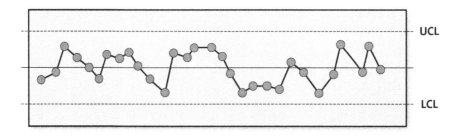

Figure 2.18 Fewer than 40% of the points in the middle third of the chart after plotting at least 25 points. This signal may be missed by an operator and is sometimes noted by chart analysis off-line. Again, there is a very high probability that the process has changed.

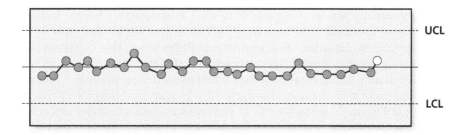

Figure 2.19   More than 90% of the points in the middle third of the chart after plotting at least 25 points. This signal may be missed by an operator and is sometimes noted by chart analysis off-line. Again, there is a very high probability that the process has changed.

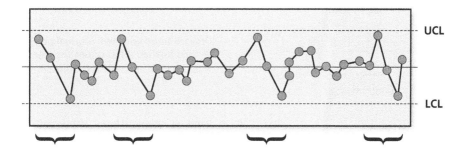

Figure 2.20   Nonrandom pattern. This indicator must be used with caution—the human brain will discover patterns where none exist. The bracketed points might be a nonrandom pattern. Or not. This signal may be missed by an operator and is sometimes noted by chart analysis off-line. Again, there is a very high probability that the process has changed.

6. Data Plotting

Identify the advantages and limitations of using this method to analyze data visually. (Understand)

Body of Knowledge II.C.6

One of the hazards of using software for statistical analysis is the temptation to perform analysis on data without first "looking" at them. One example would be the calculation of linear correlation coefficients. This number helps determine whether two variables have a relationship that permits the prediction of one variable using the other variable in a straight-line formula. The correct procedure is to construct a scatter diagram of the data as shown in Chapter 1. If the points seem to be grouped around a straight line in the scatter diagram, it would be appropriate to calculate the coefficient. Otherwise, the calculation may be misleading. In some cases (especially with small data sets) a fairly high correlation coefficient may result from data that, when plotted, are clearly not related.

Some information can be discovered just by staring at the plots. In the examples shown in Figure 2.21, knowledge of the mean and standard deviation would not help discover as much about the data as our minds intuitively can deduce from the plotted graphs. These examples are intended to support the position that it is often useful to look at plots of data in conjunction with mathematical analysis.

Time related graphs

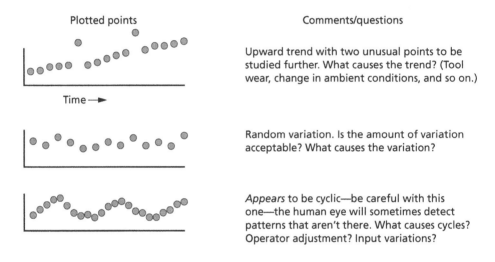

Plotted points

Time ⟶

Comments/questions

Upward trend with two unusual points to be studied further. What causes the trend? (Tool wear, change in ambient conditions, and so on.)

Random variation. Is the amount of variation acceptable? What causes the variation?

Appears to be cyclic—be careful with this one—the human eye will sometimes detect patterns that aren't there. What causes cycles? Operator adjustment? Input variations?

Histograms (vertical dashed lines designate specification limits)

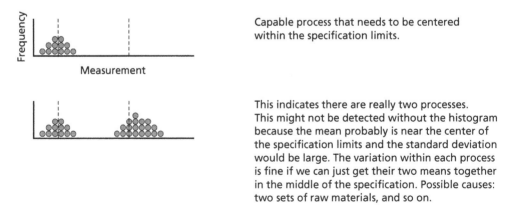

Frequency

Measurement

Capable process that needs to be centered within the specification limits.

This indicates there are really two processes. This might not be detected without the histogram because the mean probably is near the center of the specification limits and the standard deviation would be large. The variation within each process is fine if we can just get their two means together in the middle of the specification. Possible causes: two sets of raw materials, and so on.

Figure 2.21   Examples of analyzing plots visually.

One of the disadvantages of data plotting is that the choice of scale and group size can cause misinterpretation.

The two graphs in Figure 2.22 plot the same data using different scales.

The two graphs in Figure 2.23 show that group size can mask the bimodal characteristic of the distribution.

To summarize, graphs can aid in data analysis but the choice of basis parameters can unintentionally (or intentionally) be misleading.

Date	Defects/1000
19	42
20	40
21	38
22	38
23	37

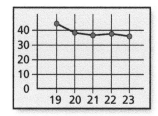 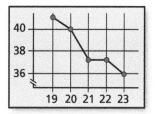

Figure 2.22   Two plots of the same data giving different impressions of the change.

Measurement	150	151	152	153	154	155	156	157	158	159	160	161	162	163	164	165
Frequency	4	6	10	5	5	6	6	7	10	11	9	6	6	7	7	7

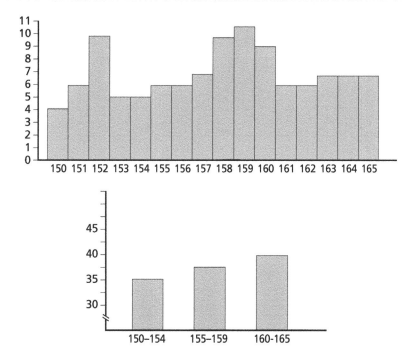

Figure 2.23   The effect of histogram group size.

Chapter 3

III. Metrology and Calibration

A. TYPES OF MEASUREMENT AND TEST EQUIPMENT (M&TE)

Describe, select, and use the following types of M&TE, and evaluate their measurement results to determine conformance to specifications. (Evaluate)

1. Hand tools (e.g., calipers, micrometers, linear scales, analog, digital, vernier scales)

2. Gauges (e.g., pins, thread, custom gauges, gauge blocks)

3. Optical tools (e.g., comparators, profiles, microscopes)

4. Coordinate measuring machines (CMM) (e.g., touch probes, vision, laser)

5. Electronic measuring equipment (e.g., digital displays, output)

6. Weights, balances, and scales

7. Hardness testing equipment (e.g., Brinell, Rockwell)

8. Surface plate methods and equipment

9. Surface analyzers (e.g., profilometers, roughness reference standards)

10. Force measurement tools (e.g., torque wrenches, tensometers)

11. Angle measurement tools (e.g., protractors, sine bars, angle blocks)

12. Color measurement tools (e.g., spectrophotometer, color guides, light boxes)

13. Automated in-line inspection methods (e.g., vision systems, laser inspection systems, pyrometers)

Body of Knowledge III.A.13

Metrology, the science of weights and measures—also defined as the science of precision measurements—has many applications and requires a wide variety of instruments in just about every facet of science and industry. In the competitive manufacture of precision-engineered products where a high degree of quality is required it is particularly important that the proper measuring and gauging instruments be employed to provide accurate, reliable, and cost-effective inspection results. Some industry studies have indicated that the dimensional tolerances on state-of-the-art manufactured products are shrinking by a factor of three every 10 years. Thus, the selection of appropriate measuring and gauging instruments will become even more critical and demanding in the future.

Dimensional metrology is concerned with the measurement or gauging of a variety of workpiece characteristics including length, diameter, thickness, angle, taper, roughness, concentricity, and profile. Different sensing technologies may be employed to measure or gauge those characteristics, depending on the requirements for accuracy and other considerations. There are basically five different technologies that may be used individually or in combination to perform these inspection functions:

1. *Mechanical.* Small displacements are amplified by a mechanical system.

2. *Electronic.* These utilize an electric or electronic phenomenon such as electrical resistance.

3. *Air or pneumatic.* Small variations made in the dimension are measured with respect to a reference dimension and are shown by a variation in air pressure or the velocity of airflow.

4. *Light waves.* These utilize the phenomenon of the interference of light waves to provide a standard. Such a standard is the wavelength of a monochromatic light, expressed in terms of the meter.

5. *Electron beam.* Stabilized lasers are used as working standards for dimensional measurements, providing a precise and stable frequency for the standard.

In general, the mechanical and electronic types of measuring and gauging instruments that have sensing devices or probes that come in contact with the workpiece are referred to as *contact instruments. Air instruments*, while employing contacting elements, rely on air pressure difference to effect measurement. Thus, they are basically noncontact instruments. Although different technologies are involved in the light-wave and electron-beam instruments, they both utilize a variety of optical systems. Thus, they are often grouped together as optical noncontact instruments.

The term M&TE refers to any device that is used to perform a test or undertake, certify, calibrate, gauge, or inspect in order to certify that a measurement or a measuring service conforms to a certain standard of measurement.

All dimensional metrology laboratories are temperature-controlled as nearly as is practical to 68°F, and thermal expansion corrections are made for any deviations that may occur. It is seldom necessary to correct for thermal expansion to achieve the accuracy required in industrial movement. Since the majority of precision parts, like the masters against which they are measured, are made of steel, it is generally safe to assume that their thermal expansion coefficients are identical and that no temperature correction need be made. Temperature corrections are also unnecessary when angles alone are measured, since a uniform temperature change can not change the size of an angle. This will definitely change with the introduction of new materials (Zipin 1971).

Concepts in Measurements

A *measurement* is a series of manipulations of physical objects or systems, according to a defined protocol, that results in a number. The number is purported to uniquely represent the magnitude (or intensity) of a certain satisfaction, which depends on the properties of the test object. This number is acquired to form the basis of a decision affecting some human goal or satisfying some human object need, the satisfaction of which depends on the properties of the test subject. These needs or goals can be usefully viewed as requiring three general classes of measurements (Simpson 1981):

1. *Technical.* This class includes those measurements made to assure dimensional compatibility, conformation to design specifications necessary for proper function, or, in general, all measurements made to ensure fitness for intended use of some object.

2. *Legal.* This class includes those measurements made to ensure compliance with a law or regulation. This class is the concern of weights and measures bodies, regulators, and those who must comply with those regulations. The measurements are identical in kind with those of technical metrology but are usually embedded in a much more formal structure. Legal metrology is more prevalent in Europe than in the United States, although this is changing.

3. *Scientific.* This class includes those measurements made to validate theories of the nature of the universe or to suggest new theories. These measurements, which can be called scientific metrology (properly the domain of experimental physics), present special problems.

Measurement Error. Error in measurement is the difference between the indicated value and the true value of a measured quantity. The true value of a quantity to be measured is seldom known. Errors are classified as *random* and *systematic*. *Random errors* are accidental in nature. They fluctuate in a way that can not be predicted from the detailed employment of the measuring system or from knowledge of its functioning. Sources of error such as hysteresis, ambient influences, or variations in the workpiece are typical but not completely all-inclusive in the random category. *Systematic errors* are those not usually detected by repetition of the measurement operations. An error resulting from either faulty calibration of a local standard or a defect in contact configuration of an internal measuring system is typical but not completely inclusive in the systematic class of errors (Darmody 1967).

It is important to know all the sources of error in a measuring system rather than merely to be aware of the details of their classification. Analysis of the causes of errors is helpful in attaining the necessary knowledge of achieved accuracy (Darmody 1967).

There are many different sources of error that influence the precision of a measuring process in a variety of ways according to the individual situation in which such errors arise. The permutation of error sources and their effects, therefore, is quite considerable. In general, these errors can be classified under three main headings (Rashed and Hamouda 1974):

1. Process environment

2. Equipment limitation

3. Operator errors, which include errors made in the identification of the measuring situation, analysis of alternative methods, selection of equipment, and application (or measurement)

The identification of measuring situations has become increasingly complex in modern metrology. As parts become smaller and more precise, greater attention has to be paid to geometric qualities such as roundness, concentricity, straightness, parallelism, and squareness. Deficiencies in these qualities may consume all of the permitted design tolerance, so that a simple dimensional check becomes grossly insufficient.

Operators have to be knowledgeable about what they have to measure and how satisfactorily the requirements of the situation will be met by the measuring instrument. Correct identification of the measuring situation will eliminate those methods found unsuitable for the situation. A proper selection of measuring equipment can therefore be made from a smaller range of measuring process alternatives. Method analysis can then be applied to such alternatives to determine which best satisfies the situation. This usually involves examining each method for different characteristics and evaluating the relative accuracies between the different methods.

Accuracy. Accuracy is the degree of agreement of individual or average measurements with an accepted reference value or level (ASTM 1977).

Precision. Precision is the degree of mutual agreement among individual measurements made under prescribed like conditions, or simply, how well identically performed measurements agree with each other. This concept applies to a process or a set of measurements, not to a single measurement, because in any set of measurements the individual results will scatter about the mean (Schrader and Elshennawy 2000).

Repeatability and Reproducibility. *Repeatability* refers to how close the measurements of an instrument are to each other if such measurements were repeated on a part under the same measuring conditions.

Reproducibility is a measure of the degree of agreement between two single test results made on the same object in two different, randomly selected measuring locations or laboratories.

While repeatability is normally used to designate precision for measurements made within a restricted set of conditions (for example, individual operators), reproducibility is normally used to designate precision for measurements involving variation between certain sets (for example, laboratories) as well as within them.

1. Hand Tools

Measuring instruments may be *direct reading* or of the *transfer* type. An ordinary steel rule, such as the ones shown in Figure 3.1 (items A–D), contains a graduated scale from which the size of a dimension being measured can be determined directly. The spring caliper in Figure 3.1 (item F) contains no scale graduations. It is adjusted to fit the size of a dimension being measured and then is compared to a direct-reading scale to obtain the size of the dimension (Schrader and Elshennawy 2000).

Most of the available measuring instruments may be grouped according to certain basic principles of operation. Many simple instruments use only a graduated scale as a measurement basis, while others may have two related scales and use the vernier principle of measurement. In a number of instruments the movement of a precision screw is related to two or three graduated scales to form a basis for measurement. Many other instruments utilize some sort of mechanical, electrical, or optical linkage between the measuring element and the graduated scale so that a small movement of the measuring element produces an enlarged indication on the scale. Air pressure or metered airflow are used in a few instruments as a means of measurement. These operating principles will be more fully explained later in the descriptions of a few of the instruments in which they are applied.

Most of the basic or general-purpose linear measuring instruments are typified by the steel rule, the vernier caliper, or the micrometer caliper.

Steel Rules. *Steel rules* are used effectively as line-measuring devices, which means that the ends of a dimension being measured are aligned with the graduations of the scale from which the length is read directly. A depth rule (Figure 3.1, item I) for measuring the depth of slots, holes, and so on, is a type of steel rule. Steel rules are also incorporated in vernier calipers, as shown in Figure 3.1 (item K), where they are adapted to end-measuring operations. These are often more accurate and easier to apply than inline measuring devices.

Verniers. The *vernier caliper* shown in Figure 3.2 typifies instruments using the vernier principle of measurement. The main or beam scale on a typical metric vernier caliper is numbered in increments of 10 mm, with the smallest scale division being equivalent to 1 mm. The vernier scale slides along the edge of the main scale and is divided into 50 divisions, and these 50 divisions are the same in total length as 49 divisions on the main scale. Each division on the vernier scale is then equal to 1/50 of (49 × 1) or 0.98 mm, which is 0.02 mm less than each division

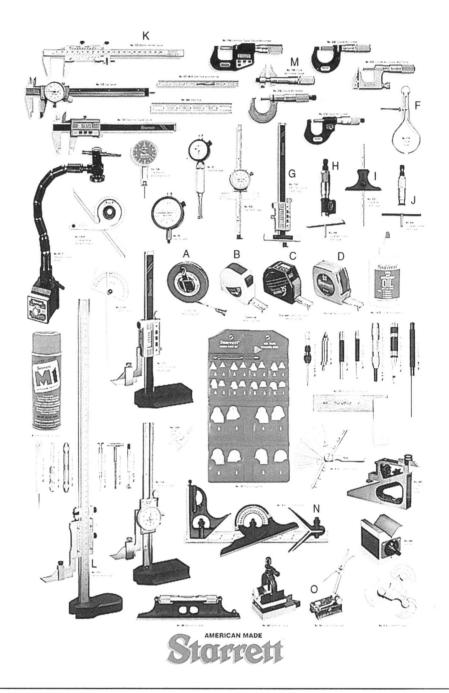

Figure 3.1 Standard measuring instruments including steel rules (A-D), spring caliper (F), micrometer depth gauges (G, H, J), depth rule (I), vernier caliper (K), vernier height gauge (L), inside micrometer (M), combination set (N), and surface gauge (O). (Courtesy the L. S. Starrett Company.)

on the main scale. Aligning the zero lines of both scales would cause the first lines on each scale to be 0.02 mm apart, the second lines 0.04 mm apart, and so on. A measurement on a vernier is designated by the positions of its zero line and the line that coincides with a line on the main scale. For example, the metric scale in Figure 3.2a shows a reading of 12.42 mm. The zero index of the vernier is located just beyond the line at 12 mm on the main scale, and line 21 (after 0) coincides with a line on the main scale, indicating that the zero index is 0.42 mm beyond the line at 12 mm. Thus, 12.00 + 0.42 = 12.42 mm.

The vernier caliper illustrated in Figure 3.2 also has an inch scale so that it can be used interchangeably for either inch or millimeter measurements. The smallest division on the main scale represents 0.25 in and the vernier is divided into .001 in increments. Thus, the measurement illustrated is .475 away from the main scale plus .014 from the vernier scale, for a total of .489 in.

The vernier caliper shown in Figure 3.2b consists of a steel rule with a pair of fixed jaws at one end and a pair of sliding jaws affixed to a vernier. Outside dimensions are measured between the lower jaws, inside dimensions over the tips of the upper jaws.

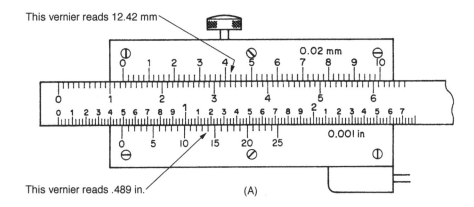

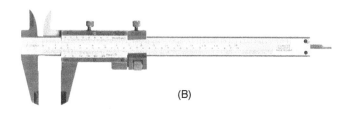

Figure 3.2 Fine-adjustment style vernier caliper.
(Courtesy Fred V. Fowler Company, Inc.)

Digital Calipers. The *digital reading caliper* shown in Figure 3.3 provides LCD readouts in either millimeters or inches and operates by a microprocessor-based system. The caliper has a measuring range of 0–152 mm (0–6 in) with readings in increments of 0.013 mm (.0005 in). The unit is capable of retaining a reading in the display when the tool is used in an area where visibility is restricted.

The *vernier height gauge* in Figure 3.1 (item L) is similar to a vernier caliper except the fixed jaw has been replaced by a fixed base, and the sliding jaw may have a scriber attached to it for layout work or a dial indicator for measuring or comparing operations. A more sophisticated version of the vernier height gauge is represented by the microprocessor-based digital height gauge shown in Figure 3.4. This instrument can easily measure in two dimensions in either angular or polar coordinates. It can measure external, internal, and distance dimensions, as well as perpendicularity, flatness, straightness, centers, and diameters.

Vertical measurements are made on the gauge shown in Figure 3.4 in either metric or inch units to a resolution of 0.0005 mm (.00002 in) by an optoelectronic sensor moving over a high-accuracy glass scale. The gauge head moves on a cushion of air generated by a completely self-contained pneumatic system. Dedicated function programs, along with a keypad and interactive LCD display, are designed to guide operators smoothly and efficiently through a variety of measurement operations.

Micrometers. The *micrometer caliper* illustrated in Figure 3.5 is representative of instruments using a precision screw as a basis for measuring. The measuring elements consist of a fixed anvil and a spindle that moves lengthwise as it is turned.

The thread on the spindle of a typical metric micrometer has a lead of ½ or 0.5 mm so that one complete revolution of the thimble produces a spindle movement of this amount. The graduated scale on the sleeve of the instrument has major divisions of 1.0 mm and minor divisions of 0.5 mm. Thus, one revolution of the spindle causes the beveled edge of the thimble to move through one small division on the sleeve scale. The periphery of the beveled edge of the thimble is graduated into 50 equal divisions, each space representing 1/50 of a complete rotation of the thimble, or a 0.01 mm movement of the spindle. Micrometers with scales in inch

Figure 3.3 LCD digital-reading caliper with 0-152 mm (0-6 in) range.
(Courtesy Fred V. Fowler Company, Inc.)

Figure 3.4   Digital-reading, single-axis height gauge for two-dimensional measurements.
(Courtesy Brown and Sharpe Manufacturing Company.)

Figure 3.5   A 0–25 mm micrometer caliper.
(Courtesy Fred V. Fowler Company, Inc.)

units operate in a similar fashion. Typically, the spindle thread has a lead of .025 in and the smallest division on the sleeve represents .025 in. The periphery of the beveled edge of the thimble is graduated into 25 equal divisions, each space representing 1/25 of a complete rotation of the thimble or a spindle movement of .001 in.

A reading on a micrometer is made by adding the thimble division that is aligned with the longitudinal sleeve line to the largest reading exposed on the sleeve scale. For example, in Figure 3.6 the thimble has exposed the number 10, representing 10.00 mm, and one small division worth 0.50 mm. The thimble division 16 is aligned with the longitudinal sleeve line, indicating that the thimble has moved 0.16 mm beyond the last small division on the sleeve. Thus the final reading is obtained by summing the three components, 10.00 + 0.50 + 0.16 = 10.66 mm.

A *vernier micrometer caliper,* such as that represented by the scales shown in Figure 3.7, has a vernier scale on the sleeve permitting measurement to 0.001 mm. The vernier scale shown has 10 divisions over a length equivalent to 19 divisions around the periphery of the thimble. Thus, the difference in length of a division on the vernier scale and two divisions on the thimble is 0.02 − (1/10)(19 × 0.01) = 0.001 mm. Thus, the reading illustrated in Figure 3.7 is 10.00 + 0.50 + 0.16 + 0.006 = 10.666 mm.

Digital Micrometers. Micrometers with digital readouts are also available to make readings faster and easier for inspection personnel regardless of their degree of experience. The digital micrometer shown in Figure 3.5 represents one instrument of this type for use in measuring to a resolution of 0.01 mm. The instrument shown in Figure 3.8 has a digital readout with a resolution to .0001 in. When equipped with vernier scales, the resolution may be increased to 0.001 mm (commonly .0001 in in the case of an inch-reading device).

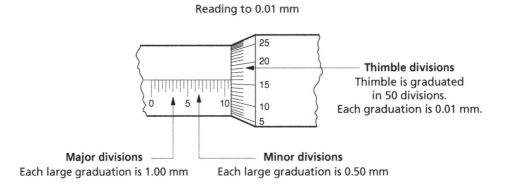

Reading to 0.01 mm

Thimble divisions
Thimble is graduated in 50 divisions. Each graduation is 0.01 mm.

Major divisions
Each large graduation is 1.00 mm

Minor divisions
Each large graduation is 0.50 mm

Figure 3.6 Micrometer reading of 10.66 mm.
Reprinted with permission of the Society of Manufacturing Engineers, *Manufacturing Processes and Materials,* 4th Edition, Copyright 2000.

Reading to 0.001 mm

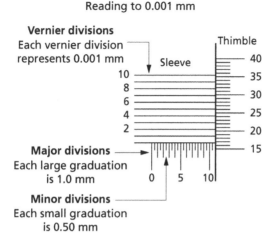

Vernier divisions
Each vernier division represents 0.001 mm

Thimble

Sleeve

Major divisions
Each large graduation is 1.0 mm

Minor divisions
Each small graduation is 0.50 mm

Figure 3.7 Scales of a vernier micrometer showing a reading of 10.666 mm.
Reprinted with permission of the Society of Manufacturing Engineers, *Manufacturing Processes and Materials,* 4th Edition, Copyright 2000.

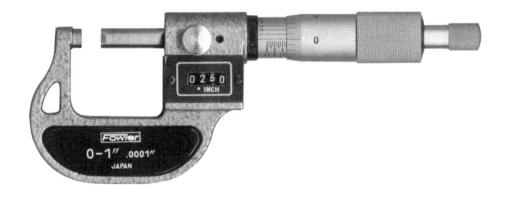

Figure 3.8 A digital micrometer.
(Courtesy Fred V. Fowler Company, Inc.)

Micrometer Calipers. The *micrometer caliper,* or mike as it is often called, is an end-measuring instrument for use in measuring outside dimensions. Although the mike is fairly easy to apply, the accuracy it gives depends on the application of the proper amount of torque to the thimble. Too much torque is likely to spring the frame and cause error. Thus, it is important that personnel using these instruments be trained in their use, and also that they be periodically required to check their measurements against a standard to minimize errors. The indicating micrometer in Figure 3.9 has a built-in dial indicator to provide a positive indication of measuring pressure applied. The instrument can be used like an indicating snap gauge.

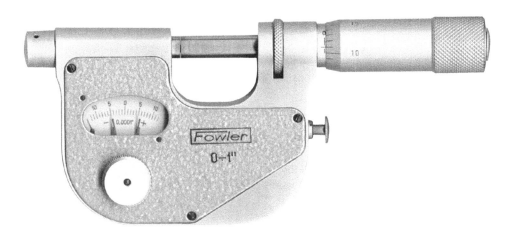

Figure 3.9 An indicating micrometer.
(Courtesy Fred V. Fowler Company, Inc.)

A standard metric micrometer is limited to a range of 25 mm (1 in for a micrometer reading in inch units). Thus, different micrometers are needed to measure a wide range of dimensions. The precision screw principle is applied directly in other measuring instruments such as the type of inside micrometer shown in Figure 3.1 (item M), the micrometer depth gauge in Figure 3.1 (items H and J), and the internal micrometer plug. It is also used as a device to provide precise calibrated linear movement to staging devices and other moving components of toolmakers' microscopes and optical projecting comparators.

Transfer-type linear measuring devices are typified by the spring caliper, spring divider, firm joint caliper, telescoping gauge, and small-hole gauge. Examples of each of these are shown in Figure 3.1.

The outside caliper is used as an end measure to measure or compare outside dimensions, while the inside caliper is used for inside diameters, slot and groove widths, and other internal dimensions. They are quite versatile but, due to their construction and method of application, their accuracy is somewhat limited.

2. Gauges

Classes. In mass-manufacturing operations it is often uneconomical to attempt to obtain absolute sizes during each inspection operation. In many cases it is only necessary to determine whether one or more dimensions of a mass-produced part are within specified limits. For this purpose a variety of inspection instruments referred to as *gauges* are employed. However, the distinction between gauging and measuring devices is not always clear as there are some instruments referred to as gauges that do not give definite measurements.

To promote consistency in manufacturing and inspection, gauges may be classified as working, inspection, and reference, or master, gauges. *Working gauges* are used by the machine operator or shop inspector to check the dimensions of parts as they are being produced. They usually have limits based on the piece being inspected. *Inspection gauges* are used by personnel to inspect purchased parts when received, or manufactured parts when finished. These gauges are designed and made so as not to reject any product previously accepted by a properly designed and functioning working gauge. *Reference,* or *master, gauges* are used only for checking the size or condition of other gauges, and represent as exactly as possible the physical dimensions of the product.

A gauge may have a single size and be referred to as a *nonlimit* gauge, or it may have two sizes and be referred to as a *limit gauge*. A limit gauge, often called a *go/no-go gauge,* establishes the high and low limits prescribed by the tolerance on a dimension. A limit gauge may be either double-end or progressive. A *double-end gauge* has the "go" member at one end and the "no-go" member at the other. Each end of the gauge is applied to the workpiece to determine its acceptability. The "go" member must pass into or over an acceptable piece, but the "no-go" member should not. A *progressive gauge* has both the "go" and "no-go" members at the same end so that a part may be gauged with one movement.

Some gauges are fixed in size while others are adjustable over certain size ranges. *Fixed gauges* are usually less expensive initially, but they have the disadvantage of not permitting adjustment to compensate for wear.

Most gauges are subjected to considerable abrasion during their application and therefore must be made of materials resistant to wear. High-carbon and alloy steels have been used as gauge materials for many years because of their relatively high hardenability and abrasion resistance. Further increases in surface hardness and abrasion resistance may be obtained from the use of chrome plating or cemented carbides as surface material on gauges. Some gauges are made entirely of cemented carbides, or they have cemented carbide inserts at certain wear points. Chrome plating is also used as a means of rebuilding and salvaging worn gauges.

Common Gauges. Typical common functional gauges can be classified on the basis of whether they are used to check outside dimensions, inside dimensions, or special features. Some examples of typical gauges are shown in Figure 3.10. They include ring and snap gauges for checking outside dimensions, plug gauges for checking inside dimensions, and other gauges for checking other geometrical shapes such as tapers, threads, and splines. Typical *plug gauges,* such as the ones shown in Figure 3.12a, consist of a hardened and accurately ground steel pin with two gauge members: one is the "go" gauge member and the other the "no-go" gauge member (top view of Figure 3.10a). *Progressive plug gauges* (bottom view of Figure 3.10a) combine both go and no-go members into one. The design of the gauge member and the method used to attach it to the handle depend on its size, as shown in Figure 3.10b. The gauge members are usually held in the handle by a threaded collet and bushing (view 1), a taper lock where gauge members have a taper shank on one end that fits into the end of the handle (view 2), or a trilock where the gauge members have a hole drilled through the center and are counterbored on both ends to receive a standard socket-head screw (view 3). One way of checking a hole for out-of-roundness is to have flats ground on the side of the gauge member as shown in Figure 3.10c.

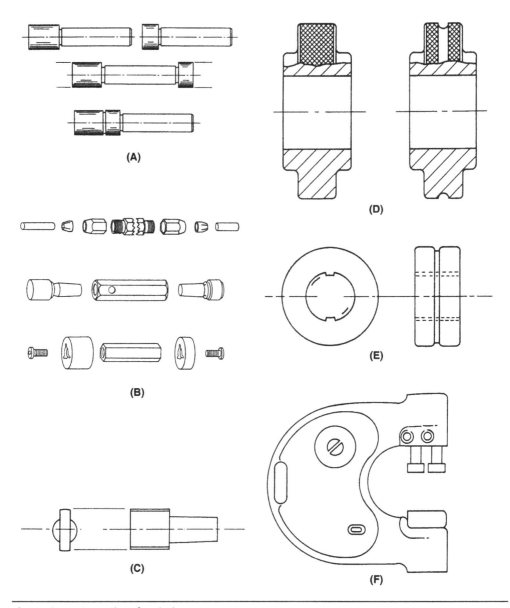

Figure 3.10 Examples of typical gauges.
Reprinted with permission of the Society of Manufacturing Engineers, *Manufacturing Processes and Materials,* 4th Edition, Copyright 2000.

Ring Gauges. *Ring gauges,* such as those shown in Figure 10d, are used for checking the limit sizes of a round shaft. They are generally used in pairs: the go gauge for checking the upper limit of the part tolerance and no-go gauge for checking the lower limit. The no-go ring has a groove in the outside diameter of the gauge to distinguish it from the go ring. It is possible that a shaft is larger at its ends than in the middle, or it could suffer an out-of-roundness condition. This situation can not be detected with a standard cylindrical ring gauge. Such an out-of-roundness condition can be checked by a ring gauge that has the inside diameter relieved such as the one shown in Figure 3.10e.

Snap Gauges. A *snap gauge* is another fixed gauge with the gauging members specially arranged for measuring diameters, thicknesses, and lengths. A typical (may also be called adjustable) *external measuring snap gauge* is shown in Figure 3.10f. It consists of a C-frame with gauging members in the jaw of the frame. Figure 3.10g shows other types of snap gauges. Threads can be checked with thread plug gauges, thread ring gauges, thread snap gauges, or a screw thread micrometer. *Thread snap gauges* have two pairs of gauging elements combined in one gauge. With appropriate gauging elements, these gauges may be used to check the maximum and minimum material limit of external screw threads in one path. An example of a thread snap gauge is shown in Figure 3.10h. In some cases special snap gauges may be desired. The example in Figure 3.10i illustrates the use of a special double-end snap gauge for inspecting the outside diameter of a narrow groove.

Spline Gauges. The use of a *spline gauge* is a common way of inspecting splined workpieces prior to assembly. External splines are checked with internal-toothed rings, whereas internal splines are checked with external-toothed plugs. Figure 3.10j shows the two basic types of fixed-limit spline gauges: composite and sector gauges. *Composite gauges* have the same number of teeth as that of the part. *Sector gauges* have only two sectors of teeth 180° apart. These gauges are further subdivided into go and no-go gauges. View 1 of Figure 3.10j shows a go composite ring gauge, and a no-go sector ring gauge is illustrated in view 2.

A *screw thread micrometer*, such as the one shown in Figure 3.12k, has a specially designed spindle and anvil so that externally threaded parts can be measured. Screw thread micrometers are generally designed to measure threads within a narrow range of pitches. *Thread plug gauges* are similar in design to cylindrical lug gauges except that they are threaded. They are designed to check internal threads. Typical thread plug gauges, such as those shown in Figure 3.10l, consist of a handle and one or two thread gauge members. Depending on the size of the gauging member, the member can be held in the handle using a threaded collet and bushing design (view 1), a taper lock design (view 2), or a trilock design (view 3).

Templates. To check a specified profile, *templates* may be used. They also may be used to control or gauge special shapes or contours in manufactured parts. These templates are normally made from thin, easy-to-machine materials. An example of a contour template for inspecting a turned part is shown in Figure 3.10m. To visually inspect or gauge radii or fillets, special templates, such as those shown in Figure 3.10n, may be used. The five basic uses of such templates are inspection of an inside radius tangent of two perpendicular planes (view 1), inspection of a groove (view 2), inspection of an outside radius tangent to two perpendicular planes (view 3), inspection of a ridge segment (view 4), and inspection of roundness and diameter of a shaft (view 5).

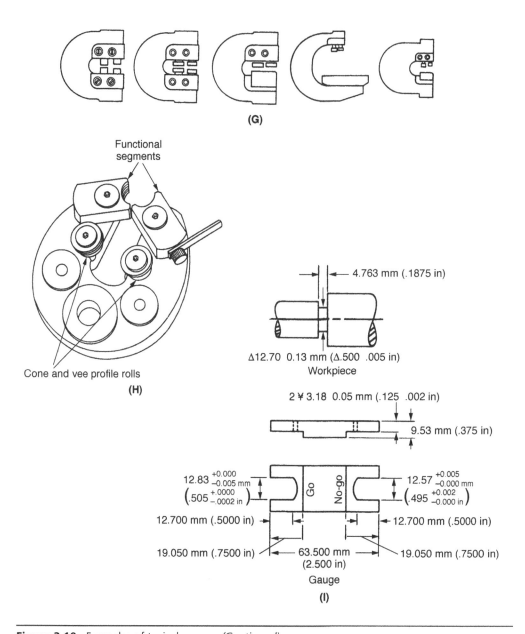

Figure 3.10 Examples of typical gauges *(Continued).*

Screw Pitch Gauges. The pitch of a screw may be checked with a *screw pitch gauge.* To determine the pitch, the gauge is placed on the threaded part as shown in Figure 3.10o. A drawback of using screw pitch gauges is their inability to give an adequate check on thread form for precision parts.

Special Gauges. It is sometimes necessary to design special gauges for checking special part features such as square, hexagonal, or octagonal holes. Figure 3.10p shows some special plug gauges for checking the profile or taper of holes.

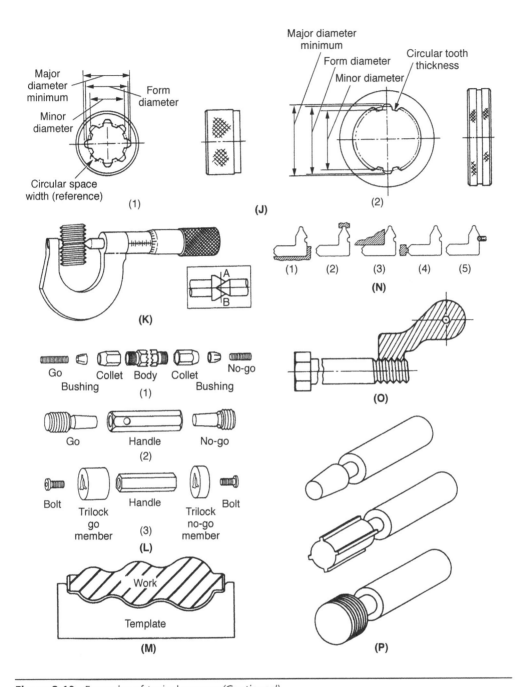

Figure 3.10   Examples of typical gauges *(Continued)*.

As an inspection tool, a snap gauge is sometimes a better choice to use than a ring gauge. Figure 3.10q illustrates how a ring gauge may accept an out-of-roundness condition that would otherwise be rejected by a snap gauge.

Ring gauge accepting part that is out-of-round

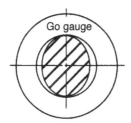
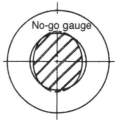

Step 1: Go gauge slips over shaft   Step 2: No-go gauge will not slip over shaft

Snap gauge rejecting part that is out-of-round

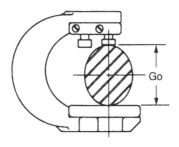
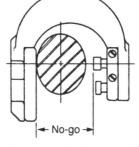

Step 1: Part enters go gauge   Step 2: Same part when inspected 90 from
and does not enter no-go   first position will enter no-go gauge

(Q)

Figure 3.10 Examples of typical gauges *(Continued)*.

Functional Gauges. A *functional gauge* checks the fit of a workpiece with a mating part. It normally just simulates the pertinent features of the mating part. An example of a functional gauge would be a plate with four plugs, each located in true position as nearly as possible. Any part that would fit on that gauge would pass inspection for hole positions.

Flush Pin Gauges. A *flush pin gauge* checks the limits of dimension between two surfaces in the manner illustrated in Figure 3.11. The step on pin B is the same size as the tolerance on the depth of the hole being checked. Thus, the step on pin B must straddle the top of collar A for the depth of the hole to be within limits. An inspector can compare the surfaces quickly and reliably by feeling them with a fingernail.

Sizes. In gauge making, as in any other manufacturing process, it is economically impractical to attempt to make gauges to an exact size. Thus, it is necessary that some tolerance be applied to gauges. It is desirable, however, that some tolerance still be available for the manufacturing process. Obviously, though, the smaller the *gauge tolerance,* the more the gauge will cost. Along with the gauge maker's tolerance, it is usually necessary to provide a *wear allowance.*

Tolerances. There are three methods of applying tolerances to gauges, each of which affects the outcome of the inspection operation differently. These three methods are illustrated in Figure 3.12. The first is to use a unilateral gauge tolerance and make the gauge within the work tolerance, as shown in A. This will result in some acceptable products being rejected. The second method is to use a bilateral gauge tolerance about the limiting specifications on the part, as shown in B. This might allow some acceptable parts to be rejected or some rejectable parts to be accepted. The third method is to use a unilateral tolerance and make the gauge outside the work tolerance, as in C. Gauges made according to this method will permit defective parts to be accepted at the start and continue to be accepted as long as the gauge is in use, but it provides the most manufacturing tolerance.

There is no universally accepted policy for the amount of gauge tolerance. A number of industries where part tolerances are relatively large use 20% of the part tolerance for working gauges and 10% for inspection gauges. For each of these gauges, one-half of the amount is used for wear on the go member and one-half for the gauge makers' tolerance on both the go and no-go members. This method has been used to determine the tolerances for the plug gauges shown in Figure 3.13 to check a hole with a diameter of 40.010 +0.10/–0.00 mm (1.5752 +.004/–.000 in). The total part tolerance is 0.10 mm (.004 in). Thus 20% of 0.10 mm (.004 in) gives 0.020 mm (.0008 in) for the working gauge, and 10% of 0.10 mm (.004 in) gives 0.010 mm (.0004 in) for the inspection gauge, applied unilaterally.

Indicating Gauges and Comparators. *Indicating gauges* and *comparators* magnify the amount a dimension deviates above or below a standard to which the gauge is set. Most indicate in terms of actual units of measurement, but some show only whether a tolerance is within a given range. The ability to measure to 25 nanometers (nm) (.00001 in) depends on the magnification, resolution, and accuracy of the setting gauges, and staging of the workpiece and instrument. Graduations on a scale should be 1.5–2.5 mm (.06–.10 in) apart to be clear. This requires magnification of 60,000× to 100,000× for a 25 nm (.00001 in) increment; less is needed, of course,

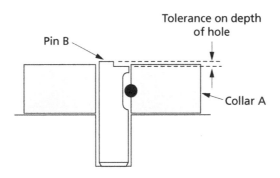

Figure 3.11   Typical flush pin gauge for gauging the depth of a hole.
Reprinted with permission of the Society of Manufacturing Engineers, *Manufacturing Processes and Materials,* 4th Edition, Copyright 2000.

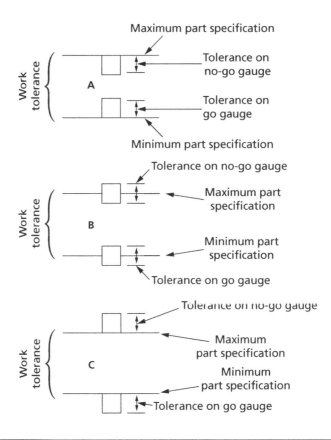

Figure 3.12 Methods of assigning gauge tolerances.
Reprinted with permission of the Society of Manufacturing Engineers, *Manufacturing Processes and Materials,* 4th Edition, Copyright 2000.

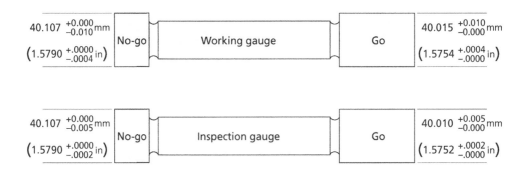

Figure 3.13 Specifications on working and inspection limit plug gauges.
Reprinted with permission of the Society of Manufacturing Engineers, *Manufacturing Processes and Materials,* 4th Edition, Copyright 2000.

for larger increments. Mechanical, air, electronic, and optical sensors and circuits are available for any magnification needed and will be described in the following sections. However, measurements have meaning and are repeatable only if based on reliable standards, like gauge blocks. In addition, when measuring quantities such as roundness, cylindrical parts must be appropriately supported. Either the probe or part must be rotated on a spindle that must run true with an error much less than the increment to be measured.

Mechanical Indicating Gauges. *Mechanical indicating gauges* are comparators. Mechanical indicating gauges and comparators employ a variety of devices. One type is the dial indicator depicted in Figure 3.14. Movement of stem A is transmitted from the rack to compound gear train (B and C) to pointer D, which moves around a dial face. Springs exert a constant force on the mechanism and return the pointer to its original position after the object being measured is removed.

Dial indicators are used for many kinds of measuring and gauging operations. One example is that of inspecting a workpiece such as the one illustrated in Figure 3.15. They also serve to check machines and tools, alignments, and cutter runout. Dial indicators are often incorporated in special gauges in measuring instruments, as exemplified by the indicating micrometer in Figure 3.9.

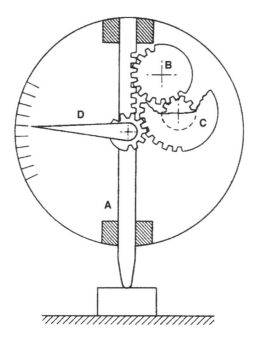

Figure 3.14 Simple dial indicator mechanism.
Reprinted with permission of the Society of Manufacturing Engineers, *Manufacturing Processes and Materials*, 4th Edition, Copyright 2000.

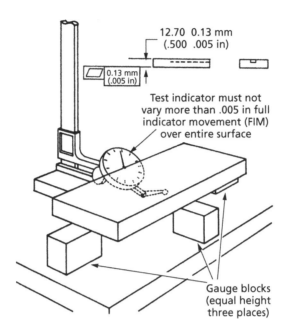

12.70 0.13 mm
(.500 .005 in)

0.13 mm
(.005 in)

Test indicator must not
vary more than .005 in full
indicator movement (FIM)
over entire surface

Gauge blocks
(equal height
three places)

Figure 3.15   An application of dial indicators for inspecting flatness by placing the workpiece on gauge blocks and checking full indicator movement (FIM).
Reprinted with permission of the Society of Manufacturing Engineers, *Manufacturing Processes and Materials*, 4th Edition, Copyright 2000.

Gauge Blocks. *Gauge blocks* are the practical length standards for the manufacturing industry. They are rectangular, square, or round blocks of steel, carbide, or ceramic materials. Each has two faces that are flat, level, and parallel to within approximately ±0.00003 mm to +0.00015 or -0.00005 mm (±0.000001 to +0.000006 or -0.000002 in.), depending on the length and accuracy grade. There are four basic classes of gauge blocks that conform to specified federal accuracy standards (Federal Specification GGG-G-15). *Laboratory master blocks,* which conform to federal accuracy grade 0.5 (formerly AAA grade), must be accurate to about ±0.00003 mm per 25 mm of length (±0.000001 in./in.) and are intended for use in checking other gauge blocks or setting very precise laboratory equipment. *Federal accuracy grade 1 blocks* (formerly AA grade) are accurate to about ±0.00005 mm per 25 mm of length (±0.000002 in./in.) and are used as reference blocks to calibrate measuring instruments, set gauges, and for very close layout work. *Federal accuracy grade 2 and 3 blocks* are normally used as working gauge blocks in manufacturing operations for establishing machine settings and layout inspection. Grade 2 blocks through 25.4 mm (1 in.) length have a length accuracy of +0.00010 mm or -0.000050 mm (+0.000004 in. or -0.00002 in.), while grade 3 blocks of similar lengths have a length accuracy of +0.00015 mm or -0.00005 mm (+0.000006 in. or -0.000002 in.) (Elshennawy and Weheba, 2015).

A number of quality factors other than just length tolerance are considered in the selection of gauge blocks for a particular activity. Flatness, parallelism, dimensional stability, surface finish, hardness, or resistance to abrasion may contribute to the utility and reliability of gauge block applications. One of the major sources of error in gaging to submillimeter tolerances in precision-engineered products is temperature variation. When a gauge block is said to have a certain length, it is understood to be the length at the standard temperature of 20° C (68° F). Thus, steel, carbide, or ceramic gauge blocks used in a laboratory environment maintained at standard temperature would be expected to retain a high degree of dimensional stability. If the blocks are to be used in a work environment wherein considerable temperature variation occurs, then a gauge block material would need to be selected that responds to temperature variations in about the same manner as the workpiece or machine on which they are used. Since wear resistance is related to hardness, most steel gauge blocks are hardened to about 65–68 RC, while chrome carbide and tungsten carbide blocks have hardness values in the 70–73 RC range (Elshennawy and Weheba, 2015).

3. Optical Tools

Optical Comparators. Many industrial products and component parts are so small and of such complex configuration that they require magnification for accurate discernment. For this purpose, a number of measuring and gauging instruments using various optical systems—such as the toolmakers' microscope, the binocular microscope, and the optical projecting comparator—find wide application for the inspection of small parts and tools.

The *optical projecting comparator* projects a magnified image of the object being measured onto a screen. A workpiece is staged on a table to cast a shadow in a beam of light in *diascopic projection*, as shown in Figure 3.16. The outline of the part is magnified and displayed on a screen. In *episcopic projection* the light rays are directed against the side of the object and then reflected back through the projection lens.

Optical projection provides a means to check complex parts quickly to small tolerances. Commonly, a translucent drawing is placed over the screen with lines drawn to scale for the contour of the part, the limits of the outline, or critical features such as angles. For instance, the outline of a part can be compared with a drawing on the screen, and deviations in the whole contour can be quickly seen. A fixture or stage may be supplied for a part in order to mount all pieces in the same way in rapid succession. The table can be adjusted in coordinate directions by micrometer screws or servomotors to 2 μm (.0001 in). Table positions can be determined from the micrometer readings or from digital readout devices. Thus, a part can be displaced to measure precisely how far a line is from a specified position. In addition, the screen can be rotated to a vernier scale to measure angular deviations in minutes or small fractions of a degree. Magnifications for commercial comparators range from 5× to as much as 500×. For example, at 250×magnification 0.0020 mm (.0008 in) on a part becomes 0.500 mm (.0197 in) on the screen, which is readily discernible. The horizontal optical comparator shown in Figure 3.17 is table mounted and has a 356 mm (14 in) diameter viewing screen. The designation "horizontal" means that the lens system is mounted horizontally as illustrated in Figure 3.16. Comparators are also commercially available with a vertical lens configuration to facilitate the staging of thin parts.

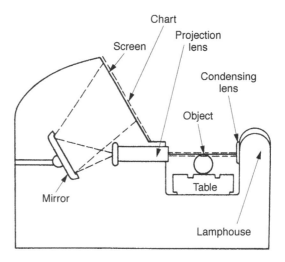

Figure 3.16 Optical comparator system.
Reprinted with permission of the Society of Manufacturing Engineers, *Manufacturing Processes and Materials*, 4th Edition, Copyright 2000.

One of the features of the comparator shown in Figure 3.17 is a computerized digital readout (DRO) located on the top of the machine. The DRO has a two-axis digital display for establishing measurements in the x–y plane. In addition, a 12-character, alphanumeric readout displays help messages, setup options, and the results of calculations. A fiber-optic edge-sensing device is also shown extending down the upper left portion of the screen. This device permits the digital readout to precisely indicate the edges of a part. A 16-key external keypad mounted on the lower bases provides the option of using the dedicated keys as they are identified, or redefining any or all of those keys to execute any of 20 different programs containing up to 100 keystrokes each. The keypad includes a joystick capable of x-, y-, and z-axis control.

Another feature of the comparator shown in Figure 3.17 is an electric screen protractor that reads angles directly to either a minute or 0.01°. The angular setting of the protractor is displayed on an LED readout at the bottom right of the screen. The machine has built-in provisions for either diascopic projection (contour illumination) or episcopic projection (surface illumination) via a high-intensity, tungsten-halogen light source. Lens changing is facilitated by the use of quick-change, bayonet-type lens holders. Seven different lens magnifications are available, ranging from 5× to 100×, all with an optical focusing range of 76 mm (3 in).

4. Coordinate Measuring Machines

The *coordinate measuring machine* (CMM) is a flexible measuring device capable of providing highly accurate dimensional position information along three mutually perpendicular axes. This instrument is widely used in manufacturing

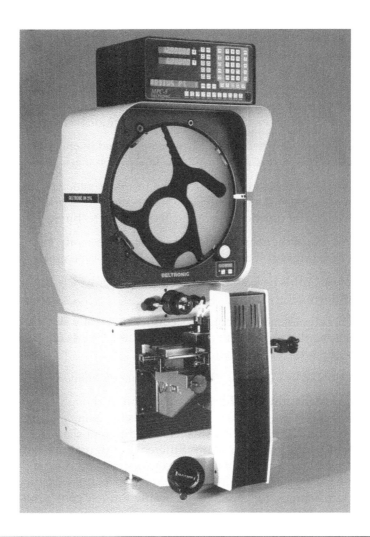

Figure 3.17   Horizontal optical comparator with a 356 mm (14 in) viewing screen, digital
readout, and edge-sensing device.
(Courtesy Deltronic Corporation.)

industries for the post-process inspection of a large variety of products and their
components. It is also very effectively used to check dimensions on a variety of
process tooling, including mold cavities, die assemblies, assembly fixtures, and
other work holding or tool positioning devices.

Over the last decade, coordinate measuring machines have become a primary
means of dimensional quality control for manufactured parts of complex form where
the volume of production does not warrant the development of functional gauging.
The advent of increasingly inexpensive computing power and more fully integrated
manufacturing systems will continue to expand the use of these machines into an
even larger role in the overall quality assurance of manufactured parts.

Coordinate measuring machines (CMMs) can most easily be defined as
physical representations of a three-dimensional rectilinear coordinate system.

Coordinate measuring machines now represent a significant fraction of the measuring equipment used for defining the geometry of different-shaped workpieces. Most dimensional characteristics of many parts can be measured within minutes with these machines. Similar measurements would take hours using older measuring equipment and procedures. Besides flexibility and speed, coordinate measuring machines have several additional advantages:

1. Different features of a part can be measured in one setup. This eliminates errors introduced due to setup changes.

2. All CMM measurements are taken from one geometrically fixed measuring system, eliminating the accumulation of errors resulting from using functional gauging and transfer techniques.

3. The use of digital readouts eliminates the necessity for the interpretation of readings, such as with the dial or vernier-type measuring scales.

4. Most CMMs have automatic data recording, which minimizes operator influence.

5. Part alignment and setup procedures are greatly simplified by using software supplied with computer-assisted CMMs. This minimizes the setup time for measurement.

6. Data can be automatically saved for further analysis.

Coordinate Measuring Machine Classification. Although coordinate measuring machines can be thought of as representations of a simple rectilinear coordinate system for measuring the dimensions of different-shaped workpieces, they naturally are constructed in many different configurations, all of which offer different advantages. CMMs provide means for locating and recording the coordinate location of points in their measuring volumes. Traditional coordinate measuring machines are classified according to their configurations, as follows (ANSI/ASME 1997):

1. *Cantilever configuration,* in which the probe is attached to a vertical machine ram (z-axis) moving on a mutually perpendicular overhang beam (y-axis) that moves along a mutually perpendicular rail (x-axis). Cantilever configuration is limited to small- and medium-sized machines. It provides for easy operator access and the possibility of measuring parts longer than the machine table.

2. *Bridge-type configuration,* in which a horizontal beam moves along the x-axis, carrying the carriage that provides the y motion. In other configurations, the horizontal beam (bridge structure) is rigidly attached to the machine base, and the machine table moves along the x-axis. This is called *fixed bridge configuration.* A bridge-type coordinate measuring machine provides more-rigid construction, which in turn provides better accuracy. The presence of the bridge on the machine table makes it a little more difficult to load large parts.

3. *Column-type configuration*, in which a moving table and saddle arrangement provides the x and y motions and the machine ram (z-axis) moves vertically relative to the machine table.

4. *Horizontal-arm configuration* features a horizontal probe ram (z-axis) moving horizontally relative to a column (y-axis), which moves in a mutually perpendicular motion (x-axis) along the machine base. This configuration provides the possibility for measuring large parts. Other arrangements of horizontal-arm configuration feature a fixed horizontal-arm configuration in which the probe is attached and moving vertically (y-axis) relative to a column that slides along the machine base in the x direction. The machine table moves in a mutually perpendicular motion (z-axis) relative to the column.

5. *Gantry-type configuration* comprises a vertical ram (z-axis) moving vertically relative to a horizontal beam (x-axis), which in turn moves along two rails (y-axis) mounted on the floor. This configuration provides easy access and allows the measurement of large components.

6. *L-shaped bridge configuration* comprises a ram (z-axis) moving vertically relative to a carriage (x-axis), which moves horizontally relative to an L-shaped bridge moving in the y direction.

Figure 3.18 shows CMM types according to this classification. The most advanced configuration, that of the ring-bridge, is not illustrated.

In addition to classifying coordinate measuring machines according to their physical configuration, they can also be classified according to their mode of operation: manually oriented, computer-assisted, or direct computer-controlled. In *manual* machines, the operator moves the probe along the machine's axes to establish and manually record the measurement values that are provided by digital readouts. In some machines, digital printout devices are used.

Computer-assisted coordinate measuring machines can be either manually positioned (free-floating mode) by moving the probe to measurement locations, or manually driven by providing power-operated motions under the control of the operator. In either case, data processing is accomplished by a computer. Some computer-assisted CMMs can perform some or all of the following functions: inch to metric conversion, automatic compensation for misalignment, storing of premeasured parameters and measurement sequences, data recording, means for disengagement of the power drive to allow manual adjustments and manipulations of the machine motions, and geometric and analytical evaluations.

Direct computer-controlled CMMs use a computer to control all machine motions and measuring routines and to perform most of the routinely required data processing. These machines are operated in much the same way as CNC machine tools. Both control and measuring cycles are under program control. Off-line programming capability is also available.

The effective use of computers for CMM applications is a principal feature differentiating available CMM systems. The value of a measurement system depends a great deal on the sophistication and ease of use of the associated software and its functional capabilities. The functional capabilities of a CMM software package depend on the number and types of application programs available. The following is a list of many of the different types of system software available for coordinate measuring machines:

1. Printout instructions, measurement sequence, zero reference, and so on.

2. Automatic compensation for misalignment of the workpiece with the machine axes.

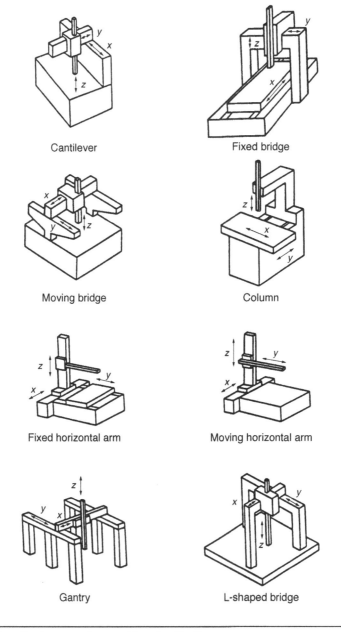

Cantilever

Fixed bridge

Moving bridge

Column

Fixed horizontal arm

Moving horizontal arm

Gantry

L-shaped bridge

Figure 3.18   Coordinate measuring machine classifications.

3. Coordinate conversion between Cartesian and polar coordinates.

4. Tolerance calculations providing out-of-tolerance condition.

5. Defining geometric elements such as points, lines, circles, planes, cylinders, spheres, cones, and their intersections.

6. Automatic redefinition of coordinate systems or machine axes, and printout of origin and inspection planes.

7. Inspection of special shapes or contours, such as gears and cams.

8. Multiple-point hole checking using least squares techniques for determining best fit center, mean diameter, roundness, and concentricity.

9. Evaluating geometric tolerance conditions by defining type of form and positional relationship, such as roundness, flatness, straightness, parallelism, or squareness.

10. Hold diameter and location checking considering maximum and minimum material conditions as defined in ANSI/ASME Y14.5.1M-1994 (R2012).

11. Friendly operator interfaces for self-teaching or part programs.

12. Other software for statistical analysis includes graphic data display, histograms, integration of areas under a curve, contour plotting, automatic part or lot acceptance or rejection based on statistical evaluation, and so on.

Moving Bridge CMM. The two most common structural configurations for CMMs are the *moving bridge* and the *cantilever type*. The basic elements and configuration of a typical moving bridge–type coordinate measuring machine are shown in Figure 3.19. The base or worktable of most CMMs is constructed of granite or some other ceramic material to provide a stable work locating surface and an integral guideway for the superstructure. As indicated in Figure 3.19, the two vertical columns slide along precision guideways on the base to provide y-axis movement. A traveling block on the bridge gives x-axis movement to the quill, and the quill travels vertically for a z-axis coordinate.

The moving elements along the axes are supported by air bearings to minimize sliding friction and compensate for any surface imperfections on the guideways. Movement along the axes can be accomplished manually on some machines by light hand pressure or rotation of a hand wheel. Movement on more expensive machines is accomplished by axis drive motors, sometimes with joystick control. Direct computer-controlled (DCC) CMMs are equipped with axis drive motors, which are programmed to automatically move the sensor element (probe) through a sequence of positions.

To establish a reference point for coordinate measurement, the CMM and probe being used must be *datumed*. In the datuming process, the probe, or set of probes, is brought into contact with a calibrated sphere located on the worktable. The center of the sphere is then established as the origin of the x-y-z axes coordinate system.

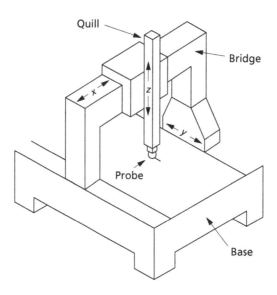

Figure 3.19   Typical moving bridge coordinate measuring machine configuration.
Reprinted with permission of the Society of Manufacturing Engineers,
Manufacturing Processes and Materials, 4th Edition, Copyright 2000.

The coordinate measuring machine shown in Figure 3.20 has a measuring envelope of about $0.5 \times 0.5 \times 0.4$ m ($18 \times 20 \times 16$ in) and is equipped with a disengageable drive that enables the operator to toggle between manual and direct computer control. It has a granite worktable, and the *x*-beam and *y*-beam are made of an extruded aluminum to provide the rigidity and stability needed for accurate measuring. The measurement system has a readout resolution of 1 μm (.0004 in), and the DCC system can be programmed to accomplish 445–600 measurement points/min (Elshennawy and Weheba 2015).

Contacting Probes. CMM measurements are taken by moving the small stylus (probe) attached to the end of the quill until it makes contact with the surface to be measured. The position of the probe is then observed on the axes readouts. On early CMMs, a rigid (hard) probe was used as the contacting element. The hard probe can lead to a variety of measurement errors, depending on the contact pressure applied, deflection of the stylus shank, and so on. These errors are minimized by the use of a pressure-sensitive device called a touch trigger probe.

The touch trigger probe permits hundreds of measurement to be made with repeatabilites in the 0.25–1.0 μm (.00001–.00004 in) range. Basically, this type of probe operates as an extremely sensitive electrical switch that detects surface contact in three dimensions. The manual indexable *touch trigger probe* shown in Figure 3.21 can be used to point and probe without re-datuming for each position measured.

Figure 3.20 Coordinate measuring machine.
(Courtesy Brown and Sharpe Manufacturing Company.)

Noncontacting Sensors. Many industrial products and components that are not easily and suitably measured with surface contacting devices may require the use of noncontact sensors or probes on CMMs to obtain the necessary inspection information. This may include two-dimensional parts such as circuit boards and very thin stamped parts, extremely small or miniaturized microelectronic devices and medical instrument parts, and very delicate, thin-walled products made of plastic or other lightweight materials.

The *multisensor coordinate measuring machine* (MSCMM) shown in Figure 3.22 incorporates three sensing technologies—optical, laser, and touch probe—for highly accurate noncontact and/or contact inspection tasks. The machine uses two quills, or measuring heads, to accomplish high-speed data acquisition within a four-axis (x, y, $z1$, $z2$) configuration, thus permitting noncontact or contact inspection of virtually any part in a single setup.

The sensing head on the left quill in Figure 3.22 contains an optical/laser sensor with a high-resolution CCD video camera and a coaxial laser. The video camera has advanced image-processing capabilities via its own microprocessor, enabling subpixel resolutions of 0.05 μm (2 μin). The coaxial laser shares the same optical path as the video image and assists in the focusing of the CCD camera.

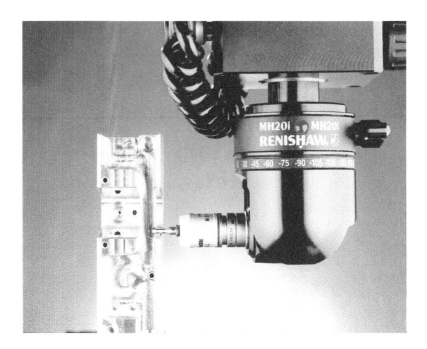

Figure 3.21 Manual indexable probe.
(Courtesy Renishaw, Inc.)

This eliminates focusing errors associated with optical systems and increases the accuracies of z measurements. Single-point measurements can be obtained in less than 0.2 sec, and high-speed laser scanning/digitizing can be accomplished at up to 5000 points/sec.

The right-hand quill in Figure 3.22 contains the z2-axis touch probe sensor used to inspect features that are either out of sight of the optical/laser sensor or are better suited to be measured via the contact method.

The MSCMM in Figure 3.22 is being used to inspect a valve body with the z1-axis optical/laser probe and a transmission case with the z2-axis touch probe. The machine shown is a benchtop type with a maximum measuring range of 900 mm (≈35 in), 800 mm (≈32 in), and 600 mm (≈24 in) for the *x*, *y*, and z1 and z2 axes, respectively. Positioning of the moving elements is accomplished by backlash-free, recirculating-ball lead screws and computer-controlled DC motors. Position information is provided by high-precision glass scales.

Laser Scanning Probes. *Laser scanning probes* are ideal for non-contact measurements of soft materials or those with textured surfaces. The probe operates at a certain distance (e.g., 50 mm) above the workpiece, with a measuring range +/- 5 mm about the point of focus and takes up to 200 readings per second. Point-taking accuracy can be further enhanced by an internal data averaging facility (Bosch, 1995).

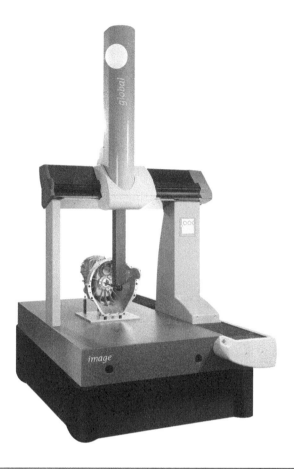

Figure 3.22   A multisensor coordinate measuring machine with optical, laser, and
touch probes for noncontact and contact measurements.
(Courtesy Brown and Sharpe Manufacturing Company)

5. Electronic Measuring Equipment

Electric and Electronic Gauges. Certain gauges are called *electric limit gauges*
because they have the added feature of a rack stem that actuates precision
switches. The switches connect lights or buzzers to show limits, and also may
energize sorting and corrective devices.

An *electronic gauge* gives a reading in proportion to the amount a stylus is
displaced. It may also actuate switches electronically to control various functions.
An example of an electronic gauge and diagrams of the most common kinds of
gauge heads are shown in Figure 3.23. The *variable inductance* or *inductance-bridge
transducer* has an alternating current fed into two coils connected into a bridge
circuit. The reactance of each coil is changed as the position of the magnetic core
is changed. This changes the output of the bridge circuit. The *variable transformer*,
or *linear variable displacement transformer* (LVDT) *transducer*, has two opposed coils
into which currents are induced from a primary coil. The net output depends on

the displacement of the magnetic core. The deflection of a strain gauge transducer is sensed by the changes in length and resistance of strain gauges on its surface. This is also a means for measuring forces. Displacement of a variable capacitance head changes the air gap between plates of a condenser connected in a bridge circuit. In every case an alternating current is fed into the gauge as depicted in Figure 3.23e. The output of the gauge head circuit is amplified electronically and displayed on a dial or digital readout. In some cases the information from the gauge may be recorded on tape or stored in a computer.

Figure 3.23e shows an electronic height gauge with an amplifier and digital display. A digital-reading height gauge like the instrument shown in Figure 3.23f can be used for transferring height settings in increments of 0.0025 mm (.00010 in) with an accuracy of 0.001127 mm (.000050 in).

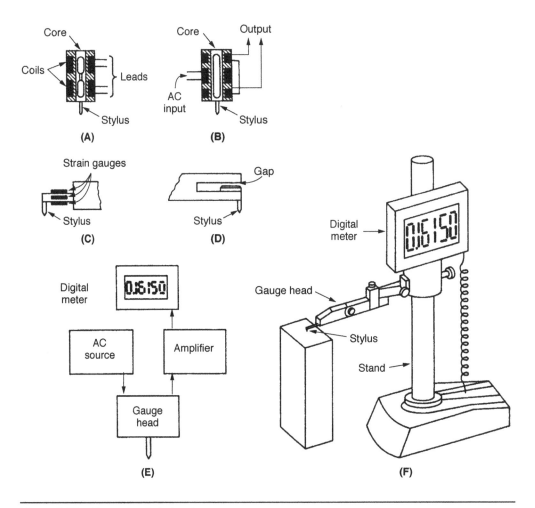

Figure 3.23 Elements of electronic gauges.
Reprinted with permission of the Society of Manufacturing Engineers, *Manufacturing Processes and Materials,* 4th Edition, Copyright 2000.

Electronic gauges have several advantages: they are very sensitive (they commonly read to a few micrometers), output can be amplified as much as desired, a high-quality gauge is quite stable, and they can be used as an absolute measuring device for thin pieces up to the range of the instrument. The amount of amplification can be switched easily, and three or four ranges are common for one instrument. Two or more heads may be connected to one amplifier to obtain sums or differences of dimensions, as for checking thickness, parallelism, and so on.

Air Gauges. An *air gauge* is a means of measuring, comparing, or checking dimensions by sensing the flow of air through the space between a gauge head and workpiece surface. The gauge head is applied to each workpiece in the same way, and the clearance between the two varies with the size of the piece. The amount the airflow is restricted depends on the clearance. There are four basic types of air gauge sensors shown in Figure 3.24. All have a controlled constant-pressure air supply.

The *back-pressure gauge* (A) responds to the increase in pressure when the airflow is reduced. It can magnify from 1000:1 to over 5000:1, depending on range, but is somewhat slow because of the reaction of air to changing pressure. The *differential gauge* (B) is more sensitive. Air passes through this gauge in one line to the gauge head and in a parallel line to the atmosphere though a setting valve. The pressure between the two lines is measured. There is no time lag in the *flow gauge* (C), where the rate of airflow raises an indicator in a tapered tube. The dimension is read from the position of the indicating float. This gauge is simple and does not have a mechanism to wear, is free from hysteresis, and can amplify to over 500,000:1 without accessories. The *venturi gauge* (D) measures the drop in pressure of the air flowing through a venturi tube. It combines the elements of the back-pressure and flow gauges and is fast, but sacrifices simplicity.

A few of the many kinds of gauge heads and applications are also shown in Figure 3.24. An *air gauge* is basically a comparator and must be an asset to a master for dimension or to two masters for limits. The common single gauge head is the plug. Practically all inside and outside linear and geometric dimensions can be checked by air gauging. Air *match gauging*, depicted in Figure 3.24i, measures the clearance between two mating parts. This provides a means of controlling an operation to machine one part to a specified fit with the other. A *multidimension gauge* has a set of cartridge or contact gauge heads (Figure 3.24h) to check several dimensions on a part at the same time. The basic gauge sensor can be used for a large variety of jobs, but a different gauge head and setting master are needed for almost every job and size.

A major advantage of an air gauge is that the gauge head does not have to tightly fit the part. A clearance of up to 0.08 mm (.003 in) between the gauge head and workpiece is permissible, even more in some cases. Thus, no pressure is needed between the two to cause wear, and the gauge head may have a large allowance for any wear that does occur. The flowing air helps keep surfaces clean. The lack of contact makes air gauging particularly suitable for checking against highly finished and soft surfaces. Because of its loose fit, an air gauge is easy and quick to use. An inexperienced worker can measure the diameter of a hole to 25 nm (.000001 in) in a few seconds with an air gauge; the same measurement (to 25 μm [.001 in]) with a vernier caliper by a skilled inspector may take up to one minute. The faster types of air gauges are adequate for high-rate automatic gauging in production.

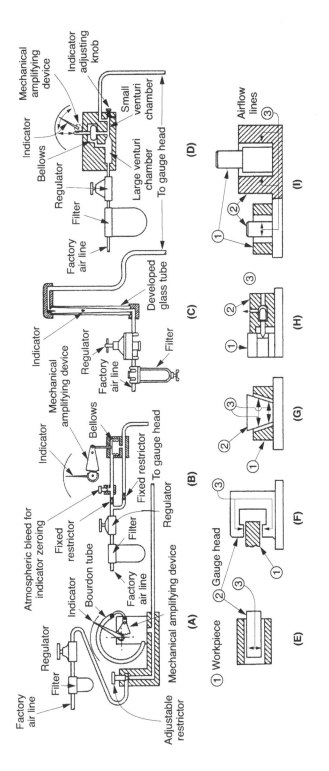

Figure 3.24 Diagrams of air gauge principles.
Reprinted with permission of the Society of Manufacturing Engineers, *Manufacturing Processes and Materials*, 4th Edition, Copyright 2000.

6. Weights, Balances, and Scales

Weight is a measure of how hard an object presses down on a scale, resulting from the action of gravity. Weight and mass are two different quantities that are fundamentally different. The weight of an object can provide an indication of the quantity that we are actually measuring—*mass*.

Measuring Weight and Mass. SI units are used to measure physical quantities. The SI unit of mass is the kilogram, which is also used in the everyday language of measuring weights. In the United States, the pound can be either a unit of weight or a unit of mass.

Adopting Newton's law $(F = ma)$, we can convert between weight and mass. F (or W) is the force due to gravity (weight), m is the mass of the object, and a (or g) is the gravitational acceleration, approximately equal to $9.8 \ m/s^2$ or $32.2 \ ft/s^2$.

Balances and Scales. There are numerous types of balances and scales that are used to measure a wide range of weights for different applications, such as laboratory, industrial, research, and other applications. They offer different capacities, resolutions, requirements, and configurations. Examples include:

- Lab balances

- Analytical balances

- Precision balances

- Industrial scales

- Bench scales

- Counting scales

- Mechanical balances

- Spring scales

- Jewelry scales

There are several national and international organizations that establish standards for weights and measures, such as:

- National Institute of Standards and Technology (NIST) is the U.S. standards-defining authority. NIST Handbook 44 *(Specifications, Tolerances, and Other Technical Requirements for Weighing and Measuring Devices)* sets forth the minimum requirements for standards used primarily to test commercial or legal-for-trade weighing devices for compliance. NIST's Special Publication 881, *Guide for the Use of the International System of Units (SI)*, is also a good source.

- The American Society for Testing and Materials (ASTM) is an organization that establishes test standards for materials, products, systems, and services for a wide range of industries. ASTM developed the E617-97 standard *(Specification for Laboratory Weights and Precision*

Mass Standards) to cover various classes of weights and mass standards used in laboratories.

- The International Organization of Legal Metrology (OIML) is an intergovernmental treaty organization. OIML has two grades of membership: *member states*—these are countries who actively participate in technical activities—and *corresponding members*— these are countries who join the OIML as observers. OIML was established in 1955 in order to promote the global harmonization of legal metrology procedures. It has since developed a worldwide technical structure providing metrological guidelines for the elaboration of national and regional requirements concerning the manufacture and use of measuring instruments for legal metrology applications.

- ISO (International Organization for Standardization) is the world's largest developer and publisher of international standards. ISO is a network of the national standards institutes of 164 countries, one member per country, with a central secretariat in Geneva, Switzerland, that coordinates the system.

7. Hardness Testing Equipment

Brinell. The Brinell hardness test is based on applying forces on an object using a steel or carbide ball that has a 10 mm diameter and subjected to a load of 6614 lb, which can be reduced for softer material to avoid excessive indentation. The diameter of the indentation will be measured after a certain amount of time using a low-powered microscope, and then the Brinell hardness number is calculated by dividing the load applied by the surface area of the indentation (Surface Engineering Forum 2008).

Rockwell. The Rockwell hardness test method is also based on applying force on an object to create indentation, but using a diamond cone or hardened steel ball indenter. A preliminary force will be applied on the indenter to be forced into the test material under minor load. When equilibrium has been reached, an additional major load is applied with resulting increase in penetration. When equilibrium has again been reached, the additional major load is removed, leaving the preliminary load as is. The removal of the additional major load will allow a partial recovery. The indentation from that load is measured and is used to calculate the Rockwell hardness number (Surface Engineering Forum 2008).

Other Measuring Standards. Along with working standards for length and angle measurements, there must be standards of geometric shape to serve as masters for the inspection of manufactured components and systems. Standards of this type are simply defined in common geometric terms and require no special definition. Taking the form of flats, straightedges, right angles, circles, balls, and the like, they are manufactured of hardened and stabilized steel to extremely close tolerances (as close as manufacturing technology permits) so that they approximate the geometric shape that they embody. A precision straightedge may be used to determine the straightness of travel of a slide on a machine tool. A master square may be used to determine the deviation from orthogonality of machine axes. A master circle may be used to inspect the truth of rotation of a machine-tool spindle. Such measurements are ultimately essential to the quality of manufactured parts since a machine tool can not produce parts to precise specifications if it is not precisely produced itself (Zipin 1971).

8. Surface Plate Methods and Equipment

The Surface Plate. A *surface plate* provides a true reference plane from which measurement can be made. A cast-iron surface plate is a heavy ribbed, box-like casting that stands on three points (establishing a plane) and has a thick and well-supported flat top plate. New plates generally have an average of 18 bearing spots on an area of 6.5 cm² (≈1 in²) that do not vary from a true plane by more than 0.005 mm (.0002 in). The use of natural stones for surface plates is becoming increasingly popular because of their hardness, resistance to corrosion, minimum response to temperature change, and nonmagnetic qualities. Figure 3.25 shows a granite surface plate used in inspection work. Reference surfaces also may be obtained by the use of bar parallels, angle irons, V-blocks, and toolmakers' flats.

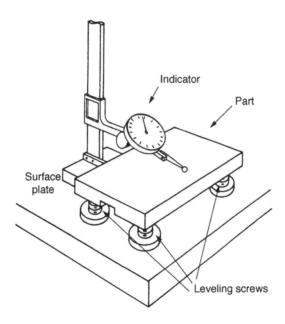

Figure 3.25 Application of a granite surface plate for checking the flatness of a part with a dial indicator and leveling screws.
Reprinted with permission of the Society of Manufacturing Engineers, *Manufacturing Processes and Materials*, 4th Edition, Copyright 2000.

A variety of hand-marking tools, such as the scriber, spring divider, and center punch, are employed by the layout person. These tools are shown in Figure 3.1. The *surface gauge*, Figure 3.1 (item O), consists of a base, an adjustable spindle, and a scriber, and may be used as a layout instrument. The scriber is first adjusted to the desired height by reference to a steel rule of gauge blocks, and then the gauge is moved to the workpiece, and a line is scratched on it at the desired location. The vernier height gauge may be employed in a similar manner.

Surface Metrology. *Surface metrology* may be broadly defined as the measurement of the difference between what the surface actually is and what it is intended to be. It is treated separately from length measurement, which is concerned with the relationship of two surfaces on a workpiece. Surface measurement, however, involves the relationship of a surface on the workpiece to a reference that is not actually on the workpiece. The most common aspect of surface metrology is the measurement of surface roughness as an average deviation from a mean center line (Bosch 1984).

The quality of surface finish is commonly specified along with linear and geometric dimensions. This is becoming more common as product demands increase because surface quality often determines how well a part performs. Heat-exchanger tubes transfer heat better when their surfaces are slightly rough rather than highly finished. Brake drums and clutch plates work best with some degree of surface roughness. On the other hand, bearing surfaces for high-speed engines wear-in excessively and fail sooner if not highly finished, but still need certain surface textures to hold lubricants. Thus, there is a need to control all surface features, not just roughness alone.

Surface Characteristics. The American National Standards Institute (ANSI) has provided a set of standard terms and symbols to define such basic surface characteristics as profile, roughness, waviness, flaws, and lay. A *profile* is defined as the contour of any section through a surface. Roughness refers to relatively finely spaced surface irregularities such as might be produced by the action of a cutting tool or grinding wheel during a machining operation. Waviness consists of those surface irregularities that are of greater spacing than roughness. Waviness may be caused by vibrations, machine or work deflections, warping, and so on. *Flaws* are surface irregularities or imperfections that occur at infrequent intervals and at random locations. Such imperfections as scratches, ridges, holes, cracks, pits, checks, and so on, are included in this category. *Lay* is defined as the direction of the predominant surface pattern. These characteristics are illustrated in Figure 3.26.

Surface Quality Specifications. Standard symbols to specify surface quality are included in Figure 3.26c. Roughness is most commonly specified and is expressed in units of micrometers (μm), nanometers (nm), or microinches (μin). According to the American National Standard ANSI/ASME B46.1-2009, the standard measure of surface roughness adopted by the United States and many other countries around the world is the arithmetic average roughness, Ra (formerly AA or CLA). Ra represents the arithmetic average deviation of the ordinates of profile height increments of the surface from the centerline of that surface.

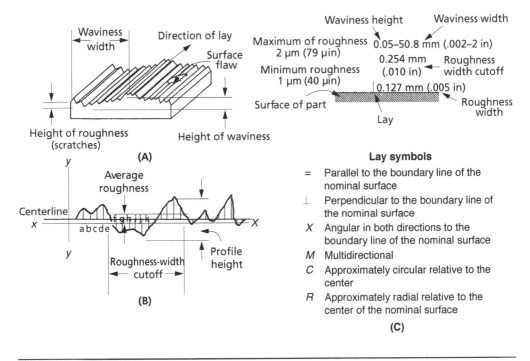

Figure 3.26   (A) Typical surface highly magnified; (B) profile of surface roughness; (C) surface quality specifications.
Reprinted with permission of the Society of Manufacturing Engineers, *Manufacturing Processes and Materials*, 4th Edition, Copyright 2000.

An approximation of the average roughness may be obtained by

$$R_{a+} \frac{y_a + y_b + y_c + \ldots + y_n}{n}$$

where

R_{a+} = Approximation of the average roughness

$y_a \ldots y_n$ = Absolute values of the surface profile coordinates

n = Number of sample measurements

The longest length along the centerline over which the measurements are made is the roughness-width cutoff, or sampling length. In many cases the maximum peak-to-valley height on a surface (R_y) is about four to five times greater than the average surface roughness as measured by R_a. This may present a problem for precision parts having small dimensional tolerances. For example, a flat surface on a part with an R_a of 0.4 μm (16 μin) might very well have a peak-to-valley height (R_y) of 1.6 μm (64 μin) or greater. If the tolerance on that dimension is 0.0025 mm (.0001 in), then the 0.4 μm (16 μin) surface finish represents nearly two-thirds of the permissible tolerance.

Waviness height alone may be specified, or it may be accompanied by a width specification. Thus, in Figure 3.26c, the specification 0.05–50.8 mm (.002–2 in) means that no waves over 0.05 mm (.002 in) high are allowed in any 50.8 mm (2 in) of length. If no width specification is given, it is usually implied that the waviness height specified must be held over the full length of the work. Other specifications in Figure 3.26c are less common (Schrader and Elshennawy 2000).

9. Surface Analyzers

Measurement of Surface Finish. Waviness and roughness are measured separately. Waviness may be measured by sensitive dial indicators. A method of detecting gross waviness is to coat a surface with a high-gloss film, such as mineral oil, and then reflect it in a regular pattern, such as a wire grid. Waviness is revealed by irregularities or discontinuities in the reflected lines.

Many optical methods have been developed to evaluate surface roughness. Some are based on interferometry. One method of interference contrast makes different levels stand out from each other by lighting the surface with two out-of-phase rays. Another method projects a thin ribbon of light at 45° onto a surface. This appears in a microscope as a wavy line depicting the surface irregularities. For a method of replication, a plastic film is pressed against a surface to take its imprint. The film then may be plated with a thin silver deposit for microscopic examination or may be sectioned and magnified. These are laboratory methods and are only economical in manufacturing where other means are not feasible, such as on a surface inaccessible to a probe.

Except for extremely fine surface finishes that require laboratory measurement, most manufacturers measure surface texture at or near the workplace. A variety of instruments, called *surface finish instruments,* are commercially available, either handheld or table mounted. These require only moderate sill, and roughness measurements are displayed on a dial, digital readout, chart, or a digital output for statistical process control (SPC) depending on the type of instrument used. Most of these instruments employ a diamond-tipped stylus that is moved across the surface of the part to sense the point-to-point roughness of that surface. As illustrated in Figure 3.27, there are two basic types of gauges, the *skid* or the *skidless* type. The skid type shown in Figure 3.27a has a hinged probe that rides the worksurface in close proximity to a fairly large skid that also contacts the work surface. The skid-type instruments usually have inductive transducers and are used predominantly for averaging measurements of surface roughness, but not waviness. The skid filters out waviness. Most portable (handheld) instruments are the skid type, and they are reasonably accurate for roughness measurements in the range of 0.30–0.51 μm (12–20 μin) R_a.

The skidless type of instrument illustrated in Figure 3.27b has a built-in reference surface that permits the probe to sense both long- and short-wavelength variations in surface conditions. Thus, these can be used to measure waviness and roughness, as well as surface inclination (straightness). These instruments are often referred to as "profiling" gauges and they usually generate a profile chart on paper or on a computer screen.

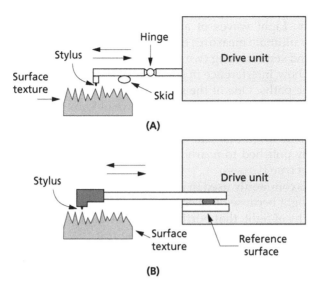

Figure 3.27 (A) Skid-type or average surface-finish measuring gauge; (B) skidless, or profiling, gauge. Reprinted with permission of the Society of Manufacturing Engineers, *Manufacturing Processes and Materials,* 4th Edition, Copyright 2000.

Roughness Reference Standards

Several international standards for the assessment of surface texture define three parameters: R_a (CLA), R_z, and r_{Max}, all measured relative to a straight mean line (Spragg 1976):

1. R_a (center line average) value is the arithmetic mean of the departures of a profile from the mean line. It is normally determined as the mean result of several consecutive sample lengths L.

2. R_z (ten-point height) is the average distance between the five height peaks and five deepest valleys within the sampling length and measured perpendicular to it.

3. R_{Max} is the maximum peak-to-valley height within the sampling length.

Other parameters of surface measurement are defined as follows (Machinability Data Center 1980):

1. R_{tm} is the average value of RMax's for five consecutive sampling lengths.

2. R_p is the maximum profile height from the mean line within the sampling length. R_{pm} is the mean value of R_p's determined over five sampling lengths.

3. PC (peak count) is the number of peak/valley pairs per inch projecting through a band of width b centered about the mean line.

Optical Flats. Light waves of any kind are of invariable length and are the standards for ultimate measures of distance. Basically, all interferometers divide a light beam and send it along two or more paths. Then the beams are recombined and always show interference in some proportion to the differences between the lengths of the paths. One of the simplest illustrations of the phenomenon is the optical flat and a monochromatic light source of known wavelength.

The *optical flat* is a plane lens, usually a clear fused quartz disk, from about 51–254 mm (2–10 in) in diameter and 13–25 mm (.5–1 in) thick. The faces of a flat are accurately polished to nearly true planes; some have surfaces within 25 nm (.000001 in) of true flatness.

Helium is commonly used in industry as a source of monochromatic or single-wavelength light because of its convenience. Although helium radiates a number of wavelengths of light, that portion that is emitted with a wavelength of 587 nm (.00002313 in) is so much stronger than the rest that the other wavelengths are practically unnoticeable.

The principle of light-wave interference and the operation of the optical flat are illustrated in Figure 3.28a wherein an optical flat is shown resting at a slight angle on a workpiece surface. Energy in the form of light waves is transmitted from a monochromatic light source to the optical flat. When a ray of light reaches the bottom surface of the flat, it is divided into two rays. One ray is reflected from the bottom of the flat toward the eye of the observer, while the other continues on downward and is reflected and loses one-half wavelength on striking the top of the workpiece. If the rays are in phase when they re-form, their energies reinforce each other, and they appear bright. If they are out of phase, their energies cancel and they are dark. This phenomenon produces a series of light and dark fringes or bands along the workpiece surface and the bottom of the flat, as illustrated in Figure 3.28b. The distance between the workpiece and the bottom surface of the optical flat at any point determines which effect takes place. If the distance is equivalent to some whole number of half wavelengths of the same monochromatic light, the reflected rays will be out of phase, thus producing dark bands. This condition exists at positions X and Z of Figure 3.28a. If the distance is equivalent to some odd number of quarter wavelengths of the light, the reflected rays will be in phase with each other and produce light bands. The light bands would be centered between the dark bands. Thus a light band would appear at position Y in Figure 3.28a.

Since each dark band indicates a change of one-half wavelength in distance separating the work surface and flat, measurements are made very simply by counting the number of these bands and multiplying that number by one-half the wavelength of the light source. This procedure is illustrated in Figure 3.28b. There, the diameter of a steel ball is compared with a gauge block of known height. Assume a monochromatic light source with a wavelength of 0.5875 μm (23.13 μin). From the block, it is obvious that the difference in elevations of positions A and B on the flat is equal to (4 × 0.5875)/2 or 1.175 μm ([4 × 23.13]/2 or 46.26 μin). By simple proportion, the difference in elevations between points A and C is equal to (1.175 × 63.5)/12.7 = 5.875 μm ([46.26 × 2.5]/.5 = 231.3 μin). Thus, the diameter of the ball is 19.05 + 0.005875 = 19.055875 mm (.750 + .0002313 = .7502313 in).

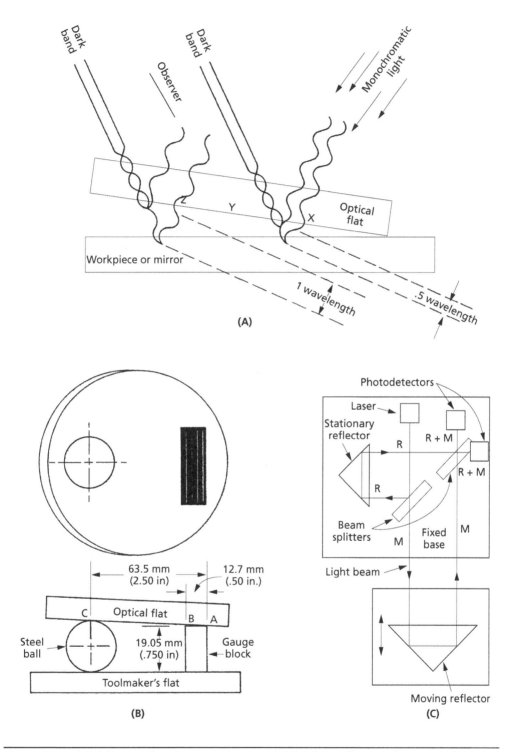

Figure 3.28 (A) Light wave interference with an optical flat; (B) application of an optical flat; (C) diagram of an interferometer.

Reprinted with permission of the Society of Manufacturing Engineers, *Manufacturing Processes and Materials,* 4th Edition, Copyright 2000.

Optical flats are often used to test the flatness of surfaces. The presence of interference bands between the flat and the surface being tested is an indication that the surface is not parallel with the surface of the flat.

The way dimensions are measured by interferometry can be explained by moving the optical flat in Figure 3.28a in a direction perpendicular to the face of the workpiece or mirror. It is assumed that the mirror is rigidly attached to a base, and the optical flat is firmly held on a true slide. As the optical flat moves, the distance between the flat and mirror changes along the line of traverse, and the fringes appear to glide across the face of the flat or mirror. The amount of movement is measured by counting the number of fringes and fraction of a fringe that pass a mark. It is difficult to precisely superimpose a real optical flat on a mirror or the end of a piece to establish the end points of a dimension to be measured. This difficulty is overcome in sophisticated instruments by placing the flat elsewhere and by optical means reflecting its image in the position relative to the mirror in Figure 3.28a. This creates interference bands that appear to lie on the face of and move with the workpiece or mirror. The image of the optical flat can be merged into the planes of the workpiece surfaces to establish beginning and end points of dimensions.

A simple interferometer for measuring movements of a machine tool slide to nanometers (millionths of an inch) is depicted in Figure 3.28c. A strong light beam from a laser is split by a half mirror. One component becomes the reference R and is reflected solely over the fixed machine base. The other part, M, travels to a reflector on the machine side and is directed back to merge with ray R at the second beam splitter. Their resultant is split and directed to two photodetectors. The rays pass in and out of phase as the slide moves. The undulations are converted to pulses by an electronic circuit; each pulse stands for a slide movement equal to one-half the wavelength of the laser light. The signal at one photodetector leads the other according to the direction of movement.

When measurements are made to nanometers (millionths of an inch) by an interferometer, they are meaningful only if all causes of error are closely controlled. Among these are temperature, humidity, air pressure, oil films, impurities, and gravity. Consequently, a real interferometer is necessarily a highly refined and complex instrument; only its elements have been described here.

10. Force Measurement Tools

Tools such as torque wrenches and tensiometers are common tools for measuring force. A *torque wrench* is a tool used to apply a certain amount of torque to nuts and bolts. It allows the measurement of the torque that is applied to a fastener in order to match the required specification for a particular application. A *tensiometer* is a device that is used to measure the surface tension of a liquid.

11. Angle Measurement Tools

The unit standard of angular measurement is the *degree*. The measurement and inspection of angular dimensions are somewhat more difficult than with linear measures and may require instruments of some complexity if a great deal of angular precision is required.

Simple Tools. The *combination* set consists of a center head, protractor, and square with a 45° surface, all of which are used individually in conjunction with a steel rule. The heads are mounted on the rule and clamped in any position along its length by means of a lock screw. The parts of such a set are shown in Figure 3.1 (item N). The center head is used to scribe bisecting diameters of the end of a cylindrical piece to locate the center of the piece. The protractor reads directly in degrees. Both the square head and the protractor may contain a small spirit level. A *bevel protractor* utilizes a vernier scale to show angles as small as five minutes.

The Sine Bar. The *sine bar* is a relatively simple device for precision measuring and checking of angles. It consists of an accurately ground, flat steel straightedge with precisely affixed round buttons a definite distance apart, and of identical diameters.

Figure 3.29 illustrates one method of applying a sine bar in the determination of the angle α on the conical surface of the part located on the surface plate. For precise results, a sine bar must be used on true surfaces. In Figure 3.10, the center-to-center distance of the sine bar buttons is 127 mm (5 in) and the distances A and B are determined by means of gauge blocks or a vernier height gauge to be 25.400 mm (1.0000 in) and 89.794 mm (3.5352 in), respectively. Thus the sine α equals (89.794 − 25.400)/127.00 = 0.50704, and from trigonometric tables the angle α is 30°28′.

Dividing Heads. *Mechanical* and *optical dividing heads* are often employed for the circular measurement of angular spacing. The optical dividing head performs the same function but more precisely.

Layout Instruments and Locating Devices. Considerable metalworking and woodworking—particularly in job shops, for pattern building, and for tool and die work—are done to lay out lines, circles, center locations, and so on, scribed on the workpiece itself. Chalk or dye is often applied to the work surface before scribing so that the lines can be readily seen.

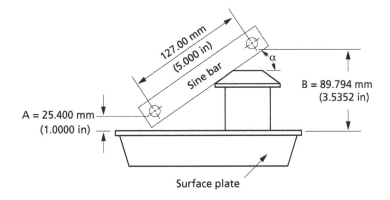

Figure 3.29 Application of a sine bar.
Reprinted with permission of the Society of Manufacturing Engineers, *Manufacturing Processes and Materials*, 4th Edition, Copyright 2000.

12. Color Measurement Tools

Spectrophotometers. The *spectrophotometer* is an instrument that measures the amount of light of a specified wavelength that passes through a medium. According to Beer's law, the amount of light absorbed by a medium is proportional to the concentration of the absorbing material or solute present. Thus, the concentration of a colored solute in a solution may be determined in the lab by measuring the absorbency of light at a given wavelength. Wavelength (often abbreviated as lambda) is measured in nm. The spectrophotometer allows selection of a wavelength passing through the solution, usually the wavelength chosen that corresponds to the absorption maximum of the solute. Absorbency is indicated with a capital A (Frankhauser 2003).

Color Guides. *Color guides* come in different forms and shapes. They are used by designers, manufacturers, product sellers, marketers, and other consumers in many industries. The purpose is to provide guidance for accurate identification of colors, product specifications, quality control, communications, and other identification means for product brands and services.

13. Automated In-Line Inspection Methods

As industrial processes are automated, gauging must keep pace. Automated gauging is performed in two general ways. One is in-process or on-the-machine control by continuous gauging of the work. The second way is post-process or after-the-machine gauging control. Here, the parts coming off the machine are passed through an automatic gauge. A control unit responds to the gauge to sort pieces by size and adjust or stop the machine if parts are found out of limits.

SUMMARY OF GAUGE USES AND APPLICATIONS

Table 3.1 shows a useful summary of the gauges that are presented in the chapter and their uses and applications.

Table 3.1 Summary of commonly used gauges and their applications.

Gauge	Uses and applications
Steel rule	Used effectively as a line measuring device, which means that the ends of a dimension being measured are aligned with the graduations of the scale, from which the length is read directly.
Depth rule	Used for measuring the depth of slots, holes, and so on.
Vernier caliper	Typifies the type of instrument using the vernier principle of measurement. Outside dimensions are measured between the lower jaws, inside dimensions over the tips of the upper jaws.
Digital reading caliper	Provides LCD readouts in either millimeters or inches and operates by a microprocessor-based system. It is capable of retaining a reading in the display when the tool is used in an area where visibility is restricted.

(continued)

Table 3.1   Summary of commonly used gauges and their applications *(continued)*.

Gauge	Uses and applications
Vernier height gauge	Similar to a vernier caliper except that the fixed jaw has been replaced by a fixed base, and the sliding jaw may have been a scriber attached to it for layout work, or a dial indicator for measuring or comparing operations.
Digital micrometer	Used in measuring diameters, thicknesses, inside dimensions, heights, and outside dimensions.
Dial indicator	Used for different applications such as heights, flatness, diameters, and so on.
Optical comparator	Used for measuring complicated or difficult shapes and other configurations.
Gauge block	Dimensional measurement standards that are used to calibrate other measuring devices. They come in sets of different grades depending on the desired measurement accuracy required. Each set has many blocks of incremental lengths. These blocks are stacked together (wringed) to build a desired length.
Working gauge	Used by the machine operator or shop inspector to check the dimensions of parts as they are being produced. They usually have limits based on the piece being inspected.
Inspection gauge	Used by personnel to inspect purchased parts when received or manufactured parts when finished. These gauges are designed and made so as not to reject any product previously accepted by a properly designed and functioning working gauge.
Reference, or master, gauge	Used for checking the size or condition of other gauges, and represent as exactly as possible the physical dimensions of the product.
Limit gauge	Often called a "go/no-go" gauge, establishes the high and low limits prescribed by the tolerance on a dimension. A limit gauge may be either double-ended or progressive.
Ring gauge	Used for checking outside dimensions such as the limit sizes of a round shaft.
Plug gauge	Used for checking inside dimensions.
Snap gauge	Another fixed gauge with the gauging members specially arranged for measuring diameters, thickness, and lengths.
Spline gauge	Commonly used to inspect splined workpieces prior to assembly.
Screw thread micrometer	Generally designed to measure threads within a narrow range of pitches.
Template	Used to check a specified profile. They may also be used to control or gauge special shapes or contours in manufactured parts.
Screw pitch gauge	Used to check the pitch of a screw.
Oscilloscope	Commonly used to troubleshoot electronic equipment failure by graphically showing signals that indicate failures or malfunctioning.
Multimeter	An electronic gauge that combines more than one function in a single unit. Multimeters use either analog or digital displays. Common uses for a multimeter are fault discovery, field work of electronic or telecommunications technicians, or as a basic workshop instrument. Standard measurements of a multimeter include voltage, current, and resistance.

(continued)

Table 3.1 Summary of commonly used gauges and their applications *(continued)*.

Gauge	Uses and applications
Pneumatic gauge	A means of measuring, comparing, or checking dimensions by sensing the flow of air through the space between a gauge head and workpiece surface.
Optical flat	Often used to test the flatness of surfaces. The presence of interference bands between the flat and the surface being tested is an indication that the surface is not parallel with the surface of the flat.

B. CONTROL AND MAINTENANCE OF M&TE

1. M&TE Identification, Control, and Maintenance

> Describe various methodologies for identifying and controlling M&TE to meet traceability requirements, and apply appropriate techniques for maintaining such equipment to obtain optimum performance. (Apply)
>
> **Body of Knowledge III.B.1**

ISO/IEC 17025 emphasizes that:

- Test and calibration items should be uniquely identified.

- Handling, protection, storage, retention, and/or disposal should follow documented procedures.

- The procedures should prevent deterioration and damage during storage and inventory.

- Calibration of equipment should be made traceable to national or international standards.

- Traceability of equipment is a prerequisite for compatibility of test and calibration results.

Equipment Traceability. *Traceability* is a process intended to quantify a laboratory's measurement uncertainty in relation to national standards. Traceability is based on analyses of error contributions present in each of the measurement transfers: the calibration of the laboratory's reference standards by NIST, the measurements made in the calibration transfers within the laboratory, and the measurements made on a product. Evidence of traceability is normally required. Such traceability may be as simple as retention of certificates and reports of calibration or as complex as reproduction of the analyses demonstrating the uncertainties claimed for the measurements (Rice 1986).

A laboratory that maintains its own reference standards (that is, it relies on no laboratory other than NIST for calibration of its standards) must continuously monitor its own performance. Measurements on check standards, intercomparisons of standards, and participation in measurement assurance programs sponsored by NIST are means to quantify laboratory error sources as well as to provide indications of the causes (Rice 1986).

Gauge Maintenance, Handling, and Storage. ISO 9001 standards require the organization to:

1. Determine the monitoring and measurements to be undertaken

2. Determine the monitoring and measuring devices to be used to provide evidence of conformity of products to requirements

3. Establish processes to ensure that monitoring and measurement are carried out in a manner that is consistent with the monitoring and measurement requirements

The standards also require the organization to ensure that measuring instruments satisfy the following requirements:

- They are calibrated at specified requirements against measurement standards traceable to international or national measurement standards, such as NIST standards.

- Where no such international or national standards exist, the basis used for calibration or verification must be recorded.

- They are adjusted or pre-adjusted as necessary.

- They are identified to determine the calibration status.

- They are safeguarded from adjustments that would invalidate the measurement status.

- They are protected from damage and deterioration during handling, maintenance, and storage.

In addition, the standards require the organization to assess and record the validity of previous measurement results when the equipment is not found to be conforming to requirements, and to take appropriate action on the equipment and any product affected.

2. Customer-Supplied M&TE

Describe and apply requirements for validation and control of customer-supplied equipment. (Apply)

Body of Knowledge III.B.2

Customers may need to keep track of their own test and measuring equipment and instruments, their operating procedures, calibration history, and other documentation related to their inventory of test and measuring equipment and instrumentation.

The following are the recommendations that are provided through ISO/IEC 17025, *General requirements for the competence of testing and calibration laboratories:*

- Equipment should conform to specifications relevant to the tests.

- Equipment and software should be identified and documented.

- Calibration certificates should not contain any recommendation on the calibration interval except where this has been agreed on with the client.

- Customers should keep a database that tells them in advance when to take a unit out of service and send it for recalibration.

- The customers managing the M&TE keep a documentation/procedure to keep track of calibration schedules.

- Equipment should be calibrated and/or checked to establish that it meets the laboratory's specification requirements.

- Calibration status should be indicated on the instruments, as well as the next calibration date.

- Records of equipment and associated software should be maintained and properly updated.

C. CALIBRATION OF M&TE

Any metrologist's ability to measure is affected by the environment, the functional features of the instrument, and his or her training. These factors, along with the design features of the instrument, combine in precision; these factors, combined with precision, interpret accuracy. You must be able to trace the accuracy of any part feature measured directly back to the international standard. At each step, all the factors contribute error that distorts the accuracy; however, only the inherent accuracy carries the accuracy forward. Ensuring accuracy is the function of the calibration group (Busch, Harlow and Thompson, 1998)

Calibration refers to measurements where the individual values are reported, rather than to measurements indicating only that an instrument is functioning within prescribed limits. It also refers to the disciplines necessary to control measuring systems to assure their functioning within prescribed accuracy objectives (Darmody, 1967).

Gauge Repeatability and Reproducibility

In any production process, natural or inherent variability is the cumulative effect of many small causes. When other causes are present, these are referred to as *special* or *assignable causes*. This variability usually arises from sources such as improperly adjustment machines or equipment, operator errors, or defective raw materials. Such variability is generally large when compared to the natural process variability and it usually represents an unacceptable level of process performance. A process that is operating in the presence of assignable causes is said to be "out of control." Often, production processes operate in the in-control state. Occasionally, however, assignable causes occur, seemingly at random, resulting in a shift to a state of out-of-control. A control chart is widely used to quickly detect the occurrence of assignable causes, and corrective action may be undertaken before many nonconforming units are manufactured.

Control charts mainly detect the presence of assignable causes. The concept of *gauge repeatability and reproducibility* (GR&R) can be employed to identify real root causes of the problem in a process. After process adjustment, factors that affect the measurement system variation can then be studied using the GR&R technique. Measurement system variation can be characterized by location (stability, bias, linearity) and width or spread (repeatability and reproducibility). A general discussion on estimating total measurement variation is outlined below (AIAG 2010).

A GR&R study is appropriate to apply in most manufacturing-related measurement systems. It may be used as:

- A criterion for judging new measuring equipment

- A comparison between measuring devices

- A means for improving performance of measuring instruments

- A comparison for measuring equipment before and after repair

- A required component for calculating process variation and the acceptability level for a production process

- A measure of the need for training on how to use measuring instruments

Calibration Systems

A calibration system, like any type of system, is composed of inputs, processes, outputs, and feedback, as identified in Figure 3.30.

1. Calibration Intervals

> Apply calibration schedules on the basis of M&TE usage history and risk. (Apply)
>
> **Body of Knowledge III.C.1**

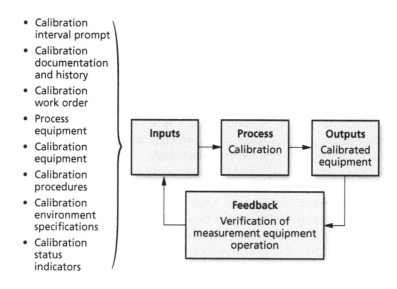

- Calibration interval prompt
- Calibration documentation and history
- Calibration work order
- Process equipment
- Calibration equipment
- Calibration procedures
- Calibration environment specifications
- Calibration status indicators

| Inputs | Process Calibration | Outputs Calibrated equipment |

Feedback
Verification of measurement equipment operation

Figure 3.30 The calibration system.

The aim of all calibration activities is to ascertain that a measuring system will function to assure attainment of its accuracy objectives. The general calibration provisions for a measuring system include (Darmody, 1967):

1. Acceptance calibration of a new system

2. Periodic calibration of the system in use or when placed in use after storage

3. Availability of standards traceable to the national standard for the unit of measure under consideration

Periodic calibration of measuring and test equipment is accepted by most as necessary for measurement accuracy. A little more controversial is the question of determining the basis of the period of recalibration. There are a number of techniques in use to establish calibration intervals initially and to adjust the intervals thereafter. These methods include the same interval for all equipment in the user's inventory, the same interval for families of instruments (for example, oscilloscopes, digital volumeters, gauge blocks, and so on), and the same interval for a given manufacturer and model number. Adjustments of these initial intervals are then made for the entire inventory, individual families, or manufacturer and model numbers, respectively, based on analyses or history. A study conducted for NIST in connection with a review of government laboratory practices identifies these and other methods. It is generally not possible or advisable to lengthen the duration of a calibration interval without a detailed analysis of equipment performance and, in the case of regulatory control, authorization by an agent of the cognizant department or agency (Vogt, 1980).

A *calibration interval* is an interval based on time, such as weekly, monthly, quarterly, semiannually, annually, or biannually. A calibration interval may also be an interval based on cycles of operation, such as every 1000 uses. A calibration interval is established for equipment identified as being influenced by, or characteristic of, any of the following:

1. Regulatory or oversight control

2. Importance in process operation

3. Manufacturer guidelines or requirements, and/or

4. Historical performance accuracy and consistency

2. Calibration Results

> Interpret calibration results and the potential impact of using out-of-calibration tools or failing to calibrate equipment on a regular basis. (Analyze)
>
> **Body of Knowledge III.C.2**

The purpose of calibration is to ensure that various types of measurement and process equipment accurately and consistently perform as designed and intended. Further, the purpose of calibration is to ensure that equipment accuracy and consistency remains correlated with known quantities or values, which are commonly referred to as standards. The basic principle of calibration, then, refers to the process of aligning measurement and process equipment performance with known quantities or values as specified in standards.

A typical calibration program may involve all or most of the following tasks (Rice, 1986):

1. Evaluation of equipment to determine its capability

2. Identification of calibration requirements

3. Selection of standards to perform calibration

4. Selection of methods/procedures to carry out the measurements necessary for the calibration

5. Establishment of the initial interval and the rules for adjusting the interval thereafter

6. Establishment of a recall system to assure instruments due for calibration are returned

7. Implementation of a labeling system to visually identify the instrument's due date

8. Use of a quality assurance program to evaluate the calibration system (process, control, audit, corrective action, and so on)

Out-of-Calibration Effects. The effects of using out-of-calibration equipment are the same as those due to type I and type II errors (also known as *producer's risk* and *consumer's risk*). In essence, the effects of out-of-calibration equipment cause stakeholders to believe that (1) the equipment is calibrated and functioning properly when it is not, or (2) the equipment has failed calibration when it is, in fact, functioning correctly (Mack, 1976).

Using out-of-calibration equipment in production or service delivery operations can cause a number of difficulties for manufacturers and service providers. In the best-case situation, once discovered, out-of-calibration equipment functions correctly, and exceptions reporting must document the out-of-calibration incident, a corrective action plan must be developed/initiated, and product or service quality must be systematically verified—all of which is wasteful, potentially compromises customer confidence and goodwill, and costs the company time and money. In the worst-case situation, once discovered, out-of-calibration equipment does not function correctly, and containment of product or service delivery must be initiated, material control and segregation procedures must be employed, a comprehensive evaluation of product/service performance must be conducted, Material Review Board action is required, a root cause analysis is required, warranty or recall may become necessary, and a company has exposure to legal/regulatory action.

At a minimum, procedures for dealing with an out-of-calibration event or discovery require the following:

1. Identification of the out-of-calibration condition (as described above in terms of type I or type II errors)

2. Determination of the magnitude of the condition (that is, how far out of calibration was the equipment?)

3. Assessment of when the out-of-calibration condition occurred

4. Quantification of the amount of product/service delivery produced/delivered during the out-of-calibration condition

5. Evaluation of product or service delivery status (that is, has any product been produced or service been provided to customers during the out-of-calibration condition?)

6. Identification of who is authorized to manage the containment efforts

3. Calibration Error

Identify the causes of calibration error and its effect on processes and products. (Understand)

Body of Knowledge III.C.3

Calibration errors do not mean that the instrument is incorrectly set: they mean that there is a disparity between the input signal and the reading. These errors are caused by false elements, such as a scale spacing that does not match the amplification, or a probe that is too long. You can detect calibration errors by correctly re-calibrating the instrument, especially to gauge blocks, and sometimes calibration errors can be corrected by adjusting the instrument. Thorough, regular evaluation of an instrument will prevent calibration errors. Calibration errors may also be caused by human errors, errors in technique or experimental errors. Such errors are usually referred to as Systematic errors. Other random or accidental errors in calibration may include judgement errors, mearing conditions, or definition (an evaluation of consistency of the measured quantity). Other errors are illegitimate errors that include mistakes, computational errors, or chaotic errors that are extreme disturbances that ruin or hide measurement results (Busch, Harlow and Thompson, 1998).

4. Hierarchy of Standards

> Explain the levels of standards (e.g., reference, primary, transfer) and their relationship to one another. (Apply)
>
> **Body of Knowledge III.C.4**

Calibration standards are known, highly accurate, and verifiable quantities used as the basis of comparison in calibration processes. Virtually all industrialized nations maintain a set of calibration standards for the measurement of various quantities and phenomena (Bucher 2004, 2006).

The National Institute of Standards and Technology (NIST) is the custodian of measurement standards in the United States. NIST was established by an act of Congress in 1901, although the need for such a body had been noted by the founders of the Constitution. NIST has two main facilities and laboratories in Gaithersburg, Maryland, and Boulder, Colorado, where research into the phenomenon of measurement, the properties of materials, and calibration of reference standards is carried out.

There are several levels of calibration standards arranged in a hierarchy. At the highest level in a calibration standard hierarchy are international standards, which serve as the basis of trade between nations. At the lowest level in a calibration standard hierarchy are transfer standards, which serve as the basis of trade between organizations. Calibration standards at the lowest levels in the hierarchy are used to support day-to-day operations by technicians and shop floor operators. Calibration standards in the middle of the hierarchy are generally used by personnel dedicated to calibration processes working in calibration laboratories. Calibration standards at the highest levels in the hierarchy are generally used by calibration specialists and government officials.

Figure 3.31 presents a hierarchy of calibration standards provided by Bucher (2004, 2006) summarized as follows.

- *International standards.* A standard recognized by international agreement to serve internationally as the basis for fixing the value of all other standards of the quantity concerned.

- *National standards.* A standard recognized by an official national decision to serve in a country as the basis for fixing the value of all other standards of the quantity concerned. Generally, a national standard in a country is also a primary standard to which other standards are traceable.

- *Primary standards.* A standard that is designed or widely acknowledged as having the highest metrological quality and whose value is accepted without reference to other standards of the same quantity. National standards are generally primary standards.

- *Secondary standards.* A standard whose value is based on comparisons with some primary standard. Note that a secondary standard, once its value is established, can become a primary standard for some other user.

- *Reference standards.* A standard having the highest metrological quality available at a given location and from which the measurements made at that location are derived.

- *Working standards.* A measurement standard, not specifically reserved as a reference standard, that is intended to verify measurement equipment of lower accuracy.

- *Transfer standards.* A standard that is the same as a reference standard except that it is used to transfer a measurement parameter from one organization to another for traceability purposes.

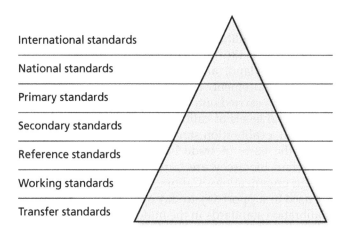

Figure 3.31 Calibration standards hierarchy.

Selection of the standards, methods, and procedures to carry out the calibration includes the decision relating to where the calibration will be performed. Some instruments may require use of a laboratory's highest level of standards and thus must be performed in the laboratory. Other instruments, however, may be calibrated in the using area by the transport of suitable standards to that area.

In order to maintain accuracy, standards in industrialized nations must be traceable to a single source, usually the country's national standards. Since the national laboratories of industrialized nations maintain close connections with the International Bureau of Weights and Measures, there is assurance that items produced from calibration standards in one country will be consistent with items produced from calibration standards in other countries.

Chapter 4

IV. Inspection and Test

A. BLUEPRINT READING AND INTERPRETATION

1. Blueprint Symbols and Components

> Interpret drawings and apply requirements in various test and inspection activities. (Analyze)
>
> **Body of Knowledge IV.A.1**

Blueprint refers to any drawing that is produced by any means, such as a drawing on paper using pencils or inks, or produced by computer-aided design (CAD) software. Blueprints provide important information that helps identify the part or assembly it represents, including:

- Information about the materials and their specifications as well as other information not provided in the drawings

- Drawing number, name of the assembly or part it represents, name and address of the person(s) who prepared the drawing, and other information that is used to define and identify that part or assembly

- Reference number

- Drawing scale

- Bill of materials

- Finish block to show the parts to be finished and their requirements

- Legends

- Symbols

- Notes and specifications

2. Geometric Dimensioning and Tolerancing (GD&T)

> Define and apply GD&T covered in the
> ASME Y14.5 standard. (Analyze)
>
> **Body of Knowledge IV.A.2**

Some parts of the discussion in this section are adapted from ASME Y14.5 standard.

Dimensioning and Tolerancing. It is expected that drawings have dimensions that provide detailed information about sizes, shapes, and the location of different components and parts. It is also expected that part and component dimensions show acceptable variation. To produce any part or component with exact dimension is nearly impossible, except by remote chance. Variations in materials, machines, manufacturing parameters, and humans make it necessary that dimensions have acceptable variations. Such variation is referred to as tolerance. Higher quality requires tighter tolerances that, in turn, require more expensive and strict production and inspection procedures to obtain. There are two types of tolerances: unilateral tolerance and bilateral tolerance. *Unilateral tolerance* specifies allowable variation in a dimension from a basic or nominal size in one direction in relation to that basic size.

For example: $2.000^{+0.000/-0.005}$ inches describes an allowable variation only in the lower limit (unilateral tolerance). Specifications on a part with this tolerance will be 2.000 inches and 1.995 inches as desired upper and lower limits, respectively. On the other hand, 2.000+0.005/−0.005 inches describes a *bilateral tolerance*. It specifies a dimension with allowable variations in both directions of the basic size. Specifications on a part with such bilateral tolerance will be 2.005 inches and 1.995 inches as desired upper and lower limits, respectively.

Geometric tolerancing defines tolerances for geometric features or characteristics on a part. Figure 4.1 shows some of the geometric dimensioning symbols as defined in ANSI Y14.5M.

The example shown in Figure 4.2 illustrates the interpretation of a geometric tolerance on a drawing.

The limit dimensions of the simple cylindrical piece at the top of Figure 4.3 define the maximum and minimum limits of a profile for the work. The form or shape of the part may vary as long as no portions of the part exceed the maximum profile limit or are inside the minimum profile limit. If a part measures its maximum material limit of size everywhere, it should be of perfect form. This is referred to as the *maximum material condition* (MMC) and is at the low limit for a hole or slot but at the high limit for parts such as shafts, bolts, or pins.

If it is desired to provide greater control on the form than is imposed by the limit dimensions, then certain tolerances of form must be applied. In most cases, these tolerances appear in the form of notations on the drawing as illustrated at the bottom of Figure 4.3.

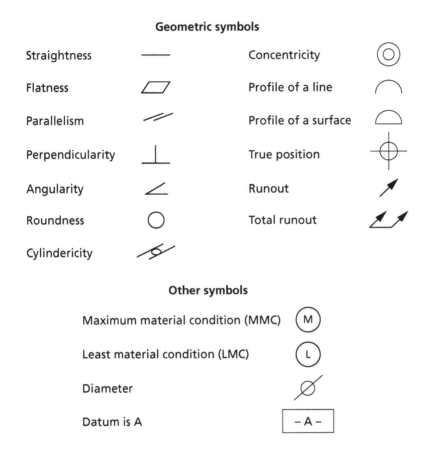

Figure 4.1   Some geometric tolerancing symbols.

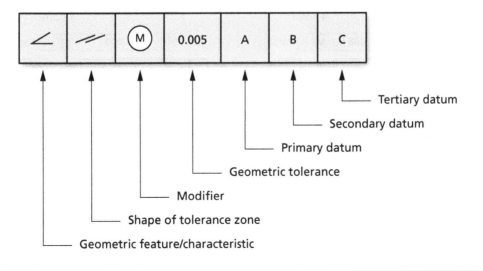

Figure 4.2   Illustration of geometric tolerances on a drawing.

Positional Tolerances. Positional tolerancing is a system of specifying the true position, size, or form of a part feature and the amount it may vary from the ideal. The advantage of the system is that it allows the one responsible for making the part to divide tolerances between position and size as he or she finds best. The principles are illustrated for two simple mating parts in Figure 4.4. The basic

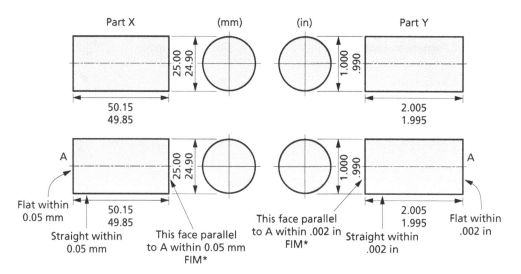

*FIM = Full indicator movement

Figure 4.3 Part drawing with and without tolerances of form.
Reprinted with permission of the Society of Manufacturing Engineers, *Manufacturing Processes and Materials*, 4th Edition, Copyright 2000.

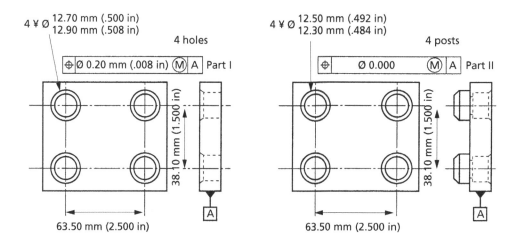

Figure 4.4 Two parts dimensioned with positional tolerances.
Reprinted with permission of the Society of Manufacturing Engineers, *Manufacturing Processes and Materials*, 4th Edition, Copyright 2000.

dimensions without tolerances are shown at the bottom and right side of each part. Beneath the size dimension for holes or posts is a box with the notations for positional tolerancing. Actually, a number of specifications are possible, but only one set is shown here as an example. The circle and cross in the first cell of the box is the convention that says the features are positionally toleranced.

Part I in Figure 4.4 introduces the idea of the MMC utilized in most positional tolerancing. This is designated by the letter M in a circle and means that the smallest hole (12.70 mm or .500 in) determines the inner boundary for any hole. The "Ø 0.20 mm (.008 in)" notation in the box specifies that the axis of any minimum-size hole must not be outside a theoretical cylinder of 0.20 mm (.008 in) diameter around the true position. A 12.50 mm (.492 in) diameter plug in true position will fit in any 12.70 mm (.500 in) diameter hole with its axis on the 0.20 mm (.008 in) diameter cylinder. Any hole that passes over such a plug is acceptable, provided that its diameter is within the high and low limits specified.

The letter "A" in the specification box designates that the theoretical cylinder bounding the hole axes must be perpendicular to the datum surface carrying the "A" flag. Features usually are referred to with three coordinate datum surfaces, but, for simplicity, in this case the holes are related only to each other and surface "A" and not to the sides of the part.

Part II of Figure 4.4 introduces the idea of zero maximum material condition specified by "Ø 0.000" before the MMC symbol. This means the axis of the largest-diameter post (12.50 mm [.492 in]) must be exactly in the true position, but smaller sizes of posts may vary in position as long as they do not lie outside the boundary set by the largest. Thus, if the posts are held to a tolerance smaller than the 0.20 mm (.008 in) specified, say to a tolerance of 0.05 mm (.002 in), the difference (0.15 mm [.006 in]) is then available for variations in post positions. The advantage of zero MMC is that only one limit of the feature, in this case the lower limit of the post diameter, needs to be checked along with position (Schrader and Elshennawy 2000).

Product and Component Characteristics. Measurement is the process of evaluating a property or characteristic of an object and describing it with a numerical or nominal value. If the value is numerical, reflecting the extent of the characteristic, then the measurement is said to be on a *quantitative* scale and the actual property is referred to as a *variable*. Examples of variables inspection are measurements related to weight, length, temperature, and so on.

If the value assigned to each unit is other than numerical, then the measurement is on a *qualitative*, or *classification*, scale and is referred to as an *attribute*. In most inspection situations involving nominal or attribute data, there are two possible nominal values: conforming (good) and nonconforming (defective). Each product unit is assigned one of these two labels according to inspection operation results. It is then possible to derive a numerical measure of many units' quality or processes output from a qualitative scale. This is achieved by calculating the *fraction nonconforming* (fraction defective) as the ratio between the number of units labeled as nonconforming and the total number of units inspected.

A common method of inspection by attributes involves the use of *limit gauges,* also known as *go/no-go gauges.* Limit gauges are made to sizes essentially identical with the design specification limits of the dimension to be inspected. If a specific gauge can properly mate with a part, then the part can be assembled with another part whose physical boundaries do not exceed those of the gauge. Consequently, the part is acceptable for assembly. Limit gauges designed to identify this condition are called *go gauges*.

The "go" end of a go/no-go gauge contains the reverse physical replica of the dimension inspected at the maximum material condition (minimum size for interior features, maximum size for exterior features). The maximum material condition produces the minimum clearance required for assembly.

The "no-go" end is designed to detect conditions of excessive clearance. It contains the reverse physical replica of the dimension inspected at its minimum material condition. A part will not mate with a no-go gauge unless the actual condition of the part feature is below the specified minimum. Thus, if the no-go gauge mates with the part, then the part dimension is incorrect and the part should be rejected.

In practice, go/no-go gauges are used together and often appear at opposite ends of an inspection instrument. An acceptable part should mate with the go end but should not mate with the no-go end. Parts that mate with neither or both ends do not meet design specifications and should be rejected.

Inspection by Attributes. Most methods of inspection by attributes, other than gauging, are largely subjective and depend on the ability of human inspectors to make the right decision. In many cases, inspection by attributes involves visual characteristics, such as color, shape, smoothness, and other visual defects (Raz 1992).

3. Classification of Product Defect Characteristics

> Define and distinguish between defect characteristics (e.g. critical, major, minor). (Analyze)
>
> **Body of Knowledge IV.A.3**

In certain types of products, more than one defect could be present, and a relatively small number of minor defects could be acceptable to the customer. Product quality in such cases may be judged by the total number of defects or the number of defects per unit. Control charts for attributes are a tool that may be used for this purpose. In such cases, the objective of inspection is to determine the number of defects or nonconformities present rather than to classify units as conforming or nonconforming.

Defect and *nonconformity* are two terms that may be used interchangeably in many situations. For other purposes, definitions for both terms are slightly different. A *nonconformity* is defined as a failure of a quality characteristic to meet its intended level or state occurring with severity sufficient to cause the product not to meet a specification. A *defect* is a nonconformity severe enough to cause the product not to satisfy normal usage requirements. Thus, the difference between the term *nonconformity* and the term *defect* is based mainly on the perspective. The former is defined based on specifications, while the latter is defined based on fitness for use. Thus, the numerical result generated by inspection consists of the count of defects or nonconformities for each product unit. Often, it is possible to classify the different types of defects according to their severity, then assign a weight to each class based on the importance of the affected quality characteristic in relation to the product specifications. The selection of the weights should reflect the relative importance of the various defect categories and their likelihood of causing product failure or customer dissatisfaction. A typical seriousness classification includes four levels of defect seriousness:

1. *Critical* defect may lead directly to severe injury or catastrophic economic loss.

2. *Serious* defect may lead to injury or significant economic loss.

3. *Major* defect may cause major problems during normal use. A major defect will likely result in reducing the usability of the product.

4. *Minor* defect may cause minor problems during normal use.

B. INSPECTION CONCEPTS

Inspection is the evaluation of product quality by comparing the results of measuring one or several product characteristics with applicable standards. From this definition it is evident that the inspection function involves a number of tasks (Raz 1992):

1. Measurement, which could be on a qualitative or quantitative scale. The objective is to make a judgment about the product's conformance to specifications.

2. Comparison of the measurement results to certain standards that reflect the intended use of the product by the customer and the various production costs. If the product is found to be nonconforming, a decision as to whether nonconforming products are fit for use may be reached.

3. Decision making regarding the disposition of the unit inspected and, under sampling inspection, regarding the lot from which the sample was drawn.

4. Corrective action(s) to improve the quality of the product and/or process based on the aggregate results of inspection over a number of units.

Uses of Inspection

The results of inspection can be used for different purposes (Raz 1992):

1. To document any changes in process performance or that the production process has changed.

2. To distinguish between good lots and bad lots, as in incoming material inspection and final product inspection, using acceptance sampling plans.

3. To distinguish between good products and bad products. In this case, a 100% inspection or a scheme of defect classification may be used.

4. To determine the status of process control and whether the process is changing. This is usually done in conjunction with control charts.

5. To evaluate process capability, which is defined as the ratio of the difference between specification limits (tolerance) and the natural tolerance limits of the process, estimated as six standard deviation units (6σ). In this case, inspection is used to determine whether the process exhibits excessive variation and if it is approaching or exceeding the specification limits.

6. To determine process adjustment. Based on inspection results of process output, as depicted by a histogram, for example, the process mean may require adjustment, and/or process variation may need to be reduced. A process might require adjustment, even though all the units produced to date conform to the quality standards agreed on with the customer.

7. To rate the accuracy of inspectors or of inspection equipment by comparing the inspection results with corresponding standards. An inspection operation can result in two types of error: classification of a conforming unit as nonconforming, and classification of a nonconforming unit as conforming. The probabilities of both types of error could be easily estimated using probability theory and other statistical methods.

8. To serve as a mechanism for evaluating vendors in terms of their products' quality. Vendors that consistently deliver high-quality products can receive preferred status involving reduced inspection and priority in bidding for new contracts, while vendors that do not stand up to quality requirements could be warned or discontinued altogether. This type of procedure is known as *vendor qualification* or *vendor certification*.

1. Types of Measurements

Define and select between direct, differential, and transfer measurements. (Understand)

Body of Knowledge IV.B.1

Measuring instruments may be *direct reading* or of the *transfer type.*

- *Direct-reading* instruments, such as an ordinary steel rule, contain a graduated scale from which the size of a dimension being measured can be determined directly.

- A spring caliper contains no scale graduations and therefore is a *transfer type* measuring instrument. It is adjusted to fit the size of a dimension being measured and then is compared to a direct-reading scale to obtain the size of the dimension.

Most of the available measuring instruments may be grouped according to certain basic principles of operation. Many simple instruments use only a graduated scale as a measurement basis, while others may have two related scales and use the vernier principle of measurement. In a number of instruments the movement of a precision screw is related to two or three graduated scales to form a basis for measurement. Many other instruments utilize some sort of mechanical, electrical, or optical linkage between the measuring element and the graduated scale so that a small movement of the measuring element produces an enlarged indication on the scale. Air pressure or metered airflow are used in a few instruments as a means of measurement.

2. Gauge Selection

> Determine which measurement instrument to use considering factors such as resolution, accuracy, tolerance, environment, and product features. (Evaluate)
>
> **Body of Knowledge IV.B.1**

There are many factors to consider in the selection of a measuring or gauging instrument or system for a particular manufacturing inspection operation. In general, a reference to the *rule of ten* will serve as a baseline or beginning of that selection process. The rule of ten, often referred to as the *gauge maker's rule,* states that inspection measurements should be better than the tolerance of a dimension by a factor of 10, and calibration standards should be better than inspection measurements by a factor of 10. If, for example, the tolerance on a shaft diameter is ±0.025 mm (±.0010 in), then the increment of measurement on the inspection instrument should be as small as $0.025/10 = 0.0025$ mm (.00010 in). Similarly, the increment of measurement for the calibration standard for that inspection instrument should be as small as $0.0025/10 = 0.00025$ mm (.000010 in).

Once the smallest increment of measurement for an instrument has been determined, then candidate instruments need to be evaluated in terms of the degree of satisfaction they offer relative to the following performance criteria:

1. *Accuracy.* The ability to measure the true magnitude of a dimension

2. *Linearity.* The accuracy of the measurements of an instrument throughout its operating range

3. *Magnification.* The amplification of the output reading on an instrument over the actual input dimension

4. *Repeatability.* The ability of the instrument to achieve the same degree of accuracy on repeated applications (often referred to as "precision")

5. *Resolution.* The smallest increment of measurement that can be read on an instrument

6. *Sensitivity.* The smallest increment of difference in dimension that can be detected by an instrument

7. *Stability or drift.* The ability of an instrument to maintain its calibration over a period of time

Other selection criteria may include factors such as the shape and size of the measured part or workpiece, part material, and capabilities of the metrology laboratory.

Consideration of these factors, along with cost and operation convenience, should help in selecting an appropriate measuring or gauging device for a particular inspection operation. For operating convenience, most instruments are or can be equipped with discrete digital readout devices. Most of these can be connected to microprocessors or computers for data recording and analysis.

Test Uncertainty Ratio (TUR) and Test Accuracy Ratio (TAR). The calibration process usually involves comparison of the M&TE to a standard having like functions with better accuracies. The comparison between the accuracy of the *unit under test* (UUT) and the accuracy of the standard is known as a *test accuracy ratio* (TAR). However, this ratio does not consider other potential sources of error in the calibration process.

Errors in the calibration process are not only associated with the specifications of the standard, but could also come from sources such as environmental variations, other devices used in the calibration process, technician errors, and so on. These errors should be identified and quantified to get an estimation of the calibration uncertainty. These are typically stated at a 95% confidence level. The comparison between the accuracy of the UUT and the estimated calibration uncertainty is known as a *test uncertainty ratio* (TUR). This ratio is more reliable because it accounts for possible sources of error in the calibration process that the TAR does not (Bennett and Zion 2005).

3. Measurement Systems Analysis (MSA)

> Define and distinguish between measurement terms such as correlation, bias, linearity, precision-to-tolerance, and percent agreement. Describe how gauge repeatability and reproducibility (R&R) studies are performed and how they are applied in support of MSA. (Analyze)
>
> **Body of Knowledge IV.B.3**

Operators have to be knowledgeable about what they have to measure and how satisfactorily the requirements of the situation will be met by the measuring instrument. Correct identification of the measuring situation will eliminate those methods found unsuitable for the situation. A proper selection of measuring equipment can therefore be made from a smaller range of measuring process alternatives. Method analysis can then be applied to such alternatives to determine which best satisfies the situation. This usually involves examining each method for different characteristics and evaluating the relative accuracies between the different methods.

Accuracy. Accuracy is the degree of agreement of individual or average measurements with an accepted reference value or level.

Precision. Precision is the degree of mutual agreement among individual measurements made under prescribed like conditions, or simply, how well identically performed measurements agree with each other. This concept applies to a process or a set of measurements, not to a single measurement, because in any set of measurements the individual results will scatter about the mean.

Repeatability and Reproducibility. *Repeatability* refers to how close the measurements of an instrument are to each other if such measurements were repeated on a part under the same measuring conditions.

Reproducibility is a measure of the degree of agreement between two single test results made on the same object in two different, randomly selected measuring locations or laboratories.

While repeatability is normally used to designate precision for measurements made within a restricted set of conditions (for example, individual operators), reproducibility is normally used to designate precision for measurements involving variation between certain sets (for example, laboratories) as well as within them.

Example 4.1 Gauge Repeatability and Reproducibility (GR&R).

This example is adapted from the Certified Quality Inspector Handbook *(Walker, Elshennawy, Gupta and McShane-Vaughn, 2013)*

A manufacturer of bolts used in automotive applications has installed a new measuring gauge. In order to perform the MSA on the new gauge, the quality manager randomly selected three operators from the Department of Quality Control, who decided to take a random sample of 10 bolts. Each operator takes three measurements on each bolt, which is randomly selected. The data obtained are shown below.

Data on an experiment involving three operators, 10 bolts, and three measurements (in mm) on each bolt by each operator.

Bolt (part) number	Operator 1			Operator 2			Operator 3		
	Trial 1	Trial 2	Trial 3	Trial 1	Trial 2	Trial 3	Trial 1	Trial 2	Trial 3
1	26	22	26	21	23	21	24	22	26
2	28	26	28	24	29	26	24	25	24
3	28	31	28	28	27	28	32	30	27
4	35	33	31	35	31	30	34	35	31
5	37	35	38	36	38	35	35	34	35
6	40	38	40	40	38	40	36	37	38
7	39	42	41	40	39	43	43	41	43
8	42	43	46	42	46	42	43	44	45
9	50	52	50	53	52	53	49	53	49
10	28	31	28	28	27	28	32	30	27
	$\bar{R}_1 = 3.0$ $\bar{x}_1 = 35.40$			$\bar{R}_2 = 2.8$ $\bar{x}_2 = 34.77$			$\bar{R}_3 = 3.0$ $\bar{x}_3 = 34.93$		

Solution
We first discuss gauge R&R using the range-based method, the approach used by IBM (1986), Barrentine (2003), and others.

Step 1: Verify that gauge calibration is current.

Step 2: Identify operators. Three operators are typically used in gauge studies; however, the more operators the better.

Step 3: Select a random sample of parts and have each operator measure all parts. One operator measures all parts, taking several measurements on each part, then the second operator takes measurements, then the third operator takes measurements, and so on. All parts are measured in random order.

Step 4: Calculate the sample mean, intertrial range for each sample, and average range for each operator. The sample means and average ranges are provided above.

Step 5: Calculate the range of sample means ($R_{\bar{x}}$), that is
$$R_{\bar{x}} = Max\,(\bar{x}_i) - Min\,(\bar{x}_i)$$
$$= 35.40 - 34.77 = 0.63$$

Step 6: Calculate the average range ($\bar{\bar{R}}$) for operators
$$\bar{\bar{R}} = \frac{\bar{R}_1 + \bar{R}_2 + \bar{R}_3}{3}$$
$$= \frac{3.00 + 2.80 + 3.00}{3} = 2.93$$

Step 7: Calculate repeatability (this value is also referred to as equipment variation (EV) and the estimate of the standard deviation of repeatability ($\sigma_{repeatability}$)
Repeatability (EV) = $\bar{\bar{R}} \times K_1 = 2.93 \times 3.05 = 8.94$

(continued)

Example 4.1 Gauge Repeatability and Reproducibility (GR&R) *(continued)*.

From Tables (see below), if the number of trials $r = 3$ and $n = $ # of parts $\times$ # of operators = 30, we have $K_1 = 3.05$.

$$\sigma_{repeatability} = \frac{EV}{5.15} = \frac{8.94}{5.15} = 1.74$$

	Number of trials						
n	**2**	**3**	**4**	**5**	**6**	**7**	**8**
1	3.65	2.70	2.30	2.08	1.93	1.82	1.74
2	4.02	2.85	2.40	2.15	1.98	1.86	1.77
3	4.19	2.91	2.43	2.16	2.00	1.87	1.78
4	4.26	2.94	2.44	2.17	2.00	1.88	1.79
5	4.33	2.96	2.45	2.18	2.01	1.89	1.79
6	4.36	2.98	2.46	2.19	2.01	1.89	1.79
7	4.40	2.98	2.46	2.19	2.02	1.89	1.79
8	4.44	2.99	2.48	2.19	2.02	1.89	1.79
9	4.44	2.99	2.48	2.20	2.02	1.89	1.80
10	4.44	2.99	2.48	2.20	2.02	1.89	1.80
11	4.44	3.01	2.48	2.20	2.02	1.89	1.80
12	4.48	3.01	2.49	2.20	2.02	1.89	1.81
13	4.48	3.01	2.49	2.20	2.02	1.90	1.81
14	4.48	3.01	2.49	2.20	2.03	1.90	1.81
15	4.48	3.01	2.49	2.20	2.03	1.90	1.81
n > or = 16	4.56	3.05	2.50	2.21	2.04	1.91	1.81

$n = $ (# of parts [samples]) x (# of operators) *(continued)*

Step 8: Calculate reproducibility (this value is also referred to as appraiser or operator variation (AV) and the estimate of the standard deviation of reproducibility ($\sigma_{reproducibility}$)

Reproducibility (AV) $= \sqrt{(R_{\bar{r}} \times K_2)^2 - [(EV)^2 / m \times r]}$

From Tables (see below), if we have three operators, we have $K_2 = 2.70$, # of parts $= m = 10$, and # of trials $r = 3$. Thus, we have

Reproducibility (AV) $= \sqrt{(0.63 \times 2.70)^2 - [(8.94)^2 / 10 \times 3]}$
$\qquad\qquad = 0.48$

	Number of operators											
3	**4**	**5**	**6**	**7**	**8**	**9**	**10**	**11**	**12**	**13**	**14**	**15**
2.70	2.30	2.08	1.93	1.82	1.74	1.67	1.62	1.57	1.54	1.51	1.48	1.47

Note that if the number under the radical is negative, then AV is zero.

The estimate of the standard deviation of reproducibility ($\sigma_{reproducibility}$) is

$$(\sigma_{reproducibility}) = \frac{0.48}{5.15} = 0.09$$

With this method, since reproducibility is calculated by ignoring the interaction term, the standard deviation of reproducibility may merely be looked upon as the operator standard deviation.

Example 4.1 Gauge Repeatability and Reproducibility (GR&R) *(continued)*.

Step 9: Calculate gauge R&R (i.e., repeatability and reproducibility) and the estimate of gauge R&R standard deviation.

$$\text{Gauge R\&R} = \sqrt{(\text{Repeatability})^2 + (\text{Reproducibility})^2}$$
$$= \sqrt{(8.94)^2 + (.48)^2}$$
$$= 8.95$$

The estimate of gauge R&R standard deviation is given by

$$\sigma_{Gauge} = \frac{8.95}{5.15} = 1.74$$

$$\sigma^2_{Time} = \sigma^2_{Parts} + \sigma^2_{Gauge}$$

Where σ^2_{Time}, σ^2_{Parts}, and σ^2_{Gauge} are the variance of total variability, parts variability, and gauge variability, respectively.

4. Rounding Rules

Use truncation and rounding rules on both positive and negative numbers. (Apply)

Body of Knowledge IV.B.4

Rounding Up. The last digit kept should increase by one if the digit to its right is 5 or greater, and drop all other (following) digits.

Example: Round off to two significant digits to the right of the decimal:
39.456391 will be 39.46
21.155000 will be 21.16

Rounding Down. The last digit kept should be unchanged if the digit to its right is less than 5, and drop all other (following) digits.

Example: Round off to two significant digits to the right of the decimal:
12.454659 will be 12.45
47.153000 will be 47.15

5. Conversion of Measurements

> Convert between metric and English
> units. (Apply)
>
> **Body of Knowledge IV.B.5**

Table 4.1 provides some useful guidelines for conversion between metric and English units.

Table 4.1 Guidelines for conversion between metric and English units. (Source: NIST Publications)

	Metric	**Equivalent English**
Weight and mass	1 gram	0.03527 ounces
		2.2046×10^{-3} pounds
	1 kilogram	2.2046 pounds
Length	1 centimeter	0.3937 inches
		3.281×10^{-2} feet
		1.094×10^{-2} yards
		6.214×10^{-6} miles
	1 kilometer	3280.8399 feet
		1094.0 yards
		3.937×10^{4} inches
	1 meter	39.37 inches
		3.281 feet
		1.094 yards
	1 micron	3.937×10^{-5} inches
Volume	1 cm³	6.102×10^{-2} in3
		3.5315×10^{-5} ft3
		1.308×10^{-6} yd3
	1 liter	61.02 in³
		1.308×10^{-3} yd³
	English	**Equivalent metric**
Weight and mass	1 ounce	28.349527 grams
	1 pound	0.4536 kilograms
		453.5924 grams
Length	1 foot	30.4801 centimeters
		$3.048 \times 10-4$ kilometers
		0.3048 meters

(continued)

Table 4.1 Guidelines for conversion between metric and English units *(continued)*.

	English	**Equivalent metric**
Length	1 inch	2.540 centimeters
		$2.54 \times 10{-2}$ meters
		25.40 millimeters
		25,400 microns
Length	1 yard	0.9144 meters
		91.44 centimeters
		9.144×10^4 kilometers
Volume	1 in³	16.3871 cm³
		1.639×10^{-5} m³
		1.639×10^{-2} liters
	1 ft³	2.832×10^{-2} m³
		28,320 cm³
		28.32 liters
	1 yd³	0.7646 m³
		7.646×105 cm³
		764.5 liters

6. Inspection Points

Define and distinguish between inspection point functions (e.g., receiving, in-process, final, source, first-article), and determine what type of inspection is appropriate at different stages of production, from raw materials through finished product. (Analyze)

Body of Knowledge IV.B.6

Parts of the discussion in these sections are adapted from Raz (1992).

Inspection planning includes the determination of the location of inspection and/or quality control methods and procedures at the various points in the production process. It also involves the determination of the types of inspections to be carried out and the acceptable quality levels, identification of critical characteristics to be inspected, and classification of defects.

The location of inspection points can be determined based on the following considerations (Raz 1992):

- *Incoming material inspection.* Inspect incoming materials to prevent the entry of defective components into the production system. This could be eliminated if the suppliers provide sufficient evidence of the use of process control techniques to maintain product quality.

- *Pre-process inspection.* This could be done in three ways:
  - Inspect prior to costly operations in order to avoid further investment in an already nonconforming product.
  - Inspect prior to processing operations that may mask defects. For example, surface finish should be inspected prior to painting.
  - Inspect prior to processing operations that may cause an increase in repair costs. For example, inspect and test circuit boards prior to assembly into their enclosures.

- *Post-process inspection.* Inspect following operations known to have a relatively high defect rate.

- *Final inspection.* Inspect final or finished goods before moving the product to another department or plant prior to shipping to the customer.

- *Verification inspection.* Inspect the first few units of each new batch in order to verify that the setup is correct.

When planning for inspection, a list of characteristics to be inspected should be done. The following guidelines may prove helpful (Raz 1992):

- Inspect characteristics that affect the performance of the product. To the extent possible, product testing should be done under conditions that simulate actual use.

- Select characteristics that can be measured objectively, to the extent possible.

- Provide a seriousness classification in order to improve consistency for characteristics that are evaluated subjectively.

- Inspect characteristics that can be related to a specific production process in order to simultaneously obtain information about the process.

Inspection Plan. A detailed inspection plan should be prepared and approved by the customer and the production, engineering, and manufacturing departments prior to the start of full-scale production. The inspection plan should include the following items:

- The location of each inspection station in the sequence of production operations

- The type of inspection or test to be carried out, including a description of the environment, equipment, and procedures

- Accuracy requirements from the measurements

- The conformance criteria, normally based on product specifications
- The sample size and procedure for drawing a sample in the case of sampling inspection
- The lot size and the criteria for lot acceptance, if applicable
- The disposition of nonconforming units—for example, repair, scrap, or salvage—and of rejected lots—for example, screen or return to vendor
- The criteria for initiating a review of the process, vendor, or inspector

7. Inspection Error

> Explain various types of inspection error, including operator error (e.g., parallax, fatigue), environment (e.g., vibration, humidity, temperature), and equipment (e.g., limitations, capability, setup). (Understand)
>
> **Body of Knowledge IV.B.7**

Errors in inspection are affected by many factors, including (Raz 1992):

1. Inspector qualification. Basic requirements for inspection personnel include:

   a. The ability to perform the relevant measurements

   b. Understanding of product specifications to the point of being capable of determining product quality

   c. Basic mathematical skills for recording and analyzing data

   d. Basic understanding of statistical concepts needed for sampling inspection and process characterization

   e. Knowledge of measurements and measurement technology

   f. Understanding of company's inspection policies, inspection procedure, products, materials, and processes

2. Inspector training. Training refers to the formal procedures used to improve job-related capability. Training programs for inspection personnel should be designed to address three main generic aspects:

   a. *Attitude.* This includes developing a genuine concern for the product and for the customer, as well as fostering a positive self-image of the inspection function. To a significant extent, attitude is affected by the leadership of management and supervisory staff.

    b. *Knowledge.* This includes not only knowledge directly related to the inspection function, but also of the various production processes, materials, equipment, procedures, and so on.

    c. *Skills.* This category refers to mastering the performance of the technical activities that are part of the inspector's job.

3. Equipment limitations and capability.

4. Other operator-related errors, such as parallax, fatigue, flinching, distraction, and so on.

5. Environmental effects, such as changes in standard temperature and humidity.

6. The interaction between part material and the equipment stylus's material properties.

8. Product Traceability

> Explain the requirements for documenting and preserving the identity of a product and its origins. (Apply)
>
> **Body of Knowledge IV.B.8**

Traceability is a process that tracks a product to its point of origin. Points of origin may include a specific supplier, a specific lot or manufacturer, a plant location, or, internally, a specific production line within the organization.

Tracing products allows a quick identification of suppliers, materials and their properties, delivery and assembly locations, accurate composition, and delivery information. It also helps improve customer service, enhances product and process control, and provides traceability and information about the inspection procedure that was followed, quality activities, measuring instruments and gauges used, and other tools used for the production, manufacture, assembly, or installation of the product.

9. Certificates of Compliance (COC) and Analysis (COA)

> Define and compare these two types of certificates. (Understand)
>
> **Body of Knowledge IV.B.9**

A *certificate of compliance* (COC) is a document from an authority certifying that the supplied products or services conform to specific and required specifications. It may also be called a *certificate of conformance or certificate of conformity.*

A *certificate of analysis* (COA) is another document from an authority that certifies the quality of the materials supplied to the customers according to their requirements. A COA contains some or all of the following information, among other specifics (Juran and Gryna 2005):

- Name of supplier

- Lot numbers of shipped products

- Production/manufacture dates

- Full description of the shipment

- Date the products were shipped

- Customer specification numbers

- Locations of tests performed and nature of those tests

- Quantity of products shipped

- Results of any analysis performed and methods used to perform such analysis

- Signature of authorized officers

C. INSPECTION TECHNIQUES AND PROCESSES

Several parts in this section are adapted from the Non-Destructive Testing *book by Hull and John (2012).*

Two terms are normally associated with inspection—*gauging and testing.* *Gauging* determines product conformance with specifications with the aid of measuring instruments such as calipers, micrometers, templates, and other mechanical, optical, and electronic devices. *Testing* refers to the determination of the capability of an item to meet specified requirements by subjecting it to a set of physical, chemical, environmental, or other operating conditions and actions similar to or more severe than those expected under normal use.

Testing might be destructive or nondestructive. In testing, the product is subjected to measuring procedures that render its usefulness to the customer. Gauging, however, is the more common form of inspection and is less costly; this operation has no effect on the product's service capability. Of course, certain product characteristics, mainly those related to failure modes, may only be observed and measured by exposing the product to conditions beyond its designed limits, such as determining the maximum current that an electronic component can carry or the maximum tensile force that a mechanical part can withstand. Normally, most of these procedures are *destructive* testing procedures and may be performed in cases where mandatory requirements are to be met. *Nondestructive testing* (NDT) of products is usually applied by subjecting the product to tests such as eddy current, ultrasonic resonance, and X-ray testing.

1. Nondestructive Testing (NDT) Techniques

> Explain various NDT techniques
> (e.g., X-ray, eddy current, ultrasonic,
> liquid penetrant, magnetic particle).
> (Understand)
>
> **Body of Knowledge IV.C.1**

Screening, or 100% inspection, can not be used when the product is subjected to a destructive testing procedure, or the time needed to perform the inspection is too long. Another constraint can be that the cost of inspection is too high to justify the economics of inspection. NDT techniques are more common for automated inspection or 100% inspection. A list of the most common NDT techniques includes:

- *Eddy current testing* involves the application of an AC current passing through a coil that is placed near the surface of the part to be inspected. Thus, its application is limited to conducting materials, and the test results are made by comparison.

- *Ultrasonic testing* is normally used to check for surface defects that cause deflection of an ultrasonic wave directed at the part surface, thus giving an indication of the presence of a surface defect. For ultrasonic testing, reference standards are required.

- *X-ray techniques* cause the internal characteristics of the part to be displayed and thus provide information about the presence of defects, cracks, or other impurities.

- *Liquid penetration* is more common for detecting defects on the part surface. It is used for different part configurations and, unlike magnetic particle testing, it can be used for nonmagnetic materials. However, liquid penetration can not be used to locate subsurface discontinuities.

- *Magnetic particle testing* is used when the part material can be magnetized. Discovery of part defects like cracks or discontinuities can then be detected by the presence of pairing magnetic fields. Magnetic particle testing is limited to parts made of iron, steel, or allied materials.

- Other common NDT techniques include the application of thermal, chemical, or optical phenomena, or holographic inteferometry (employing interference patterns for checking surface displacements). These are used for special testing procedures and are often too expensive to be widely applied.

2. Destructive Testing Techniques

> Explain various destructive tests
> (e.g., tensile, fatigue, flammability).
> (Understand)
>
> **Body of Knowledge IV.C.2**

Other testing techniques are destructive in nature. Some of these techniques include:

- *Tensile testing,* also known as *tension testing,* is the method for determining behavior of materials under axial stretch loading. Data from tests are used to determine elastic limit, stretching, modulus of elasticity, proportional limit, and reduction in area, tensile strength, yield point, yield strength, and other tensile properties. This test is probably the most fundamental type of mechanical test that can be performed on a material. Tensile tests are simple, relatively inexpensive, and fully standardized. By pulling on something, you will very quickly determine how the material will react to forces being applied in tension.

- *Impact testing* is used to check the ability of a material to absorb energy under impact without fracturing. This is a dynamic test in which a test specimen is broken by a single blow, and the energy used in breaking the piece is measured in foot-pounds.

- *Crash testing* is usually performed in order to ensure safe design standards in crash compatibility for automobiles or related components.

- *Fatigue testing* is used to test the ability of a material to withstand repeated loading. The number of repeated cycles of loading is counted until a failure happens. The stress used to cause failure is then determined.

- *Flammability testing* is used to define the material's ability to handle burning when exposed to certain sources of ignition under predetermined conditions. Acceptance or rejection of the materials is determined based on the resulting flammability ratings. This test is most commonly used in fabrics.

3. Other Testing Techniques

> Describe characteristics of testing techniques
> used for electrical measurement (e.g., DC, AC,
> resistance, capacitance, continuity), chemical
> analysis (e.g., pH, conductivity, chromatography),
> physical/mechanical measurement (e.g.,
> hardness, pressure tests, vacuum, flow), and
> other techniques such as gravimetric testing,
> cleanliness testing, contamination testing, and
> environmental testing (e.g., bioburden, surface,
> air, water testing). (Remember)
>
> **Body of Knowledge IV.C.3**

Functionality Testing. Used to verify whether a product meets the intended design specifications and functional requirements stated in the development documentation. It identifies potential product defects and minimizes the cost of service and maintenance after sale, which builds better product reputation and provides the ability to compete in the market. Common functionality testing techniques include torque measurement, pressure testing, leak testing, and vacuum tests.

Software Testing and Verification. Software verification determines that the software performs its intended functions correctly, ensures that the software performs no unintended functions, and measures and assesses the quality and reliability of the software.

Physical and Mechanical Measurements. These tests include pressure testing and flow measurements. Some of the pressure measuring instruments include electronic transducers, manometers, and Bourdon gauges.

Hardness Testing. Hardness tests include indentation, bounce, or scratching. Hardness testing techniques include:

- *Brinell.* This type of hardness test is based on applying forces on an object using a steel or carbide ball that has a 10 mm diameter and subjected to a load of 6614 lb, which can be reduced for softer material to avoid excessive indentation. The diameter of the indentation will be measured after a certain amount of time using a low-powered microscope, and then the Brinell harness number is calculated by dividing the load applied by the surface area of the indentation.

- *Rockwell.* The Rockwell hardness test method is also based on applying force on an object to create an indentation, but using a diamond cone or hardened steel ball indenter. A preliminary force will be applied on the indenter to be forced into the test material under minor load.

When equilibrium has been reached, an additional major load is applied with a resulting increase in penetration. When equilibrium has again been reached, the additional major load is removed, leaving the preliminary load as is. The removal of the additional major load will allow a partial recovery. The indentation from that load is measured and is used to calculate the Rockwell hardness number.

- *Vickers.* The Vickers hardness test was developed as an alternative method to measure the hardness of materials. This method doesn't have the arbitrary unrelated scales of the Rockwell method and is often easier to use than other hardness tests. The Vickers test can be used for all metals and also can be used on ceramic materials. It has one of the widest scales among hardness tests. The unit of hardness given by the test is known as the *Vickers pyramid number* (HV). The hardness number is determined by the load over the surface area of the indentation, not the area normal to the force, and is therefore not a pressure.

- *Microhardness test.* Microhardness testing of metals, ceramics, and composites is useful for a variety of applications where other test methods are not useful, such as testing very thin materials like foils, measuring individual microstructures within a larger matrix, or measuring the hardness gradients of a part along the cross-section. Microhardness testing gives an allowable range of loads for testing with a diamond indenter; the resulting indentation is measured and converted to a hardness value.

D. SAMPLING

1. Sampling Characteristics

> Identify and define sampling characteristics such as operating characteristic (OC) curve, lot size, sample size, acceptance number, and switching rules. (Apply)
>
> **Body of Knowledge IV.D.1**

Lot-by-Lot versus Average Quality Protection. Sampling plans based on average quality protection from continuing processes have their characteristics based on the binomial and/or Poisson distributions. Plans used for lot-by-lot protection—where product is not considered to have been manufactured by a continuing process—have their characteristics based on the hypergeometric distribution, which takes the lot size into consideration for calculation purposes.

Sampling plans based on the Poisson and binomial distributions are more common than those based on the hypergeometric distribution. This is due to the complexity of calculating plans based on the hypergeometric distribution. New software on personal computers, however, may eliminate this objection.

The Operating Characteristic (OC) Curve. No matter which type of attribute sampling plan is being considered, the most important evaluation tool is the operating characteristic (OC) curve.

The OC curve allows a sampling plan to be almost completely evaluated at a glance, giving a pictorial view of the probabilities of accepting lots submitted at varying levels of percent defective. The OC curve illustrates the risks involved in acceptance sampling. Figure 4.5 shows an OC curve for a sample size, n, of 50 drawn from an infinite lot size, with an acceptance number, c, of 3.

As can be seen by the OC curve, if the lot were 100% to specifications, the probability of acceptance Pa would also be 100%. But if the lot were 13.4% defective, there would be a 10% probability of acceptance.

There are two types of OC curves to consider: (1) type A OC curves and (2) type B OC curves. Type A OC curves are used to calculate the probability of acceptance on a lot-by-lot basis when the lot is not a product of a continuous process. These OC curves are calculated using the hypergeometric distribution.

Type B OC curves are used to evaluate sampling plans for a continuous process. These curves are based on the binomial and/or Poisson distributions when the requirements for usage are met. In general, the ANSI/ASQ Z1.4-2008 standard OC curves are based on the binomial distribution for sample sizes through 80, and the Poisson approximation to the binomial is used for sample sizes greater than 80.

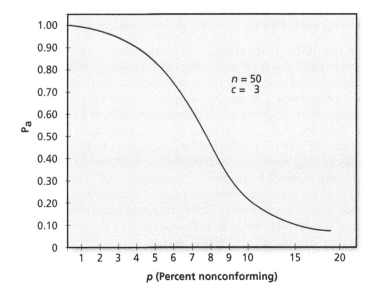

Figure 4.5 An operating characteristic (OC) curve.

2. Sampling Types

> Define and distinguish between sampling
> types such as fixed sampling, single,
> double, skip lot, 100% inspection,
> attributes, and variables sampling. (Apply)
>
> **Body of Knowledge IV.D.2**

Inspection can be done with screening (also called *sorting* or *100% inspection*), in which all units are inspected, or with *sampling*. *Acceptance sampling* is the process of inspecting a portion of the product in a lot for the purpose of making a decision regarding classification of the entire lot as either conforming or nonconforming to quality specifications. Sampling provides the economic advantage of lower inspection costs due to fewer units being inspected. In addition, the time required to inspect a sample is substantially less than that required for the entire lot, and there is less damage to the product due to reduced handling. Most inspectors find that selection and inspection of a random sample is less tedious and monotonous than inspection of a complete lot. Another advantage of sampling inspection is related to the supplier/customer relationship. For example, in the case of *rectifying inspection*—where a small fraction of the lot is inspected, and if the lot is rejected, the supplier is forced to screen (or 100% inspect) the remainder of the lot—the customer emphasizes that the supplier must be more concerned about quality. On the other hand, the variability inherent in sampling results in sampling errors: rejection of lots of conforming quality and acceptance of lots of nonconforming quality.

Sampling versus 100% Inspection. Acceptance sampling is most appropriate when inspection costs are high and when 100% inspection is monotonous and can cause inspector fatigue and boredom, resulting in degraded performance and increased error rates. Obviously, sampling is the only choice available for destructive inspection. Rectifying sampling is a form of acceptance sampling. Sample units detected as nonconforming are discarded from the lot, replaced by conforming units, or repaired. Rejected lots are subject to 100% screening, which can involve discarding, replacing, or repairing units detected as nonconforming.

In certain situations it is preferable to inspect 100% of the product. This would be the case for critical or complex products, where the cost of making the wrong decision would be too high. Screening is appropriate when the fraction nonconforming is extremely high. In this case most of the lots would be rejected under acceptance sampling, and those accepted would be so as a result of statistical variations rather than better quality. Screening is also appropriate when the fraction nonconforming is not known and an estimate based on a large sample is needed.

It should be noted that the philosophy now being espoused in supplier relations is that the supplier is responsible for ensuring that the product shipped meets the user's requirements. Many larger customers are requiring evidence of product quality through the submission of process control charts showing that the product was produced by a process that was in control and capable of meeting the specifications.

Sampling may be performed according to the type of quality characteristics to be inspected. There are three major categories of sampling plans: sampling plans for attributes, sampling plans for variables, and special sampling plans. It should be noted that acceptance sampling is not advised for processes in continuous production and in a state of statistical control. For these processes, Deming (1986) provides decision rules for selecting either 100% inspection or no inspection.

Acceptance Sampling by Attributes. Acceptance sampling by attributes is generally used for two purposes: (1) protection against accepting lots from a continuing process whose average quality deteriorates beyond an acceptable quality level, and (2) protection against isolated lots that may have levels of nonconformances greater than can be considered acceptable. The most commonly used form of acceptance sampling is sampling plans by attributes. The most widely used standard of all attribute plans, although not necessarily the best, is ANSI/ASQ Z1.4-2008. The following sections provide more details on the characteristics of acceptance sampling and discussion of military standards in acceptance sampling.

Acceptable Quality Level (AQL). AQL is defined as the maximum percent or fraction of nonconforming units in a lot or batch that, for the purposes of acceptance sampling, can be considered satisfactory as a process average. This means that a lot that has a fraction defective equal to the AQL has a high probability (generally in the area of 0.95, although it may vary) of being accepted. As a result, plans that are based on AQL, such as ANSI/ASQ Z1.4-2008, favor the producer in getting lots accepted that are in the general neighborhood of the AQL for fraction defective in a lot.

Lot Tolerance Percent Defective (LTPD). The LTPD, expressed in percent defective, is the poorest quality in an individual lot that should be accepted. The LTPD has a low probability of acceptance. In many sampling plans, the LTPD is the percent defective having a 10% probability of acceptance.

Producer's and Consumer's Risks. There are risks involved in using acceptance sampling plans. The risks involved in acceptance sampling are: (1) producer's risk, and (2) consumer's risk. These risks correspond with type 1 and type 2 errors in hypothesis testing. The definitions of producer's and consumer's risks are:

- *Producer's risk (α).* The producer's risk for any given sampling plan is the probability of rejecting a lot that is within the acceptable quality level (ASQ Statistics Division 2004). This means that the producer faces the possibility (at level of significance a) of having a lot rejected even though the lot has met the requirements stipulated by the AQL level.

- *Consumer's risk (β).* The consumer's risk for any given sampling plan is the probability of acceptance (usually 10%) for a designated numerical value of relatively poor submitted quality (ASQ Statistics Division 2004). The consumer's risk, therefore, is the probability of accepting a lot that has a quality level equal to the LTPD.

Average Outgoing Quality (AOQ). The *average outgoing quality* (AOQ) is the expected average quality of outgoing products, including all accepted lots, plus all rejected lots that have been sorted 100% and have had all of the nonconforming units replaced by conforming units.

There is a given AOQ for specific fractions nonconforming of submitted lots sampled under a given sampling plan. When the fraction nonconforming is very low, a large majority of the lots will be accepted as submitted. The few lots that are rejected will be sorted 100% and have all nonconforming units replaced with conforming units. Thus, the AOQ will always be less than the submitted quality. As the quality of submitted lots becomes poor in relation to the AQL, the percent of lots rejected becomes larger in proportion to accepted lots. As these rejected lots are sorted and combined with accepted lots, an AOQ lower than the average fraction of nonconformances of submitted lots emerges. Therefore, when the level of quality of incoming lots is good, the AOQ is good; when the incoming quality is bad and most lots are rejected and sorted, the result is also good.

To calculate the AOQ for a specific fraction nonconforming and a sampling plan, the first step is to calculate the probability of accepting the lot at that level of fraction nonconforming. Then, multiply the probability of acceptance by the fraction nonconforming for the AOQ. Thus,

$$AOQ = P_a p[1 - \text{sample size/lot size}]$$

If the desired result is a percentage, multiply by 100.

Average Outgoing Quality Limit (AOQL). The AOQ is a variable dependent on the quality level of incoming lots. When the AOQ is plotted for all possible levels of incoming quality, a curve as shown in Figure 4.6 results. The AOQL is the highest value on the AOQ curve. The average outgoing quality limit (AOQL) is the maximum AOQ for all possible levels of incoming quality.

Assuming an infinite lot size, the AOQ may be calculated as $AOQ = P_a\, p$. Probability of acceptance (P_a) may be obtained from tables as explained earlier and then multiplied by p (associated value of fraction nonconforming) to produce a value for AOQ as shown in the next example, using the previous equation.

Example: Given OC curve points (Pa and p) as shown in Figure 4.6, the AOQ curve can then be constructed.

Probability of acceptance	Fraction defective	AOQ
0.998	0.01	0.00998
0.982	0.02	0.01964
0.937	0.03	0.02811
0.861	0.04	0.03444
0.760	0.05	0.03800
0.647	0.06	0.03882
0.533	0.07	0.03731
0.425	0.08	0.03400
0.330	0.09	0.02970
0.250	0.10	0.02500

As can be seen, the AOQ rises until the incoming quality level of 0.06 nonconforming is reached. The maximum AOQ point is 0.03882, which is called the AOQL. This is the AOQL for an infinite lot size, sample size = 50, accept on three or less nonconformances.

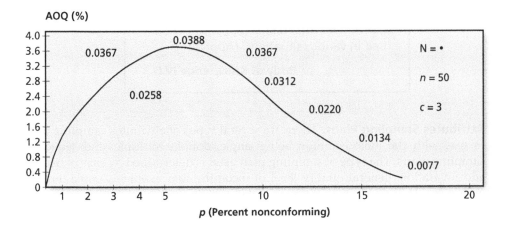

Figure 4.6 Average outgoing quality curve for $n = 50$, $c = 3$.

Acceptance Sampling by Variables. *Variables sampling plans* use the actual measurements of sample products for decision making rather than classifying products as conforming or nonconforming, as in attribute sampling plans. Variables sampling plans are more complex in administration than attribute plans, thus they require more skill. They provide some benefits, however, over attribute plans. Two of these benefits are:

1. Equal protection to an attribute sampling plan with a much smaller sample size. There are several types of variables sampling plans in use, three of these being (1) known, (2) unknown but can be estimated using sample standard deviation S, and (3) unknown and the range R is used as an estimator. If an attribute sampling plan sample size is determined, the variables plans previously listed can be compared as a percentage to the attribute plan.

Plan	Sample size (%)
Attribute	100
σ unknown, range method	60
σ unknown and estimated from sample	40
σ known	

2. Variables sampling plans allow the determination of how close to nominal or a specification limit the process is performing. Attribute plans either accept or reject a lot; variables plans give information on how well or poorly the process is performing.

3. Selecting Samples from Lots

> Determine sample size (e.g., AQL),
> selection method and accept/reject criteria
> used in various situations. (Apply)
>
> **Body of Knowledge IV.D.3**

Attributes Sampling Plans. There are several types of attributes sampling plans in use, with the most common being single, double, multiple, and sequential sampling plans. The type of sampling plan used is determined by ease of use and administration, general quality level of incoming lots, average sample number, and so on.

Single Sampling Plans. When single sampling plans are used, the decision to either accept or reject the lot is based on the results of the inspection of a single sample of n items from a submitted lot. In the example shown earlier, the OC curve and AOQ curve were calculated for a single sampling plan where $n = 50$ and $c = 3$. Single sampling plans have the advantage of ease of administration, but due to the unchanging sample size, they do not take advantage of potential cost savings of reduced inspection when incoming quality is either excellent or poor.

Double Sampling Plans. When using double sampling plans, a smaller first sample is taken from the submitted lot, and one of three decisions is made: (1) accept the lot, (2) reject the lot, or (3) draw another sample. If a second sample is drawn, the lot will either be accepted or rejected after the second sample. Double sampling plans have the advantage of a lower total sample size when the incoming quality is either excellent or poor because the lot is either accepted or rejected on the first sample.

Example: A double sampling plan is to be executed as follows: take a first sample (n_1) of 75 units and let c_1 (the acceptance number for the first sample) = 0. The lot will be accepted based on the first sample results if no nonconformances are found in the first sample. If three nonconformances are found in the first sample, the lot will be rejected based on the first sample results. If, after analyzing the results of the first sample, one or two nonconformances are found, take a second sample ($n_2 = 75$). The acceptance number for the second sample (c_2) is set to 3. If the combined number of nonconformances in the first and second samples is three or less, the lot will be accepted, and if the combined number of nonconformances is four or more, the lot will be rejected. The plan is represented as follows:

Sample number	Acceptance number (c)	Rejection number (r)
$n_1 = 75$	$c_1 = 0$	$r_1 = 3$
$n_2 = 75$	$c_2 = 3$	$r_2 = 4$

Multiple Sampling Plans. Multiple sampling plans work in the same way as double sampling with an extension of the number of samples to be taken up to seven, according to ANSI/ASQ Z1.4-2008. In the same manner that double sampling is performed, acceptance or rejection of submitted lots may be reached before the seventh sample depending on the acceptance/rejection criteria established for the plan.

ANSI/ASQ Z1.4-2008. ANSI/ASQ Z1.4-2008 is probably the most commonly used standard for attribute sampling plans. The wide recognition and acceptance of the plan could be due to government contracts stipulating the standard rather than its statistical importance. Producers submitting products at a nonconformance level within AQL have a high probability of having the lot accepted by the customer.

Levels of Inspection. There are seven levels of inspection used in ANSI/ASQ Z1.4-2008: reduced inspection, normal inspection, tightened inspection, and four levels of special inspection. The special inspection levels should only be used when small sample sizes are necessary and large risks can be tolerated. When using ANSI/ASQ Z1.4-2008, a set of switching rules must be followed as to the use of reduced, normal, and tightened inspection.

The following guidelines are taken from ANSI/ASQ Z1.4-2008:

- *Initiation of inspection.* Normal inspection level II will be used at the start of inspection unless otherwise directed by the responsible authority.

- *Continuation of inspection.* Normal, tightened, or reduced inspection shall continue unchanged for each class of defect or defectives on successive lots or batches except where the following switching procedures require change. The switching procedures shall be applied to each class of defects or defectives independently.

Switching Procedures. Switching rules are graphically shown in Figure 4.7

Types of Sampling. ANSI/ASQ Z1.4-2008 allows for three types of sampling:

1. Single sampling

2. Double sampling

3. Multiple sampling

The choice of the type of plan depends on many variables. Single sampling is the easiest to administer and perform, but usually results in the largest average total inspection. Double sampling in ANSI/ASQ Z1.4-2008 results in a lower average total inspection than single sampling, but requires more decisions to be made, such as:

- Accept the lot after first sample

- Reject the lot after first sample

- Take a second sample

- Accept the lot after second sample

- Reject the lot after second sample

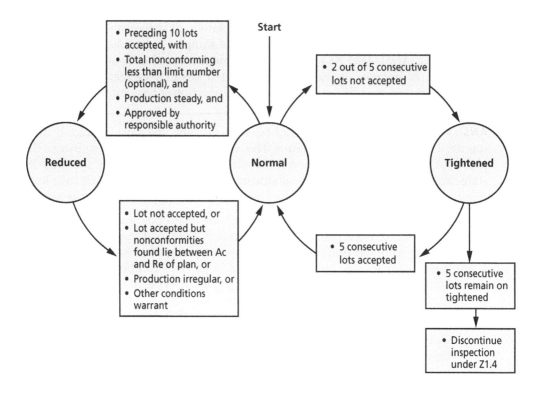

Figure 4.7 Switching rules for normal, tightened, and reduced inspection.

Multiple sampling plans further reduce the average total inspection but also increase the number of decisions to be made. As many as seven samples may be required before a decision to accept or reject the lot can be made. This type of plan requires the most administration.

A general procedure for selecting plans from ANSI/ASQ Z1.4-2008 is as follows:

1. Decide on an AQL.

2. Decide on the inspection level.

3. Determine the lot size.

4. Find the appropriate sample size code letter.

5. Determine the type of sampling plan to be used: single, double, or multiple.

6. Using the selected AQL and sample size code letter, consult the appropriate table to find the desired plan to be used.

7. Determine the normal, tightened, and reduced plans as required from the corresponding tables.

Variables Sampling Plans. Variables sampling plans, such as ANSI/ASQ Z1.9-2008, have some disadvantages and limitations:

1. The assumption of normality of the population from which the samples are being drawn.

2. Unlike attribute sampling plans, separate characteristics on the same parts will have different averages and dispersions, resulting in a separate sampling plan for each characteristic.

3. Variables plans are more complex in administration.

4. Variables gauging is generally more expensive than attribute gauging.

ANSI/ASQ Z1.9-2008. The most common standard for variables sampling plans is ANSI/ASQ Z1.9-2008, which has plans for (1) variability known, (2) variability unknown—standard deviation method, and (3) variability unknown—range method. Using the aforementioned methods, this sampling plan can be used to test for a single specification limit, a double (or bilateral) specification limit, estimation of the process average, and estimation of the dispersion of the parent population.

Figure 4.8 summarizes the structure and organization of ANSI/ASQ Z1.9-2008.

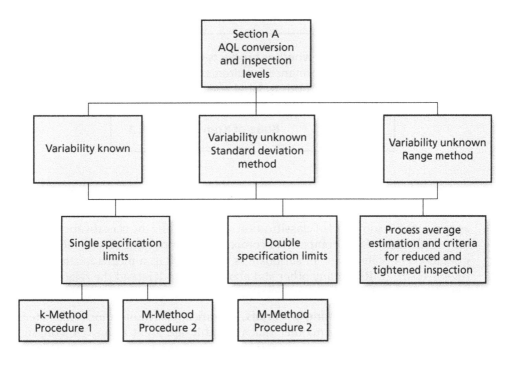

Figure 4.8   Structure and organization of ANSI/ASQ Z1.9-2008.

E. NONCONFORMING MATERIAL

In the book *Glossary and Tables for Statistical Quality Control*, written by representatives of the American Society for Quality Statistics Division (2004), a *nonconforming unit* is defined as follows: "A unit of product or service containing at least one nonconformity." And in the same book, a *nonconformity* is defined as "A departure of a quality characteristic from its intended level or state that occurs with a severity sufficient to cause an associated product or service to not meet a specification requirement."

A component of any comprehensive quality system is a subsystem designed to effectively deal with nonconforming materials as soon as they are identified—optimally as early in the production process as possible. For purposes of the Certified Quality Technician (CQT) Body of Knowledge (BoK), nonconforming material identification consists of the following:

- Determining conformance status

- Identifying nonconforming materials

- Segregating nonconforming materials

1. Identifying and Segregating

> Determine whether products or material meet conformance requirements, and use various methods to label and segregate nonconforming materials. (Evaluate)
>
> **Body of Knowledge IV.E.1**

Determining Conformance Status. Conformance status is determined in accordance with compliance or noncompliance with a quality standard or specification as compared to some sort of classification scheme. While the classification schemes may be different from company to company, the important consideration is that gradations or "categories" of seriousness are created as a means for the material review board (MRB) or any other stakeholders to understand the relative importance and magnitude of nonconformities.

Identifying Nonconforming Materials. Identification of nonconforming materials must be completed in a manner that is readily apparent to anyone coming in contact with the item(s) or material in question. To accomplish the identification, some provision must be made so as to distinguish the physical appearance of the item(s) or material as "nonconforming." The physical nature of the provision refers to altering the appearance of the item(s) or its associated production data documentation with some sort of special coloring (that is, by paint, marker, or a different-colored tag). The nonphysical nature of the provision refers to collecting and documenting data related to the nonconformity and attaching that data to the production data documentation accompanying the item(s) or material.

Segregating Nonconforming Materials. Once identified as nonconforming, any such material must be prevented from entering or continuing on in the supply chain. Segregation, then, is an important concern for both suppliers and customers as a means of ensuring product or process quality.

Segregation of nonconforming materials is accomplished by establishing a secure area (that is, a lockable area with strictly limited access). Once inside this secure area, nonconforming materials are not available to access, inspection, further processing, or shipment by anyone other than authorized MRB members or their designees.

2. Material Review Process

> Explain various elements of this process such as the function of the material review board (MRB), the steps in determining fitness-for-use, and product disposition. (Understand)
>
> **Body of Knowledge IV.E.2**

Virtually all quality standards require the creation and implementation of a clearly defined and communicated process to follow when "nonconforming" material is identified or detected. The importance of a nonconforming material review process can not be overstated as it serves as the mechanism by which to prevent nonconforming material from entering or proceeding in the supply chain. Such a process is most commonly referred to as a *nonconforming material review process*.

While specific components or steps in a nonconforming material review process will vary from company to company, and from quality standard to quality standard, at the most basic level such a process would consist of the following:

- A cross-functional team called a *material review board* composed of representatives from the quality and engineering functions and, in some cases, customers

- Appropriate quality standards and metrics

- A sampling and inspection protocol/plan

- Policies and procedures addressing when and how to trigger the MRB

- Overall process documentation

As would be expected, the successful operation of a nonconforming material review process is the responsibility of the MRB. Ultimately, the MRB must determine what to do with nonconforming material and what corrective action to take to prevent further nonconforming material. The "what to do with nonconforming material" portion of the MRB responsibility is commonly referred to as *disposition*. Disposition may take many forms as agreed to by the supplier and the customer, and this is described by Berger (2002) as follows:

- Shipped "as is"
- Sort/100% inspection
- Downgrade
- Repair
- Rework
- Scrap

Investigation of Root Causes. Andersen and Fagerhaug (2000), define and describe root cause analysis as "...a collective term to describe a wide range of approaches, tools, and techniques used to uncover causes to problems."

Investigation of root causes implies the existence of one or more problem(s) that needs to be resolved. In this context, root cause analysis is a structured approach to problem solving that uses all the traditional quality control tools such as histograms, Pareto charts, cause-and-effect diagrams, check sheets, scatter diagrams, and control charts. In fact, it can easily be argued that root cause analysis uses even more than the traditional quality control tools and techniques identified by Kolarik (1995) such as affinity diagrams, relations diagrams, systematic diagrams, matrix diagrams, process decision program charts, and arrow diagrams. Additionally, tools and techniques identified by Brassard and Ritter (1994) in the book *The Memory Jogger 2*, such as force field analysis, interrelationship diagraphs, prioritization matrices, and radar charts, can also be applied to the root cause analysis.

Emphasizing that the root cause analysis process is a series of iterative steps taken while solving a problem is important. Since there are many generally accepted approaches to problem solving (for example, PDSA/PDCA, Kepner-Tregoe) the benefits to be derived from any problem-solving approach are in the consistency and rigor involved in the problem-solving methodology or protocol.

At issue in this whole notion of problem solving is solving the "right" problem. All too often, a problem that presents itself is the result of another problem, or perhaps several other problems combined. In this case, and in the language of root cause analysis, we say the problem that presents itself as the most apparent is merely the symptom of a more deeply rooted problem. Solving symptomatic problems, therefore, gives rise to other, perhaps seemingly unrelated, problems.

It has long been understood in the quality community that until someone can ask the question why at least five times, they can not hope to be looking at anything more than symptoms of a problem rather than the actual or root cause problem. This why, why, why, why, why questioning methodology, as supported by the many problem-solving tools identified above, represents the means by which to separate symptoms from root causes. And someone would then know that a root cause problem has been identified and solved when other problems disappear or are eliminated automatically as a function of solving the root cause problem.

Chapter 5

V. Quality Audits

The intent of any audit is to protect the business, professional, and/or legal interests of the party or person requesting the audit. Implicit in this intent is a requirement that the audit be based on factual data and observations obtained from independent and objective individual(s) performing the audit in keeping with the concept of "management by fact." By extension, then, audits are formal or informal in nature and revolve around analyses of the day-to-day things actually done to meet customer expectations, as compared to customer expectations normally documented in the form of some standard or specifications.

There are generally three interests involved in quality audits. The company, party, or person that requests and authorizes the audit is known as the *client*. The company, party, team, or person that actually conducts the audit is known as the *auditor*. And the company, party, facility/location, process, or product/service that is audited is known as the *auditee*.

A. AUDIT TYPES AND TERMINOLOGY

> Define basic audit types: 1) internal,
> 2) external, 3) systems, 4) product, 5)
> process, and 6) distinguish between
> first-, second-, and third-party audits.
> (Understand)
>
> **Body of Knowledge V.A**

Key to appreciating the value of, needs served, and benefits provided by quality audits is understanding the various types of audits, differentiating between internal and external boundaries for audits, identifying who authorizes or conducts these audits, and knowing important terminology.

There are three primary types of quality audits, which include system, process(es), and/or products/services, as follows:

- *System audit.* A system audit is a comprehensive audit involving all parts of a quality system including quality management principles and practices, quality system structure and components, quality system operational procedures and instructions, quality system documentation, quality system performance, and mechanisms for continuous improvement of the quality system. While system audits focus on, and normally reveal, high-level issues related to the design and management of quality systems, quality system audits can also encompass audits of selected individual processes as well as products/ services.

- *Process audit.* A process audit is a detailed audit of one or more selected processes that constitute a quality system as it relates to the production of tangible products or the delivery of services. Process audits include process design, work flow, procedures and work instructions, documentation, provisions for the assurance and control of quality, and performance measures and metrics associated with the selected process(es).

- *Product audit.* A product audit is even more detailed than a process audit with respect to a focus on ensuring that the product or service being audited will meet customer expectations. Product or service audits include the product/service design, operational specifications, research and development or test data, trials or performance data, customer satisfaction data (if available), and failure data (internal and/ or external). Much of the work of product audits is completed at key milestones called design reviews in the development of new products and services. Product audits are, however, commonly completed by business-to-business customers purchasing products/services as a final check or approval following the design and development of these new products/services from another company or other vendor outside their company or by another division, department, or work center within their own company.

Figure 5.1 is provided to demonstrate the relationships between types of audits.

Figure 5.1 illustrates that system audits have the widest scope, and these types of audits are generally focused on elements of quality philosophies, strategies, systems, practices, procedures, and documentation that reside in multiple areas or functions of an organization. The wide scope of a system audit also generally means that the depth of analysis, or the amount of detail, examined in a system audit has inherent limitations. Also illustrated in Figure 5.1 is that process audits are not as far-reaching in terms of scope as are system audits; however, process audits do facilitate a deeper and more detailed look at the processes being audited— even if there are common processes across multiple areas or functions within an organization. Lastly, Figure 5.1 illustrates that product audits are limited in scope to the specific product or product type being audited, and that product audits are focused in greater depth on quality characteristics associated with these products.

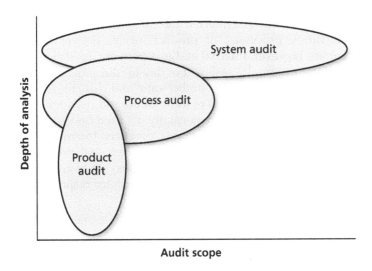

Figure 5.1 Relationships between audit types.

There are, however, other types of audits referred to as *secondary* audits that include management reviews and various forms of vendor/supplier surveillance. Information on these secondary audit types is beyond the scope of the Certified Quality Technician (CQT) Body of Knowledge or this book; however, continued learning and professional development in the field of quality will lead readers to these secondary audit types.

Next, we must consider in greater detail the boundaries of audits as being *internal* or *external*. The question here is "internal or external to what?" Audits may be considered internal or external to an organization as a whole or to a part of an organization, such as a division, department, area of production, or multiple facilities. It is important to note that whether an audit is considered to be internal or external depends on the perspective of the person(s) authorizing the audit and the audit scope, as well as the source of the auditors.

Source of Auditors

The demand for auditors as sources of independent and objective evaluation is, in many cases, greater than the supply of resources available to provide for these services. This means it is a normally accepted practice to use as auditors some individuals not formally trained or who are not working day-to-day with general or mainstream quality practices, tools, and techniques, but who have in-depth process and/or product/service knowledge. In this case, and to provide greater coverage of audit scrutiny, there has been a general approach to the deployment of auditors developed wherein system-level audits are normally conducted by auditors from outside the company or organization. These auditors are referred to as *external auditors.* Further, process and/or product/service audits may certainly be conducted by external auditors, but in many cases these audits are conducted by auditors from inside their own company or organization. These auditors are referred to as *internal auditors.* Internal auditors are normally obtained from other functions, facilities, processes, or product/service delivery lines within their same companies; however, internal auditors perform auditing functions in areas different from their normally assigned or day-to- day jobs.

As it can be somewhat more cumbersome and difficult for internal auditors to gain access to the highest levels of individuals and resources within their own organizations, internal auditors are normally not used for system audits, although there is no formal rule preventing this practice. Internal auditors are very frequently deployed, however, to conduct process and product/service audits, particularly where the internal auditors are called on to audit processes and/or products/services different from their area of primary responsibility.

Audit Types

Who actually performs the audit is important, with the level of perceived objectivity being a key consideration. In this context, a client may request or require one or more of three parties to complete any given audit. An audit is known as a *first-party* audit when it is conducted by the client actually requesting or authorizing the audit. Internal audits are first-party audits wherein the client is seeking to protect its business interests as a result of the audit. An audit is known as a *second-party* audit when it is conducted by someone or an organization other than the client, but where both the client and the auditor have a business interest in the result of the audit. External audits are second-party audits. An audit is known as a *third-party* audit when it is conducted by someone or an organization other than the client, and the auditor has no business interest in the result of the audit other than maintaining their professional credibility, reputation, and avoidance of legal liability.

Now, with an understanding of audit types and terminology, we can turn our attention to describing and understanding various elements and components of the audit process.

B. AUDIT COMPONENTS

> Describe and apply various elements of the audit process: 1) audit purpose and scope, 2) audit reference standard, 3) audit plan (preparation), 4) audit performance, 5) opening and closing meetings, 6) final report and verification of corrective action. (Apply)
>
> **Body of Knowledge V.B**

The basic components of an audit include the following:

- Purpose/scope
- Preparation
- Performance
- Documentation (that is, record keeping)
- Closure

Purpose/Scope

To be functionally effective, boundaries must be set that define what is to be audited (that is, what is to be considered/evaluated, and what is not). We call these boundaries the *scope* of the audit. Accordingly, the audit scope defines a frame of reference wherein auditors are to concentrate their focus and analyses. Audits may be very far-reaching and encompassing, such as in the case of systems audits, where virtually all aspects of quality systems are reviewed. Audits may also be more restricted in terms of what is considered part of the audit, such as is the case with process or product/service audits.

Due to a tendency for the scope of an audit to "creep," or get bigger and more encompassing as the audit progresses, it is extremely important to identify very early in the audit preparation the scope of the audit since significant financial and human resources will be required to complete a comprehensive audit, and if scope is allowed to creep, costs of the audit will escalate very quickly. Establishment and documentation of the audit scope then becomes a limitation or constraint that keeps everyone involved (that is, all stakeholders) focused on what was originally intended for and authorized by the audit.

Preparation

Preparation for any type of quality audit requires consideration of the following.

Identification of Authorization Source. Formal preparation for an audit normally does not commence until the audit is authorized by an appropriate individual within an organization. Authorization for an audit carries with it the obligation of and responsibility for allocating resources, so audit authorization decisions are normally reserved for management team members who are at or above the director level, and while any one of several management team members may have an interest in requesting and authorizing an audit of quality systems, processes, and/or products/services, it is generally the director of quality who actually issues the audit authorization.

Once audit authorization has been issued, documentation of the authorization becomes an important part of the historical records generated as part of the audit process. Documentation of the authorization becomes an important part of the documentation when a contact person is required for other interested parties to learn more about the reasons why an audit may have been authorized, when other interested parties require justification or explanation of system/process/product/ service modifications or revisions as a result of corrective actions called for in an audit, or in the case of litigation.

Determination of the Audit Purpose. An audit may be authorized for one or several purposes. The most common purposes of an audit include qualification of a vendor's quality system, process(es), and/or products/services, and meeting contractual obligations. Common purposes for initiating and authorizing an audit also include continuous improvement, identification and verification of perceived weaknesses, verification of corrective action, verification of adequacy of resources (that is, facilities, equipment, human resources, and so on), verification of new technology and/or methods, and enhancing customer satisfaction.

Determination of Audit Type. As will be described below, audit types are normally categorized as system, process, or product/service audits; these three types of audits are the most common and represent the primary audit types. There are, however, other types of audits referred to as secondary audits that include management reviews and various forms of vendor/supplier surveillance.

Determination of Resources Required. Consistent with the type and scope of audit to be performed, resources will be required to support the audit process. Primary resources needed to support an audit normally include auditing and auditee personnel, physical work space for the audit team—normally a secure work space—computer/data processing and printing support, and clerical/ administrative support. Secondary resources needed to support an audit may include travel funding, per diem for travel-related expenses, lodging/ accommodation, and ground transportation.

Formation of the Audit Team. Formation of an audit team is completed, again, in accordance with the type and scope of audit. In most cases audit team members are selected based on their knowledge of, training and certification in, and experience with auditing methods and practices. When there is not an optimal skill set or talent pool of trained and experienced auditors available, auditors are commonly selected from the most technically competent and knowledgeable personnel available, and these auditors normally work under the guidance and direction of one or more experienced auditors and with the further guidance and direction provided by detailed documentation called audit *working papers.*

Assignment of Audit Team Roles and Responsibilities. Once key individuals have been selected for an audit team, roles and responsibilities are assigned so as to facilitate the audit process. In the preparation phase of an audit it is common practice to select an audit team leader and a small complement of experienced auditors or experts in a given technical area and assign those people responsibility and authority consistent with the audit type and scope. The team leader is normally assigned the role and responsibility of leading the team, facilitating the audit process, coordinating all resources needed to support the audit, and constituting the remainder of an audit team. Other key individuals initially selected for an audit team are normally assigned roles and responsibilities consistent with their areas of expertise either in auditing practices/methods or in a specific technical area. Other individuals not initially selected for the audit team, but who are subsequently selected by the audit team leader, are assigned roles and responsibilities consistent with their expertise and ability to contribute to the effectiveness of the audit.

Identification of Requirements. To successfully complete an audit, everyone involved with the audit must complete their assigned tasks and produce any required deliverables; these assigned tasks and deliverables are referred to as *audit requirements*. While there are general requirements that are consistent with audits in general, there is much flexibility in the level of formality and detail required to "successfully" complete an audit.

Generally expected components of audits include formal documentation of the audit as described throughout this section, a final set of working papers (that is, detailed questions and notes that guided the audit process), a series of debriefings describing the audit process and the findings/results, and a detailed description of any requested/required corrective action(s). Other generally expected components of audits include documentation of and provision for verification of adequacy and completeness of corrective action(s).

Establishment of Time Schedule. The final component of an audit is establishment of a time schedule. A time schedule is a critical component for the audit team leader in the preparation of detailed work or project plans to guide the work effort of an audit. The time schedule is also important to management team members as a communications tool and as a coordination device indicating when and where certain physical or human resources will be needed to support the audit process.

Performance

Audit performance is described by a set of activities as follows:

- Managing/administering the audit process
- Creating a set of working papers
- Conducting an opening meeting
- Collecting data
- Analyzing data
- Conducting an exit meeting

Managing/Administering the Audit Process. To properly manage/administer an audit, the team leader is required to complete a set of tasks needed to keep the audit process moving. The team leader is responsible to call for and conduct regularly scheduled meetings with the audit team to discuss preliminary results and findings. During these meetings the team leader must make decisions regarding the amount and type of communications that may be warranted between the audit team and other stakeholders, possible interventions that may be needed by the audit team, and the effectiveness of the audit process. The team leader is also responsible to call for and conduct, on an as-needed basis, meetings with the auditee to discuss audit progress, significant results and findings, and changes in the audit plan (such as content to be evaluated or the time schedule).

Creating a Set of Working Papers. To ensure complete and thorough scrutiny consistent with the type and scope of audit, working papers are drafted to guide the audit work effort. Working papers consist of predefined sets of auditee interview questions, checklists of specific documents/policies/procedures/instructions to be reviewed, log sheets of personnel contacted as part of the audit, data collection forms, and so on. A more thorough discussion of working papers will be provided in a later section of this chapter.

Conducting an Opening Meeting. As a normal part of the auditing process, an opening meeting is held wherein both the audit team and management team members and appropriate personnel from the auditee are present to discuss the audit plan. While generally a short meeting, the opening meeting allows the audit team leader the opportunity to review the audit plan, answer questions about the intent of or approach to the audit, discuss the timing and logistics of the audit, as well as address/resolve any conflicts that may have developed in the time between approval of the audit plan and the audit team arriving at the audit site.

Collecting Data. Audit team members complete the next step in the audit process by collecting data consistent with the data requirements documented in the working papers mentioned above. Data collected to support the audit may encompass design parameters, performance specifications, actual performance data, process documentation, work instructions, policy statements, general quality system documentation, vendor/supplier qualification information, raw material and component part certificates of authenticity/purity, purchasing/acquisition records, defective material disposition records, compliance with selected standards, and perhaps training/certification records.

Analyzing Data. Once data are collected, it is necessary for audit team members to sort or categorize the data in some way so as to be able to identify and categorize the results and findings in a manner that indicates some level of importance. Frequently, this means that audit team members create three or more levels of concern wherein verifiable observations are recorded in categories such as "passes/meets expectations," "marginal pass/questionable response/performance," and "fails to meet expectations."

Once data are categorized in accordance with a scheme established by the audit team, it is possible for audit team members to analyze the data, looking for existing patterns or emerging trends that indicate potential problems.

Conducting an Exit Meeting. One of the final steps in the completion of an audit is conducting an exit meeting between the audit team and the auditee. At this exit meeting the primary points of discussion revolve around major findings and results of the audit. Note that this is an opportunity for the audit team to share their findings and results with the auditee, not a venue for the audit team to have to justify or debate the findings or results. Also during the exit meeting any requested or required corrective actions are presented and discussed, with particular importance being placed on creation of a corrective action plan, time schedule for the corrective actions, and verification provisions for corrections to any potential problems.

Documentation

Documentation associated with an audit includes appropriate correspondence, audit planning documents (that is, authorization, type/scope statements, audit team member assignments, and so on), audit working papers, status reports, preliminary findings and results documentation, debriefing and closure reports, corrective action requests, and follow-up report forms for corrective action verification.

By sheer volume, the amount of documentation associated with a quality audit can quickly become very large, particularly when conducting system and multiple process audits.

It is generally specified in planning/authorization documents or procurement contracts how long to maintain copies of audit records. *In many cases five years is the required time frame for care and maintenance of audit documents,* particularly where the audit involves a large, complex, or distributed quality system (that is, a quality system comprising a vendor/supplier with multiple facilities/locations). *In cases where the time frame for saving audit documentation is not specified, and where the audit does not involve particularly large or complex quality systems, one year is an acceptable time frame for saving audit documents.*

Closure

Technically, an audit is considered complete as soon as the final report has been submitted to the authorizing agent and the auditee. However, an emerging trend in auditing is to delay reaching closure on an audit until a set of terms and conditions have been met as defined by the agent authorizing the audit and the auditee. Those terms and conditions related to closure of an audit increasingly focus on resolution of problems related to unfavorable audit results or findings. In the case of one or more unfavorable audit results or findings, the terms and conditions for audit closure specify the scope of potential corrective actions and an appropriate time frame for completion of corrective action(s). Under these emerging conditions, an audit is considered closed when both parties involved with the audit are satisfied that all corrective actions have been satisfactorily completed.

C. AUDIT TOOLS AND TECHNIQUES

Define and apply various auditing tools:
1) checklists and working papers, 2) data gathering and objective evidence, 3) forward- and backward-tracing, 4) audit sampling plans and procedural guidelines. (Apply)

Body of Knowledge V.C

Application of auditing tools and techniques includes the following:

- Checklists

- Audit working papers

- Data gathering via qualitative and quantitative quality tools

- Objective evidence

- Forward and backward tracing

- Audit sampling plans

- Procedural guidelines

Checklists

Checklists are documents that support both the planning and execution/ completion of audits. Checklists typically list the major elements or procedural steps in audits. Auditors rely on checklists when planning audits to ensure that all of the major elements of an audit are addressed; in this manner, the detail documented on checklists (that is, the check marks on the checklist) provides an indication that the major element(s) have been considered for planning purposes.

Following a review of Figure 5.2, it should be clear that the value of a planning-oriented checklist is to ensure that none of the major elements in an audit have been overlooked or otherwise forgotten or omitted. It should also be clear that the value of a planning-oriented checklist is to ensure that the audit sponsor (that is, the client) approves the planning prior to beginning the audit.

Similarly, an audit *completion* checklist guides auditors in terms of the specific tasks to be completed during audits. In most cases, the audit completion checklist identifies the audit tasks and places them in the sequence in which they must be completed during an audit. Figure 5.3 provides an example of an audit completion checklist.

Following a review of Figure 5.3, it should be clear that the value of an audit planning checklist is to provide step-by-step guidance in what tasks must be completed, and also to identify resources that may be needed in order to complete each task. Beyond the audit completion checklist, additional checklists may be required to support other aspects of audits. One example of a need for additional audit completion checklists would be to provide additional detail on procedural steps needed when auditing multiple areas within a single audit, or when auditing sub-elements within a larger audit area. When additional detail or audit completion guidance is needed, multiple levels of checklists are prepared for each area, and the combination of these checklists becomes hierarchical in nature. The hierarchical set of checklists supporting audit completion is used as part of a more comprehensive set of documents used in the audit process, and this comprehensive set of documents is referred to as of the *working papers*.

Audit Planning Checklist			
Auditee:	Audited function:	Audit date(s):	
Audit source:	Lead auditor:		
Audit element	**Needed**	**Completed (✓)**	**Initials**
Authorization source confirmed?			
Audit purpose defined?			
Audit type identified?			
Audit resource secured?	Document access		
	Facility access		
	Security clearances		
	Audit personnel		
	Finances		
	Working room		
	Computer(s)		
Audit team formed?	Team members selected		
	Supervisory approval secured		
Audit team roles/responsibilities assigned?			
Time schedule established?			
Final audit plan approved by sponsor?			

Figure 5.2 Audit planning checklist.

Audit Working Papers

Audit working papers consist of the various data collection forms used to gather, categorize, summarize, and analyze selected audit data. Audit working papers for the audit team comprise the formal and informal note sheets and formal question/data sheets that guide and direct audit team members to review specific portions or sections of quality systems.

While there is no standard for the design of working papers, various forms of checklists and check sheets are used to assist auditors in collecting tabular data very quickly while providing auditors some room for detailed note-taking and specific data collection. Also used as working papers are the many qualitative and quantitative quality tools when tailored to the collection and analysis of selected audit data.

Audit Completion Checklist			
Auditee:	Audited function:	Audit date(s):	
Lead auditor:	Assigned auditor:		
Task list	**Needed**	**Completed (✓)**	**Initials**
Review previous audit results	Previous audit documentation		
Identify special concerns	Previous audit documentation		
Access and prepare final working papers	Printer access		
Request specific documentation	Access support		
Conduct opening meeting	Scheduling support		
Review requested documentation			
Schedule interviews and meetings	Scheduling support		
Conduct interviews and meetings			
Document findings	Computer(s)		
Seek additional clarification(s)			
Summarize and document results	Computer(s)		
Debrief audit team (daily)			
Submit completed audit findings/report			

Figure 5.3 Audit completion checklist.

Quantitative Quality Tools

Quantitative quality tools encompass tools such as the "traditional" Japanese tools, including flowcharting (also used for forward and backward tracing), cause–and–effect diagrams, check sheets, histograms, Pareto chart, scatter diagrams, and statistical process control charts. To avoid duplication, these tools have not been reintroduced here and readers are encouraged to review these tools as they appear in other sections of this handbook.

While there is not a standardized list of tools to be used in every audit, there are common expectations of how, when, and where the quality tools are applied. For example, many audits begin with a review of process flowcharts to help familiarize auditors with important process steps. Flow charts are also commonly used when auditors are analyzing where to look deeper into areas of concern when points of failure have been identified (i.e., backward tracing) and similarly, flow charts are commonly used when auditors are analyzing the appropriateness of quality checks and measurement points within processes (forward tracing). Cause-and-effect diagrams are commonly used, and are commonly reviewed by auditors, when analyzing potential effects such as certain types of failures and corresponding causes for those failures. Auditors commonly refer to quantitative data displays such as check sheets to understand the number, types, and/or locations of errors or defects occurring in processes. Likewise auditors may refer to histograms and/or statistical process control charts to assess variability in processes just as they may refer to Pareto charts to assess the magnitude and characteristics of process behavior.

Objective Evidence

To facilitate the process of "management by fact," the expected outcome of any audit is independent, accurate, verifiable, and traceable facts and observations. When facts and observations are independent, accurate, verifiable, and traceable to a specific source, we say these facts and observations constitute "objective evidence." Objective evidence then is said to be unbiased and a true representation. These facts and observations are needed and used as input into the management decision-making process wherein steps are planned for, authorized, and taken to assure that customer expectations are met or exceeded. Further, these facts and observations are needed and used as input into the areas of continuous improvement and corrective action, and for compliance with various standards.

Forward and Backward Tracing

Forward and backward tracing refers to how auditors approach the process of gathering objective evidence. Tracing, whether forward or backward, helps auditors systematically investigate each step in any process or type of audit. Similarly to the intent of a checklist, forward or backward tracing ensures that no steps in a process are considered out of sequence, nor are they inadvertently forgotten or omitted.

In forward tracing, auditors investigate process steps sequentially from their point of origin or beginning. As each process step is completed, and thus leads to the next step in a process, the investigation of an auditor proceeds until the last step in a process is reached. Process flowcharts are particularly helpful in guiding auditors as they investigate sequentially organized process steps.

In backward tracing, auditors investigate process steps in reverse sequence from the completion or termination point. As each process step is completed when backward tracing, the auditor moves to the previous process step for investigation until the beginning of the process is reached. As with forward tracing, process flowcharts are particularly helpful in guiding auditors as they investigate sequentially organized process steps.

Audit Sampling Plans

As auditors utilize checklists, working papers, and qualitative and quantitative data collection tools to gather and document objective evidence in a manner consistent with forward or backward tracing, it is all too commonly the case that there is much more data available than there is time to consider it during an audit. When the amount of data and/or objective evidence exceeds the amount of time available for consideration during an audit, steps must be taken to limit the amount of data and evidence collected or considered. Audit sampling plans are the tools or techniques used to select a limited set of data or evidence from a larger set of data or evidence.

Key to any sampling plan is that the data or evidence selected for further consideration must have certain characteristics as follows:

1. The data or evidence must accurately characterize the larger set of data or evidence.

2. The data or evidence must not be biased.

3. The data or evidence must be selected randomly relative to its sampling characteristics (that is, purely random, stratified, and so on).

The statistical basis for audit sampling plans lies in *acceptance sampling*. Acceptance sampling is a topic addressed elsewhere in this book, and readers are encouraged to revisit acceptance sampling following a review of the material presented here under audit sampling. Auditors or auditor candidates should be advised that the application of acceptance sampling as audit sampling is within the CQT Body of Knowledge, is commonly used in the workplace, and is commonly on the CQT examination.

Procedural Guidelines

Earlier in this chapter, checklists were introduced, and in particular two types of checklists: planning and audit completion checklists. The audit completion checklist is a tool that provides detailed identification of procedural steps needed to complete the audit. During the discussion of audit completion checklists a point was made that there could be several levels of checklists used to support an audit as multiple areas or processes are investigated as part of the audit.

Procedural guidelines are provided to auditors as high-level tools that articulate, in less detail than checklists, how to approach the completion of audits. Procedural guidelines commonly address topics such as expectations of auditors, how to handle certain types of interactions with auditees, major elements in the audit plan, what to do in certain circumstances, and so on. The hierarchy of checklists and procedural guidelines is as shown in Figure 5.4.

What can be seen in Figure 5.4, in addition to the hierarchy of procedural guidelines and checklists, are audit completion instructions. It is important to understand and appreciate the level of detail embedded within each of these guidelines, checklists, and instructions. While the detail embedded in guidelines and checklists has already been addressed, the detail provided in instructions has not yet been addressed. Instructions provide very specific detail in terms of how to complete a given task or assignment. Instructions are typically provided in the form of statements and verbal or text-based explanations, whereas checklists are much more abbreviated and seek only to identify major points, and guidelines typically address even higher-level information such as approaches or strategies.

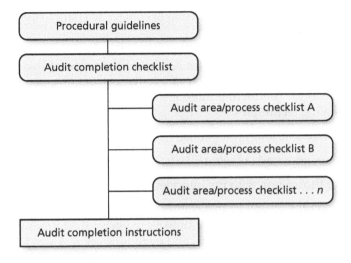

Figure 5.4 Audit guideline and checklist hierarchy.

D. AUDIT COMMUNICATION TOOLS

> Identify and use appropriate interviewing techniques and listening skills in various audit situations, and develop and use graphs, charts, diagrams, and other aids in support of written and oral presentations. (Apply)
>
> **Body of Knowledge V.D**

Application of audit communication tools includes the following:

- Interviewing techniques
- Listening skills

Interviewing Techniques

Objective evidence comes from two sources as we have discussed earlier in this chapter: *data* and *observations*. Observations can be further divided into *visual* and *verbal*. Visual observations come from actually watching as people complete certain tasks or by watching video of the same. Verbal observations are obtained by overhearing the conversations or statements made by other people or by talking directly with people. When talking directly with people in the context of their work, and in a more formal setting or context, we refer to these conversations as *formal interviews.*

A great deal of research has been devoted to interview techniques, and an exhaustive review of that literature is beyond the scope of this book. However, there are several points that are relevant to the current or aspiring CQT that will provide a basis for conducting interviews. The following guidelines are relevant for interviewing techniques:

- Be personable and professional, not excessively friendly.

- Prepare an agenda of what is to be discussed during the interview.

- Share the agenda with the interviewee prior to the interview.

- Conduct the interview in a comfortable and safe location (that is, consider the environmental controls: temperature/humidity, the location—free of distractions and ongoing work tasks and free of observations from coworkers/supervisors—a place to sit and talk, and so on).

- Ensure that the interviewee understands how and why the interview relates to the audit.

- Share with the interviewee what will be done with the results of the interview and whether or not the interview will be held in confidence.

- Have interview questions prepared and documented before the interview.

- Have an interview data collection form ready and available to document important points.

- Restrict the documentation of interviews to notes only—additional detail can be added to notes after the interview has been completed.

- Listen, listen, listen…versus talking.

- Move from open-ended to more-specific questions.

- Do not ask questions that "lead" an interviewee to a desired answer.

- Do not be distracted with other tasks or assignments during an interview (that is, answering phones, checking e-mail, reviewing audit documentation, and so on).

- Do not disagree with the interviewee or dispute statements.

- End the interview with an offer for, and time available for, the interviewee to ask questions.

It is important to remember that during an interview the intent is to obtain objective evidence. The time to assess whether or not the data and observations coming from an interview are objective is *after* the interview. It is a common mistake for people conducting interviews to be listening, recording data and observations, and assessing the objectivity of these data and observations all at the same time. To gain the intended outcome from interviews, it is necessary to focus one's attention on asking questions, listening, and then recording (that is, simple note-taking); this requires the complete attention of the interviewer.

Listening Skills

Interviews are the mechanism by which auditors access data and observations derived directly from the people involved with processes. *Active listening* is the process that makes the interview valuable and worthwhile. As with all processes, how to actively listen can be articulated so auditors can apply these techniques as follows:

- Dedicate and focus your complete attention to listening.

- Establish clear eye contact.

- Use posture to indicate attentiveness (that is, head nods, short verbal cues of agreement/interest, and so on).

- Ask clarifying questions.

- Paraphrase key aspects of the conversation to ensure understanding and demonstrate engagement.

- Summarize key points and highlights.

Chapter 6

VI. Risk Management

Corrective and preventive action (CAPA) is deeply embedded in the Certified Quality Technician (CQT) Body of Knowledge (BoK). Within the 2018 BoK, Risk Assessment and Mitigation appears as a new section (A.) while Corrective Action appears as section (B.) and Preventive Action appears as section (C.).

Career development for the CQT will entail learning more about what may be considered the greater "Quality Body of Knowledge" (QBoK), and CAPA is certainly in that greater QBoK—at multiple levels of cognition within Bloom's Taxonomy. Understanding the relationship of CAPA to the CQT and the QBoK is important when considering how the CQT will learn more about CAPA. Accordingly, CAPA is commonly addressed in technical references and professional literature under the heading of a more comprehensive set of material known as *root cause analysis* (RCA).

Surprisingly, there have been relatively few technical references on CAPA or RCA. A comprehensive listing of technical references for CAPA and RCA is compiled in the References section at the end of this book. However, it should be noted that a definitive and well-respected technical reference on CAPA and RCA is *Root Cause Analysis: Simplified Tools and Techniques,* written by Bjørn Andersen and Tom Fagerhaug. This book should be considered a prerequisite desk reference for the CQT.

It should be noted as well that the more comprehensive topic of RCA is *not* included in the 2011 CQT BoK; however, CAPA is included in the 2012 CQT BoK, so we will address CAPA next. The CQT candidate should be advised that it would not be surprising to see tools and techniques addressed in some technical references and/or professional literature as RCA that could appear on the CQT examination as tools and techniques of CAPA.

A. RISK ASSESSMENT AND MANAGEMENT

> Describe methods of risk assessment and mitigation such as trend analysis (SPC), failure mode and effects analysis (FMEA), root cause analysis (RCA), product and process monitoring reports, and control plans. (Understand)
>
> **Body of Knowledge VI.A**

In assessing and mitigating risk, the CQT must be able to understand information derived from trend analysis. There are several tools and techniques that provide trend data, all of which are identified in Section I, Quality Tools and Concepts, Sub-Section B. Quality Tools (i.e., cause-and-effect diagrams, flowcharts and process maps, check sheets, Pareto charts, scatter diagrams, control charts, and histograms) and Section II, Statistical Techniques, Sub-Section C. Control Charts (i.e., variables charts such as averages and range charts, and averages and standard deviation charts, and attribute charts such as the p, np, c, and u Charts. Since the information identified in the 2018 revision of the BoK has already been provided, and referenced here, it will not be repeated; however, readers are encouraged to carefully review this information in particular as it represents such a fundamentally important set of tools and techniques used throughout the field of quality.

Next in the 2018 CQT BoK revision that is relevant to our discussion is the addition of failure modes and effects analysis (FMEA). FMEA is both a preventive and corrective action tool. FMEA is commonly applied during the product development process to identify where problems, defects, or failures may occur and how these difficulties may be expected to present themselves. FMEA is commonly used in the corrective action process as an analysis tool to provide insights into how problems, defects, or failures actually occurred. When used as part of a prevention, it is said to be looking "down-stream" at where things *may* or *are likely* to go wrong. When used as part of a corrective action, FMEA is said to be looking "up-stream" to determine where things *did* go wrong, and why.

FMEA is a team-based problem-solving tool intended to help users identify and eliminate, or reduce, the negative effects of potential failures before they occur in systems, sub-systems, product or process design, or the delivery of a service. FMEA can be used as a stand-alone tool, or as part of comprehensive quality programs such as IATF 16949, Advanced Product Quality Planning and Control Planning (APQP), or Six Sigma. Accordingly, we will focus on terminology, theory, mechanics, and applications of FMEA as it applies to product designs, process designs, and systems.

Selecting a Standard for FMEA

The primary standard for FMEA, is published by the Society of Automotive Engineers standard (SAE J1739). The standard is limited in scope to address only design and process FMEAs. The SAE J1739 standard provides general FMEA forms and documents, identifies criteria for the quantification of risk associated with potential failures, and provides very general guidelines on the mechanics of completing FMEAs. SAE J1739 may be obtained by contacting the Society of Automotive Engineers at the following address:

> Society of Automotive Engineers
> 400 Commonwealth Drive
> Warrendale, PA 10596-0001

Planning for an FMEA

Planning for an FMEA involves a series of considerations that include, as a minimum, the following:

- Selecting appropriate applications for the analysis —An FMEA may be authorized by individuals at various levels within an organization or may be required by IATF 16949, APQP, Six Sigma methodologies, internal quality programs, or customer requirements. However authorized or required, an FMEA is expensive and should be completed only in those instances where the benefits of completing the analysis outweigh the costs.

- Identifying and allocating resources—These resources include FMEA team members and a reporting structure, physical space to conduct the analysis and store documentation, time, and clerical/ communications support.

- Defining scope—Since an FMEA can be conducted at a high level (i.e., the system level) or at a very detailed level (i.e., the component level or service delivery level), and since a high-level FMEA may lead to additional FMEAs at more detailed levels, it is very important to set the scope of the analysis before beginning.

- Expectations and deliverables—The team-based nature of completing an FMEA means FMEA team members will have dual or multiple responsibilities and reporting structures in addition to the FMEA team. It is critical, therefore, to clearly define performance expectations for all FMEA team members and to communicate those expectations directly to appropriate supervisory or managerial personnel in reporting structures outside the FMEA team. It is equally important that all FMEA team members understand what deliverables will result from the analysis and their respective roles in developing those deliverables.

- Establishing milestones, due dates, and deadlines—Key milestones for an FMEA include authorization for the analysis, establishment of a reporting structure, allocation of resources (particularly FMEA team members), gathering input for the analysis, completing the analysis, taking and monitoring corrective action, preparing documentation, and report-outs and debriefings. To ensure effectiveness, an FMEA should be conducted like a project from the perspective of establishing a schedule specifying due dates and deadlines for each of the major milestones.

Establishing a Single Point of Responsibility

As was mentioned in the Introduction, FMEA is a team-based analysis. However, there is sufficient practical experience to support the idea that assigning responsibility to a cross-functional team rather than a single individual is not the most effective policy. For a variety of reasons, one person should be assigned the responsibility of FMEA team leader, and that person needs the authority to make decisions and allocate resources to complete the FMEA as planned.

FMEA Team Members

The belief that only the one or two people closest to a system, sub-system, product or process design, or service delivery should be assigned to an FMEA violates the very intent of the analysis. FMEA is intended to be completed by team members representing a broad cross-section of expertise—technical and non-technical. For example, an FMEA should have representation from the following functional groups as a minimum:

- Design Engineering
- Manufacturing Engineering
- Production
- Quality/Reliability
- Purchasing/Material Control
- Sales & Marketing
- Customers

It cannot be overemphasized that if an FMEA is to be truly effective, the viewpoints and perspectives of every functional group above must be included—particularly customers. As Palady (1997) explains, "Excluding the customer's input from the FMEA will result in an incomplete list of the effects and low estimates of the severity."

Inputs to an FMEA

To prepare for an FMEA it is necessary to gather information from several sources—and these inputs should be gathered *prior* to the initial FMEA team meeting so as to maximize the effectiveness of team members' time. Inputs to an FMEA include, as a minimum, the following:

- Process flow chart or functional block diagram
- Design specifications
- Customer requirements/specifications
- Testing data/results
- Data on similar process/design technology
- Warranty data
- Failure/rework data
- Design/configuration change data
- Prior FMEAs
- Results from quantitative analysis (DOE, SPC, Process Capability Assessments, Reliability Assessments, etc.)

FMEA and Other Quality Tools

In addition to the inputs described above, other quality tools are frequently used during the completion of an FMEA. Other quality tools include, but are not limited to, the following:

- Cause-and-effect diagrams
- Process decision program charts
- Histograms
- Pareto diagrams
- Run charts
- Force field analysis
- Fault tree diagrams
- Root cause analysis

Outputs from an FMEA

Outputs or deliverables from an FMEA include the following:

- FMEA documentation
- System, sub-system, design, process, and/or service delivery documentation

- Recommendation reports
- Corrective action reports
- Design changes
- Compliance reports
- Debriefings and presentations

Basic Steps in an FMEA

Complexity in an FMEA is directly related to the number of levels of analysis dictated by the situation or team members. At the most fundamental level, however, every FMEA consists of the same basic steps that include the following:

- Identify a starting point for the analysis—A starting point will be a system, sub-system, product or process design, or service delivery system of interest.

- Gather all relevant inputs to support the analysis—Gathering inputs for an FMEA is a milestone to be completed prior to an initial FMEA meeting. It is far more effective, both from cost and efficiency perspectives, to have all team members at meetings participating in the analysis rather than leaving meetings to gather input!

- Identify potential failure modes as related to the following:
  - *Who* would be impacted by a failure?
  - *What* would happen in the event of a failure?
  - *When* would the failure occur?
  - *Where* would the failure occur?
  - *Why* would the failure occur?
  - *How* would the failure occur?

- Quantify the risk associated with each potential failure—Risk assessment is based on severity, occurrence, and detection of a potential failure.

- Develop a corrective action plan for the most significant risks.

- Iterate or repeat the analysis until all potential failures pose an "acceptable" level of risk—What constitutes an "acceptable" risk must be clearly defined by the individual or agent authorizing the FMEA.

- Document results.

- Report-out and/or present results.

Quantifying the Risk Associated with Each Potential Failure

To avoid confusion, the quantification of risk associated with potential failures will now be introduced—prior to detailed explanation of FMEA mechanics. While FMEA may appropriately be applied to systems, sub-systems, product or process designs, and/or service delivery, risk assessment methods and metrics remain consistent regardless of analysis level. Where the actual criteria for risk assessment change (specifically between design and process FMEAs), the criteria will be provided as needed for the discussion. Readers are encouraged to familiarize themselves with this section of risk assessment, and be prepared to review this section once specific analysis levels are discussed.

Risk Components

For purposes of FMEA, risk has three components that are multiplied to produce a risk priority number (RPN). The three components of risk are as follows:

- Severity (S)—An indicator of the severity of a failure should a failure occur. Severity is described on a 10-point scale.

- Occurrence (O)—An indicator of the likelihood of a failure occurring. Occurrence is described on a 10-point scale.

- Detection (D)—An indicator of the likelihood of detecting a failure once it has occurred. Detection is described on a 10-point scale.

$$RPN_{min} = 1 \quad while \quad RPN_{max} = 1000$$

Taking Action Based on an RPN

A common mistake in assessing FMEA risk is prioritizing corrective action based the descending order of RPNs. Logic would suggest that the largest RPNs represent the highest risk—which is true, but only to a point. When multiplying the three risk components together their importance relative to each other becomes obscured. Consider the following example:

	(S)	x	(O)	x	(D)	=	RPN
Potential failure 1	2		10		5		100
Potential failure 2	10		2		5		100
Potential failure 3	2		5		10		100
Potential failure 4	10		5		2		100

In each case the resulting RPN = 100. It is unclear which potential failure merits corrective action first. There is, however, a generally accepted strategy when taking action on an RPN, and Palady (1997) describes that strategy as follows:

1. Eliminate the occurrence

2. Reduce the severity

3. Reduce the occurrence

4. Improve detection

In the example above, the additional information provided by the generally accepted strategy used when taking action on an RPN makes it clear how to proceed.

1. Eliminating occurrences would, mathematically, re-order the RPNs.

2. Reducing severity next would focus our attention on potential failures 2 and 4. But then what? We still have two potential failures with the same level of risk.

3. Reducing occurrence as the next step in this process focuses our attention on potential failure 4 that had a higher occurrence rating than did potential failure 2.

Now our attention can turn to evaluating the remaining potential failures since potential failures 2 and 4 have been ranked as the two most important. Of the remaining two potential failures (1 and 3 respectively), potential failure 1 has the higher occurrence rating and is therefore ranked as the third most important potential failure; potential failure 3 drops to the least important position by default. The rank order by which the potential failures in the above example should be investigated for corrective action is as follows:

First priority	Potential failure 4
Second priority	Potential failure 2
Third priority	Potential failure 1
Fourth priority	Potential failure 3

Do We Rate The Failure Mode or the Cause?

A common point of confusion arises when considering what is actually rated as part of the risk assessment, the actual failure itself or the cause of a given failure. It is perfectly acceptable to rate either the failure or the cause—as long as the assumption is well documented (on actual FMEA charts, in written correspondence, and in all reports/presentations), and as long as everyone on the FMEA team and in the reporting structure is aware of the assumption. Whether rating a failure itself or a cause of that failure, an FMEA should provide consistent results and corrective actions.

Types of FMEAs

It was mentioned earlier in this chapter that FMEA can be applied to the system/ sub-system, design or process, or service delivery levels. A brief synopsis of each FMEA application is as follows:

- *System FMEA*
  A system, or sub-system, is a collection of elements or components working together to accomplish a desired task or function. FMEA is applied at the system or sub-system level to identify potential failure modes and effects that could negatively impact system or sub-system performance. At the system or sub-system level, FMEA is focused at system or sub-system boundaries where potential failures are most likely to occur. The boundaries of interest for a system or sub-system FMEA include functional (i.e., expected outcomes assuming normal operation) or operational (i.e., specific outputs expected as compared to tolerances, specifications, and timing).

- *Design FMEA*
  A design, or more accurately a product design, is a set of specifications that describes all aspects of a product (i.e., major functions, operating parameters and tolerances, materials, dimensions, etc.). FMEA is applied to product designs as early in the product design process as feasible to identify potential failure modes that could that could result from a design flaw. Design FMEAs are a normal part of key milestones in the product development process such as concept reviews, concept approvals, preliminary design reviews, and final design reviews.

- *Process FMEA*
  A process design is a set of specifications that describes all aspects of a process (i.e., functional components, flow rates, process steps, equipment to be used, steps to be performed, operators or employees to be involved, etc.). Process design FMEA is applied to process designs at the earliest possible point to identify potential failure modes that could result from a design flaw. Process FMEAs too are a normal part of key milestones in the process development process.

- *Service Delivery FMEA*
  A service delivery is the completion of a set of tasks designed to meet one or more customer expectations. Service delivery FMEA is applied to service delivery designs to identify potential failure modes that, if experienced, would result in some level of customer dissatisfaction. Service delivery FMEAs are also completed as early as possible in the design process and are a normal part of key milestones in the service delivery design process.

In most instances the practicing quality technician (QE) can be expected to work primarily on design and/or process FMEAs. A CQT would expect much less opportunity, if ever, to work on system/sub-system and/or service delivery FMEAs. Accordingly, we will focus on design and process FMEAs, and will purposefully omit system/sub-system and service delivery FMEAs. Readers are encouraged to reference Stamatis (1995) for a detailed discussion of system/sub-system and service delivery FMEAs.

Design and Process FMEA

Following the steps outlined above describing the planning functions preceding an FMEA, the analysis proceeds as the FMEA team completes appropriate documentation such as the FMEA form. For purposes of this discussion, one form applicable to either a design or process FMEA will be described. Where the criteria change between a design or process FMEA, both criteria will be provided. Figure 6.1 and Figure 6.2 are blank FMEA forms applicable to design and process FMEA. Each component of the forms will be identified and described.

Heading Information & Documentation:

Product or Process Name—Provide the formal and/or commonly used name (if different) for the product or process.

Product or Process Description—Provide a brief description of the product or process that is meaningful to the FMEA team members.

FMEA Number—Assign an FMEA Number to each FMEA for tracking and documentation purposes. There are no standards for numbering FMEAs; however, a numbering system that links the FMEA to a specific period of time and product/process family is preferred.

Design/Process Owner—Identify the individual or team assigned primary responsibility for the design or process for tracking and documentation purposes. This individual or team is also identified for reference, if needed, during the FMEA.

FMEA Team Leader—Identify the individual assigned primary responsibility for completion of the FMEA for documentation purposes. This individual is also identified so as to establish a point of contact should any stakeholder need information during or after the FMEA.

FMEA Team—List each member of the FMEA team along with any key responsibilities relative to the FMEA.

FMEA Date—Provide the date(s) during which the FMEA is completed to help establish a chronology of events. Revision dates should be noted here as well.

FMEA Risk Assessment Based On—Indicate the basis of the risk assessment. The FMEA risk assessment may be based on either Actual Failures or Failure Causes. It is important to document the team's decision to assess risk based on failures or causes to ensure everyone evaluating the FMEA understands exactly how risk was assessed.

Analysis Content & Documentation:
DFMEA Part Name, #, Function
Or

Potential
Failure Mode and Effects Analysis
(Design FMEA)

____ System
____ Subsystem
____ Component ____________________

Design responsibility ____________________

Model year(s) vehicle(s) ________________

Key date ____________________

Core team ____________________

FMEA number ____________

Page ________ of ________

Prepared by ____________________

FMEA date (orig.) ________ (rev.) ________

Item / Function	Potential failure mode	Potential effect(s) of failure	Sev	Class	Potential cause(s)/ mechanism(s) of failure	Occur	Current design controls	Detec	R.P.N.	Recommended action(s)	Responsibility and target completion date	Action results					
												Actions taken	Sev	Occ	Det	R.P.N.

Figure 6.1 Blank design FMEA form.

Potential
Failure Mode and Effects Analysis
(Process FMEA)

Item ________ Process responsibility ________ FMEA number ________

Page ____ of ____

Model year(s) vehicle(s) ________ Key date ________ Prepared by ________

Core team ________ FMEA date (orig.) ____ (rev.) ____

Process function / Requirements	Potential failure mode	Potential effect(s) of failure	Sev	Class	Potential cause(s)/ mechanism(s) of failure	Occur	Current process controls	Detec	R.P.N.	Recommended action(s)	Responsibility and target completion date	Action results: Actions taken	Sev	Occ	Det	R.P.N.

Figure 6.2 Blank process FMEA form.

PFMEA Process Function—Identify the product (i.e., part name, part number, and function) or process (i.e., functions to be completed as part of the process).

Potential Failure Mode—List each of the potential failure modes associated with the design or process. Design failure modes may include dented, deformed, fractured, loosened, leaking, warped, etc. Process failure modes may include overheating, inoperable, visual defect, etc.

Potential Effect of Failure Mode—For each potential failure mode, indicate the potential effect on customers or production/process personnel – it is entirely possible to have multiple effects for each potential failure mode.

Severity—Indicate the seriousness of the effect of the potential failure using the Severity Criteria defined in Tables 6.1 and 6.2. NOTE: The Severity rating applies only to the effect of the potential failure.

Classification—Classify any special characteristics that may require additional process controls. SAE J1739 identifies classifications that include critical, key, major, and significant.

Potential Cause of Failure Mode—For each potential effect of each failure mode, identify all possible causes. It is entirely possible to have more than one cause for each potential effect.

Occurrence—Indicate how frequently each failure is expected to occur using the Occurrence criteria defined in Tables 6.3 and 6.4.

Risk Priority Number (RPN)—For each potential failure mode, multiply the severity (S), occurrence (O), and detection (D) assessments together. Since each scale (S, O, and D) range from 1 to 10, $RPN_{min} = 1$ and $RPN_{max} = 1000$

Recommended Actions—For each potential failure mode list one or more recommended corrective actions. For further direction and guidance on prioritizing recommended corrective actions, readers are encouraged to refer to the "Taking Action Based on an RPN" section of this chapter.

Individual/Team Responsible & Completion Date—For each recommended action, assign an appropriate individual or team and an expected completion date.

Actions Taken—Provide a brief description of the actual actions taken and their respective action dates.

Resulting RPN Analysis—Following each action taken, reiterate the severity, occurrence, and detection assessments and calculate a new resulting RPN. Actions taken based on RPNs and resulting RPNs continue until the risk assessment for each potential failure is "acceptable" to the customer and/or authorizing agent for the FMEA (see Tables 6.5 and 6.6).

Table 6.1 Design FMEA severity criteria.

Effect	Severity criteria	Ranking
Hazardous without warning	Very high ranking when potential failure mode affects safe operation and/or regulation noncompliance. Failure occurs without warning.	10
Hazardous with warning	Very high ranking when potential failure mode affects safe operation and/or regulation noncompliance. Failure occurs with warning.	9
Very high	Item or product is inoperable, with loss of function. Customer very dissatisfied.	8
High	Item or product is operable, with loss of performance. Customer dissatisfied.	7
Moderate	Item or product is operable, but comfort/convenience items inoperable. Customer experiences discomfort.	6
Low	Item or product is operable, but with loss of performance of comfort/convenience items. Customer has some dissatisfaction.	5
Very low	Certain characteristics do not conform. Noticed by most customers.	4
Minor	Certain characteristics do not conform. Noticed by average customers.	3
Very minor	Certain characteristics do not conform. Noticed by discriminating customers.	2
None	No effect.	1

S × O × D = risk priority number (RPN)
Derived from Technical Standard SAE J 1739.
Reprinted by permission of The Society of Automotive Engineers (SAE).

Table 6.2 Process FMEA severity criteria.

Effect	Severity criteria	Ranking
Hazardous without warning	May endanger machine or assembly operator. Very high severity ranking when a potential failure mode affects safe operation and/or involves noncompliance with regulation. Failure will occur without warning.	10
Hazardous with warning	May endanger machine or assembly operator. Very high severity ranking when a potential failure mode affects safe operation and/or involves noncompliance with regulation. Failure will occur with warning.	9
Very high	Major disruption to production line. 100% of product may have to be scrapped. Item inoperable, loss of primary function. Customer very dissatisfied.	8
High	Minor disruption to production line. A portion of product may have to be sorted and scrapped. Item operable, but at reduced level. Customer dissatisfied.	7

(continued)

Table 6.2 Process FMEA severity criteria *(continued).*

Effect	Severity criteria	Ranking
Moderate	Minor disruption to production line. A portion of product may have to be scrapped (no sorting). Item operable, but some comfort items inoperable. Customer experiences discomfort.	6
Low	Minor disruption to production line. 100% of product may have to be reworked. Item operable, but some comfort items operable at reduced level of performance. Customer experiences some dissatisfaction.	5
Very low	Minor disruption to production line. Product may have to be sorted and a portion reworked. Minor adjustments do not conform. Defect noticed by customer.	4
Minor	Minor disruption to production line. Product may have to be reworked online, but out of station. Minor adjustments do not conform. Defect noticed by average customer.	3
Very minor	Minor disruption to production line. Product may have to be reworked online, but out of station. Minor adjustments do not conform. Defect noticed by discriminating customer.	2
None	No effect.	1

Derived from Technical Standard SAE J 1739.
Reprinted by permission of The Society of Automotive Engineers (SAE).

Table 6.3 Design FMEA occurrence criteria.

Probability of failure	Possible failure rates	Ranking
Very high: Failure almost inevitable	> 1 in 2 1 in 3	10 9
High: Repeated failures	1 in 8 1 in 20	8 7
Moderate: Occasional failures	1 in 80 1 in 400 1 in 2000	6 5 4
Low: Relatively few failures	1 in 15,000 1 in 150,000	3 2
Remote: Failure is unlikely	< 1 in 1,500,000	1

Derived from Technical Standard SAE J 1739.
Reprinted by permission of The Society of Automotive Engineers (SAE).

Table 6.4 Process FMEA occurrence criteria.

Probability of failure	Possible failure rates	Ranking
Very high: Failure almost inevitable.	> 1 in 2 1 in 3	10 9
High: Generally associated with processes similar to previous processes that have often failed.	1 in 8 1 in 20	8 7
Moderate: Generally associated with processes similar to previous processes that have experienced occasional failures.	1 in 80 1 in 400 1 in 2000	6 5 4
Low: Isolated failures associated with similar processes.	1 in 15,000	3
Very low: Only isolated failures associated with almost identical processes.	1 in 150,000	2
Remote: Failure is unlikely. No failures associated with almost identical processes.	< 1 in 1,500,000	1

Derived from Technical Standard SAE J 1739.
Reprinted by permission of The Society of Automotive Engineers (SAE).

Table 6.5 Design FMEA detection criteria.

Effect	Detection criteria	Ranking
Absolute	Design control will not and/or cannot detect a potential cause/uncertainty mechanism and subsequent failure mode or there is no design control.	10
Very remote	Very remote chance the design control will detect a potential cause/mechanism and subsequent failure mode.	9
Remote	Remote chance the design control will detect a potential cause/mechanism and subsequent failure mode.	8
Very low	Very low chance the design control will detect a potential cause/mechanism and subsequent failure mode.	7
Low	Low chance the design control will detect a potential cause/mechanism and subsequent failure mode.	6
Moderate	Moderate chance the design control will detect a potential cause/mechanism and subsequent failure mode.	5
Moderately high	Moderately high chance the design control will detect a high potential cause/mechanism and subsequent failure mode.	4
High	High chance the design control will detect a potential cause/mechanism and subsequent failure mode.	3
Very high	Very high chance the design control will detect a potential cause/mechanism and subsequent failure mode.	2
Almost	Design control will almost certainly detect a potential cause/certain mechanism and subsequent failure mode.	1

Derived from Technical Standard SAE J 1739.
Reprinted by permission of The Society of Automotive Engineers (SAE).

Table 6.6 Process FMEA detection criteria.

Effect	Detection criteria	Ranking
Absolutely impossible	No known controls to detect failure mode.	10
Very remote	Very remote likelihood current controls will detect failure mode.	9
Remote	Remote likelihood current controls will detect failure mode.	8
Very low	Very low likelihood current controls will detect failure mode.	7
Low	Low likelihood current controls will detect failure mode.	6
Moderate	Moderate likelihood current controls will detect failure mode.	5
Moderately high	Moderately high likelihood current controls will detect failure mode.	4
High	High likelihood current controls will detect failure mode.	3
Very high	Very high likelihood current controls will detect failure mode.	2
Almost certain	Current controls will almost certainly detect a failure mode. Reliable detection controls are known with similar processes.	1

Derived from Technical Standard SAE J 1739.
Reprinted by permission of The Society of Automotive Engineers (SAE).

A Final Word on Taking Corrective Action

An FMEA represents an in-depth, objective, quantitative analysis of the risk associated with potential failures that result in the calculation of one or more RPNs. Once RPNs have been calculated and the FMEA team prepares to take corrective action, the analysis necessarily takes on a subjective element as FMEA team members use the risk assessment to guide prioritization of corrective actions.

As was mentioned earlier in this chapter, the most common practice used to prioritize corrective action is based on a descending rank ordering of the RPN values. Prioritization of corrective action based solely on RPNs works effectively, however, only as long as there is a "comfortable" difference among the RPN values. When clusters of RPN values are the same or very close (say, within 25 to 50 points), taking action based on RPNs alone is not straightforward. When there are clusters of RPN values (i.e., grouping of RPN values that are the same or within a 25- to 50-point range) additional guidance in prioritizing corrective action is needed as follows:

1. Rank the RPNs in descending order.

2. For those RPNs that cluster within a predefined range of 25 to 50 points, use the strategy suggested earlier in this chapter by Palady (i.e., eliminate occurrence, then reduce severity, then reduce occurrence, then improve detection).

3. Plan, take, and monitor corrective action on the largest non-clustered RPNs.

4. Plan, take, and monitor corrective action on RPN clusters as defined in step two above.

5. Repeat steps three and four as needed to address all potential failures identified in the analysis.

As another means of eliminating the subjectivity in prioritizing corrective actions based on RPNs, a method called "Criticality Analysis" was developed as part of Mil-Std 1629A.

A Caution About Using FMEA

FMEA can be a powerful and effective tool for system/sub-system, design or process, or service delivery improvement. It should be remembered, however, that completing an FMEA has associated with it significant costs. Readers may be tempted to follow the results of an FMEA to further levels of refinement and specificity, but are cautioned to remember there is a cost/benefit relationship associated with the use of FMEA.

Design and Process FMEA Examples

The following examples of design and process FMEAs (Figures 6.3 and 6.4) have been provided to help guide the reader through an actual analysis.

FMEA is a tool to help cross-functional teams identify, eliminate, and/or reduce the negative effects of potential failures—*before they happen*. FMEA is widely used as a stand-alone tool or as part of comprehensive quality systems/ programs.

Even though two primary standards guide the use and implementation of FMEA, the theoretical basis for, risk assessment criteria, and mechanics of an FMEA are consistent across the standards. Much of the preparation for, inputs to, and prioritization of corrective action guidance are not covered in the standards to support an FMEA.

**Potential
Failure Mode and Effects Analysis
(Process FMEA)** (3)

System		
x	Subsystem	(2)
	Component 01.03/Body closures	(5)

Model year(s)/vehicle(s) 199X/Lion 4dr/wagon

Core team: T. Fender—Car product dev., Childers—Manufacturing, J. Ford—Assy ops (Dalton, Fraser, Henley assembly plants)

Design responsibility Body engineering (6)

Key date 9X 03 01 ER

FMEA number 1234 (1)
Page 1 of 1
Prepared by A. Tate—X6412—Body engr (4) (7)
FMEA date (orig.) 8X 03 22 (rev.) 8X 07 14 (8)

Item / Function (9)	Potential failure mode (10)	Potential effect(s) of failure (11)(12)	C l a s s	Potential cause(s)/ mechanism(s) of failure (13)(14)	O c c u r (15)	Current design controls (16)(17)	D e t e c	R. P. N.	Recommended action(s) (18)(19)	Responsibility and target completion date (20)	Actions taken (21)	S e v	O c c	D e t e c	R. P. N.
Front door L.H. H8HX-0000-A • Ingress to and egress from vehicle • Occupant protection from weather, noise, and side impact • Support anchorage for door hardware including mirror, hinges, latch, and window regulator • Provide proper surface for appearance items • Paint and soft trim	Corroded interior lower door panels	Deteriorated life of door leading to: • Unsatisfactory appearance due to rust through paint over time • Impaired function of interior door hardware	7	Upper edge of protective wax application specified for inner door panels is too low	6	Vehicle general durability test veh. T-118 T-109 T-301	7	294	Add laboratory accelerated corrosion testing	A Tate-Body Engrg 8X 09 30	Based on test results (Test No. 1481) upper edge spec raised 125mm	7	2	2	28
				Insufficient wax thickness specified	4	Vehicle general durability testing - as above	7	196	Add laboratory accelerated corrosion testing Conduct Design of Experiments (DOE) on wax thickness	Combine w/test for wax upper edge verification A Tate Body Engrg 9X 01 15	Test results (Test No. 1481) show specified thickness is adequate. DOE shows 25% variation in specified thickness is acceptable	7	2	2	28
				Inappropriate wax formulation specified	2	Physical and Chem Lab test - Report No. 1265	2	28	None						
				Entrapped air prevents wax from entering corner/edge access	5	Design aid investigation with non-functioning spray head	8	280	Add team evaluation using production spray equipment and specified wax	Body Engrg & Assy Ops 8X 11 15		7	1	3	21
				Wax application plugs door drain holes	3	Laboratory test using "worst case" wax application and hole size	1	21	None	Body Engrg & Assy Ops	Based on test, 3 additional vent holes provided in affected areas	7	1	1	7
				Insufficient room between panels for spray head access	4	Drawing evaluation of spray head access	4	112	Add team evaluation using design aid buck and spray head	Body Engrg & Assy Ops	Evaluation showed adequate access	7	1	1	7

SAMPLE

Figure 6.3 Design FMEA example.

Potential
Failure Mode and Effects Analysis
(Process FMEA)

FMEA number ___1450___ (1)
Page ___1___ of ___1___

Item ___Front door LH/H8HX-000-A___ (2)   Process responsibility ___Body engrg./assembly operations___ (3)   Prepared by ___J. Ford—X6521—Assy ops___ (4)

Model year(s) vehicle(s) ___199X/Lion 4dr/wagon___ (5)   Key date ___9X 03 01 ER___   ___9X 08 26 Job #1___ (6)   FMEA date (orig.) ___9X 05 17___ (rev.) ___9X 11 06___ (7)

Core team ___A. Tate—Body engrg., J. Smith—QC, R. James—Production, J. Jones—Maintenance___ (8)

Process function (9) Requirements	Potential failure mode (10)	Potential effect(s) of failure (11) (12)	C l a s s	S e v	Potential cause(s)/ mechanism(s) of failure (13) (14)	O c c u r	Current process controls (15) (16)	D e t e c (17)	R. P. N.	Recommended action(s) (18) (19)	Responsibility and target completion date (20)	Action results (22) Actions taken (21)	S e v	O c c	D e t	R. P. N.
Manual application of wax inside door	Insufficient wax coverage over specified surface	Deteriorated life of door leading to: • Unsatisfactory appearance due to rust through paint over time • Impaired function of interior door hardware		7	Manually inserted spray head not inserted far enough	8	Visual check each hour-1/shift for film thickness (depth meter) and coverage	5	280	Add positive depth stop to sprayer	Mfg Engrg 9X 10 15	Stop added, sprayer checked on line	7	2	5	70
										Automate spraying	Mfg Engrg 9X 12 15	Rejected due to complexity of different doors on same line				
To cover inner door, lower surfaces at minimum wax thickness to retard corrosion					Spray heads clogged • Viscosity too high • Temperature too low • Pressure too low	5	Test spray pattern at start-up and after idle periods, and preventative maintenance program to clean heads	3	105	Use Design of Experiments (DOE) on viscosity vs. temperature vs. pressure	Mfg Engrg 9X 10 01	Temp and press limits were determined and limit controls have been installed-control charts show process is in control Cpk=1.85	7	1	3	21
					Spray head deformed due to impact	2	Preventative maintenance programs to maintain head	2	28	None						
					Spray time insufficient	8	Operator instructions and lot sampling (10 doors / shift) to check for coverage of critical areas	7	392	Install spray timer	Maintenance 9X 09 15	Automatic spray timer installed - operator starts spray, timer controls shut-off control charts show process is in control Cpk=2.05	7	1	7	49

SAMPLE

Figure 6.4 Process FMEA example.

INVESTIGATION OF ROOT CAUSES

Note: The information on investigation of root causes does not *appear in the 2012 CQT BoK; however, this information is particularly important for the CQT in professional practice.*

Andersen and Fagerhaug (2000) define and describe root cause analysis as "a collective term to describe a wide range of approaches, tools, and techniques used to uncover causes to problems."

The title of this section, "investigation of root causes," implies the existence of one or more problems that must to be resolved. In this context, root cause analysis is a structured approach to problem solving that uses all the traditional quality control tools identified in CQT BoK Section I, Subsection B, such as histograms, Pareto charts, cause-and-effect diagrams, check sheets, scatter diagrams, and control charts. In fact, it can easily be argued that root cause analysis uses even more than the traditional quality control tools identified in Section I, Subsection B, including the nontraditional quality tools and techniques identified by Kolarik (1995), such as affinity diagrams, relations diagrams, systematic diagrams, matrix diagrams, process decision program charts, and arrow diagrams. Additionally, tools and techniques identified by Brassard and Ritter in *The Memory Jogger 2* (1994), such as force field analysis, interrelationship digraphs, prioritization matrices, and radar charts, can also be applied to root cause analysis.

It is important to emphasize that the root cause analysis process is a series of iterative steps taken while solving a problem. Since there are many generally accepted approaches to problem solving (for example, PDSA/PDCA, Kepner-Tragoe), the benefit to be derived from any problem-solving approach is in the consistency and rigor involved in the problem-solving methodology or protocol.

At issue in this whole notion of problem solving is solving the "right" problem. All too often, a problem that presents itself is the result of another problem, or perhaps several other problems combined. In this case, and in the language of root cause analysis, we say that the problem that presents itself as the most apparent is merely the symptom of a more deeply rooted problem. Solving symptomatic problems, therefore, gives rise to other, perhaps seemingly unrelated, problems.

It has long been understood in the quality community that until someone can ask the question "why?" at least five times, they can not hope to be looking at anything more than symptoms of a problem rather than the actual or root cause problem. This *why, why, why, why, why* questioning methodology, as supported by the many problem-solving tools identified above, represents the means by which to separate symptoms from root causes. And one would then know that a root-cause problem has been identified and solved when other problems disappear or are eliminated automatically as a function of solving the root cause problem.

B. CORRECTIVE ACTION

> Explain and apply elements of the corrective
> action process: identify the problem, contain the
> problem (interim action), assign responsibility
> (personnel) to determine the causes of the
> problem and propose solutions to eliminate it or
> prevent its recurrence (permanent action), verify
> that the solutions are implemented, and confirm
> their effectiveness (validation). (Apply)
>
> **Body of Knowledge VI.B**

Corrective action is defined in ANSI/ISO/ASQ Q9000-2005, *Quality management systems—Fundamentals and vocabulary* as follows:

> …an action taken to eliminate the cause of a detected non-conformity,
> which prevents the problem from recurring.

The 2012 CQT BoK identifies corrective action as being composed of the following elements:

- Identify the problem

- Contain the problem (interim action)

- Assign responsibility (personnel) to determine the causes of the problem and propose solutions to eliminate it or prevent its recurrence (permanent action)

- Verify that the solutions are implemented

- Confirm their effectiveness (validation)

Figure 6.5 provides a graphical representation of the corrective action process (CAP).

Figure 6.5 and the corrective action process begin with problem identification. Once one or more problems have been identified, steps are taken to contain the problem. *Problem containment* means that steps are taken to ensure that the problem does not impact or affect process outputs or other processes. Problem containment is commonly referred to as *interim action* because the steps taken to ensure containment are generally disruptive to normal process operation, do not add value to the final product or service, do not permanently correct or prevent the problem, and are ultimately not sustainable. An example of problem containment might be re-inspecting and/or sorting good product from bad before that product reaches customers. Once the problem has been contained for the short term, a more in-depth analysis takes place; at that time individuals involved with identifying the problem causes are in a position to propose long-term or permanent solutions. The next step in a CAP is to verify that solutions have been implemented. Verifying solution implementation is a risk point in a CAP because the potential exists to implement proposed solutions that are (1) not needed (that is, do not address the real root cause of the problem), (2) implemented incorrectly, or (3) implemented incompletely. Following solution implementation, it is imperative that solution effectiveness be validated. *Validation* is a process of ensuring that something has been completed, that whatever has been completed is in accordance with some set of instructions or specifications, that the completed action meets the intended goal(s) or outcomes(s), that the completed action does not harm or disrupt other elements of any given process or system, and that the completed action is sustained into future operations.

While Figure 6.5 shows the graphical relationship of each element in the corrective action process (CAP), it is of key importance to realize that completion of each CAP element requires the use of one or more additional tools and/or techniques. Table 6.7 provides a non-exhaustive list of the tools and/or techniques that can be or commonly are used in support of each element in the CAP.

It should be noted that some of the tools and techniques used to support the CAP are identified in the CQT BoK, and those tools and techniques are covered at various other points in this book. Similarly, not all of the tools and techniques identified in Table 6.7 are included in the 2012 CQT BoK. It should be noted as well that the level of mastery or proficiency in the use and implementation of these tools and techniques varies with each of ASQ's BoKs (for example the CQI, CQE, CMQ/OE) based on the hierarchy established with Bloom's Taxonomy. Each CQT candidate is encouraged to look closely at the CQT BoK to see which tools and techniques are requisite and at what level of mastery these tools and techniques

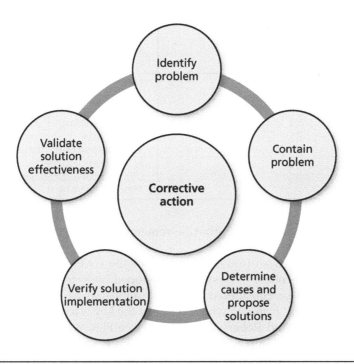

Figure 6.5 The corrective action process.

Table 6.7 Tools and techniques used to support the CAP process (non-exhaustive).

CAP element	Applicable tool or technique
Identify the problem	Process operation data Run charts Statistical process control charts Process performance data Rework data Warranty and claims data RCA Process flowcharts Critical incident techniques Matrix diagrams
Contain the problem	Brainstorming Brain writing Nominal group technique
Determine cause of problem and propose solutions	Data sampling plans Checklists Run charts Statistical process control charts Histograms Pareto charts Scatter charts Relations diagrams Affinity diagrams Cause-and-effect diagrams Failure modes and effects analysis Fault tree analysis
Verify solution implementation	Inspection techniques Observation techniques Interview techniques Tree diagrams Force field analysis
Validate solution effectiveness	Process operation data Run charts Statistical process control charts Process performance data Rework data Warranty and claims data RCA Process flowcharts Critical incident techniques Matrix diagrams

are within Bloom's Taxonomy (that is, remember, understand, apply, analyze, evaluate, and create).

Having completed an initial discussion of the CAP, we will now turn our attention to a more robust CAP system developed by Ketola and Roberts (2003). The CAP about to be considered originally appeared as Appendix A of their book *Correct! Prevent! Improve!,* which is one of the key references supporting this chapter. The Ketola and Roberts (K&R) CAP (see Figure 6.6) has gained a great deal of recognition and implementation as a definitive and robust CAP.

A review of the K&R CAP reveals many more elements than were introduced in the CAP discussed earlier in this chapter. A more detailed review, however, reveals that each of the major elements in the CAP discussed above is conceptually embedded within the K&R CAP. Accordingly, the K&R CAP extends the usefulness and robustness of the CAP previously discussed.

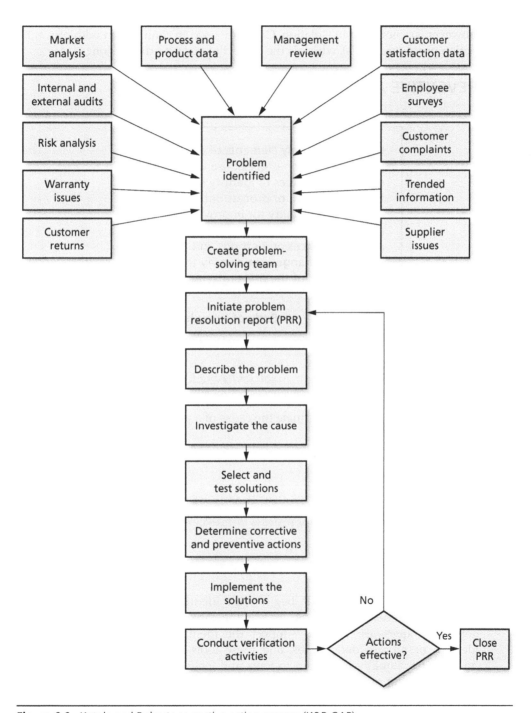

Figure 6.6   Ketola and Roberts corrective action process (K&R CAP).

The value of comparing and contrasting the two CAPs is that the reader will gain an appreciation of what is entailed in a basic versus a more robust CAP. Additionally, the comparison reveals that many tools and techniques, sources of data, and, in many cases, customer interactions come into play when using a CAP in the context of professional responsibilities associated with the CQT. CAPs, however, are not used in isolation. CAPs are used in conjunction with preventive action processes (PAPs), which is the subject of our next discussion.

C. PREVENTIVE ACTION

> Explain and apply elements of a preventive action process: use various data analysis techniques to identify potential failures, defects, or process deficiencies; assign responsibility for improving the process (e.g., develop error- or mistake-proofing devices or methods, initiate procedural changes), and verify the effectiveness of the preventive action. (Apply)
>
> **Body of Knowledge VI.C**

Preventive action is defined in ANSI/ISO/ASQ Q9000-2005, *Quality management systems—Fundamentals and vocabulary* as follows:

> … an action taken to eliminate the cause of a potential non-conformity from occurring.

The 2012 CQT BoK identifies preventive action as being composed of the following elements:

- Identify potential failures, defects, or process deficiencies

- Assign responsibility for process improvement

- Verify solution effectiveness

Figure 6.7 provides a graphical representation of the preventive action process (PAP).

Figure 6.7 and the PAP begin with identification of potential failures, defects, or process deficiencies. As was the case with the CAP, numerous tools and techniques are used to support the identification of potential failures, defects, or process deficiencies, and these tools and techniques are identified in Table 6.8. Equally important to tools and techniques used in identification is the assignment of responsibility for process improvements. With responsibility comes accountability, and it is simply imperative that members of the leadership know who is responsible for implementation of process improvements, both as a source of accountability and so that they know where to flow resources and authorizations for the processes improvements. While responsibility is normally assigned to an individual, leader, or manager, teams normally are assigned to implement the process improvements. Here, too, working in teams requires a set of knowledge, skills, and abilities as identified in Table 6.8. Team functions are covered in the CQT BoK in section I.C, and readers must review that material as as it could very possibly be embedded in the CQT exam within the CAPA section. Once the problem identification and process improvement responsibilities have been assigned and completed, the next step in the PAP is verification of solution effectiveness. Verification and validation of solution effectiveness was discussed as part of CAP, and the steps in verification in the CAP and PAP are the same.

While Figure 6.7 shows the graphical relationship of each element in the PAP, it is of key importance to realize that completion of each PAP element requires the use of one or more additional tools and/or techniques. Table 6.8 provides a non-exhaustive list of the tools and/or techniques that can be or commonly are used in support of each element in the PAP.

As was done following our initial discussion of CAP, we will now turn our attention to a more robust PAP system developed by Ketola and Roberts (2003). The PAP about to be considered originally appeared as Appendix B of their book *Correct! Prevent! Improve!*, which is one of the key references supporting this chapter. The Ketola and Roberts (K&R) PAP (see Figure 6.8) also has gained a great deal of recognition and implementation as a definitive and robust PAP.

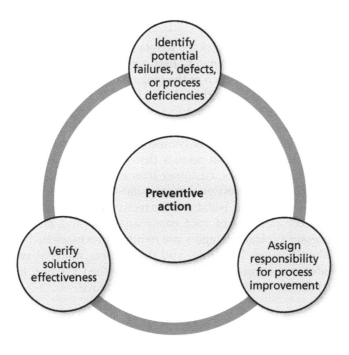

Figure 6.7   A graphical representation of the preventive action process (PAP).

Table 6.8 Tools and techniques used to support the PAP process (non-exhaustive).

PAP element	Applicable tool or technique
Identify potential failures, defects, or process deficiencies	Process operation data Run charts Statistical process control charts Process performance data Rework data Warranty and claims data RCA Process flowcharts Critical incident techniques Matrix diagrams Failure mode and effects analysis Fault tree analysis
Assign responsibility for process improvement	
Verify solution effectiveness	Process operation data Run charts Statistical process control charts Process performance data Rework data Warranty and claims data RCA Process flowcharts Critical incident techniques Matrix diagrams

Parallel to our discussion of the Ketola and Roberts CAP, a review of the K&R PAP reveals a few more elements than were introduced in the PAP discussed previously in the chapter. Each of the major elements in the PAP discussed above is conceptually embedded within the K&R PAP. Accordingly, the K&R PAP also extends the usefulness and robustness of the PAP previously discussed.

The value of comparing and contrasting both PAPs is that the reader will gain an appreciation of what is entailed in a basic versus a more robust PAP. Additionally, the comparison reveals that many tools and techniques, sources of data, and, in many cases, customer interactions come into play when using a PAP in the context of professional responsibilities associated with the CQT. PAPs, however, are not used in isolation. Corrective and preventive action processes are used as components of root cause analysis, and effective application of CAPA processes typically triggers use of other processes such as nonconforming material identification, handling, and disposition, material review boards, and so on. Readers are encouraged again to review the CQT BoK for identification of material on the topics mentioned immediately above.

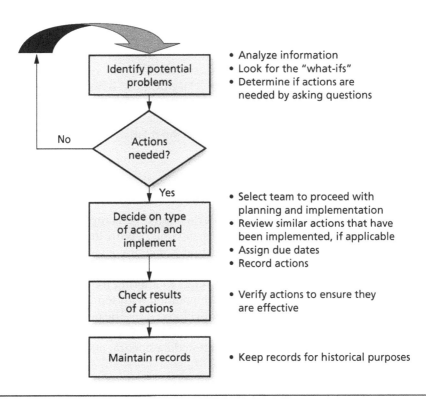

Figure 6.8 Ketola and Roberts preventive action process (K&R PAP).

NONCONFORMING MATERIAL IDENTIFICATION

Note: The information on nonconforming material identification does not appear in the 2012 CQT BoK; however, this information is particularly important for the CQT in professional practice.

In the book *Glossary and Tables for Statistical Quality Control*, written by representatives of the American Society for Quality Statistics Division (1996), a *nonconforming unit* is defined as follows: "A unit of product or service containing at least one nonconformity." And in the same book, a *nonconformity* is defined as "A departure of a quality characteristic from its intended level or state that occurs with a severity sufficient to cause an associated product or service to not meet a specification requirement."

A component of any comprehensive quality system is a subsystem designed to effectively deal with nonconforming materials as soon as they are identified—optimally as early in the production process as possible. For purposes of the CQT BoK, nonconforming material identification consists of the following:

- Determining conformance status

- Identifying nonconforming materials

- Segregating nonconforming materials

Determining Conformance Status

Conformance status is determined in accordance with compliance or noncompliance with a quality standard or specification as compared to some sort of classification scheme. While the classification schemes may be different from company to company, the important consideration is that gradations or "categories" of seriousness are created as a means for the material review board and any other stakeholders to understand the relative importance and magnitude of nonconformities.

Identifying Nonconforming Materials

Identification of nonconforming materials must be completed in a manner that is readily apparent to anyone coming in contact with the item(s) or material in question. To accomplish the identification, some provision must be made so as to distinguish the physical appearance of the item or material as "nonconforming." The physical nature of the provision refers to altering the appearance of the item or its associated production data documentation with some sort of special coloring (that is, by paint, marker, or a different-colored tag). The nonphysical nature of the provision refers to collecting and documenting data related to the nonconformity and attaching that data to the production data documentation accompanying the item(s) or material.

Segregating Nonconforming Materials

Once identified as nonconforming, any such material must be prevented from entering or continuing in the supply chain. Segregation, then, is an important concern for both suppliers and customers as a means of ensuring product or process quality.

Segregation of nonconforming materials is accomplished by establishing a secure area (that is, a lockable area with strictly limited access). Once inside this secure area, nonconforming materials are not available to access, inspection, further processing, or shipment by anyone other than authorized material review board members or their designees.

NONCONFORMING MATERIAL REVIEW PROCESS

Note: The information on nonconforming material review processes does not appear in the 2012 CQT BoK; however, this information is particularly important for the CQT in professional practice.

Virtually all quality standards require the creation and implementation of a clearly defined and communicated process to follow when "nonconforming" material is identified or detected. The importance of a nonconforming material review process cannot be overstated; it serves as the mechanism by which to prevent nonconforming material from entering or proceeding in the supply chain. Such a process is most commonly referred to as a *nonconforming material review process.*

While specific components or steps in a nonconforming material review process will vary from company to company, and from quality standard to quality standard, at the most basic level such a process would consist of the following:

- A cross-functional team called a *material review board* (MRB) composed of representatives from the quality and engineering functions and, in some cases, customers

- Appropriate quality standards and metrics

- A sampling and inspection protocol/plan

- Policies and procedures addressing when and how to trigger the MRB

- Overall process documentation

As would be expected, the successful operation of a nonconforming material review process is the responsibility of the MRB. Ultimately, the MRB must determine what to do with nonconforming material, and what corrective action to take to prevent further nonconforming material. The "what to do with nonconforming material" portion of the MRB responsibility is commonly referred to as *disposition*. Disposition may take many forms as agreed to by the supplier and the customer; it is described by Berger (2002) as follows:

- Shipped "as is"

- Sort/100% inspection

- Downgrade

- Repair

- Rework

- Scrap

Appendix A

ASQ Certified Quality Technician (CQT) Body of Knowledge

The topics in this Body of Knowledge include additional detail in the form of subtext explanations and the cognitive level at which the questions will be written. This information will provide useful guidance for both the Exam Development Committee and the candidate preparing to take the exam. The subtext is not intended to limit the subject matter or be all-inclusive of what might be covered in an exam. It is meant to clarify the type of content to be included in the exam. The descriptor in parentheses at the end of each entry refers to the maximum cognitive level at which the topic will be tested. A complete description of cognitive levels is provided at the end of this document.

I. **Quality Concepts and Tools (18 Questions)**

A. **Quality Concepts**

1. Customers and suppliers
Define internal and external customers, identify their expectations, and determine their satisfaction levels. Define internal and external suppliers and key elements of relations with them. (Understand)

2. Quality principles for products and processes
Explain basic quality principles related to products (such as features, fitness-for-use, and freedom from defects) and processes (such as monitoring, measuring, and continuous improvement) (Understand)

3. Quality standards, requirements, and specifications
Define and distinguish between national or international standards, customer requirements, and product or process specifications. (Understand)

4. Cost of quality (COQ)
Describe and distinguish between the four classic cost of quality categories (prevention, appraisal, internal failure, external failure) and classify activities appropriately. (Apply)

B. **Quality Tools**

The seven basic quality tools
Select, construct, and interpret **1.** cause and effect diagrams, **2.** flowcharts (process maps), **3.** check sheets, **4.** Pareto charts, **5.** scatter diagrams, **6.** control charts, and **7.** histograms. (Evaluate)

8. Problem solving techniques
Define, describe, and apply problem solving techniques such as 5 Whys and 8D. (Apply)

9. Six sigma
Identify key six sigma concepts and tools such as quality function deployment (QFD), design of experiments (DOE), and design, measure, analyze, improve, control (DMAIC). (Remember)

10. Lean
Identify key lean concepts and tools such as 5S, value-stream mapping, flow, and pull system. (Remember)

11. Continuous improvement techniques
Define and use various continuous improvement techniques including the Plan Do Check Act (PDCA) cycle, brainstorming, and benchmarking. (Apply)

C. **ASQ Code of Ethics for Professional Conduct**
Determine and apply appropriate behaviors and action that comply with this ethical code. (Evaluate)

II. **Statistical Techniques (17 Questions)**

A. **General Concepts**

1. Terminology
Identify and differentiate between statistical terms such as population, sample, parameter, statistic, and statistical process control (SPC). (Understand)

2. Frequency distributions
Define and compare normal, Poisson, and binomial frequency distributions. (Understand)

B. **Calculations**

1. Measures of central tendency
Define, compute, and interpret mean, median, and mode. (Analyze)

2. Measures of dispersion
Define, compute, and interpret standard deviation, range, and variance. (Analyze)

3. Confidence levels
Explain confidence levels in various situations. (Understand)

4. Confidence limits
   Explain confidence limits in various situations. (Understand)

5. Probability
   Explain probability using the basic concepts of combinations, permutations, and area under the normal curve. (Understand)

C. Control Charts

1. Control limits vs. specification limits
   Identify and distinguish the different uses of control limits and specification limits. (Analyze)

2. Variables charts
   Identify, select, construct, and interpret variables charts such as and . (Analyze)

3. Attributes charts
   Identify, select, construct, and interpret attributes charts such as p, np, c, and u. (Analyze)

4. Process capability measures
   Define the prerequisites for capability, and calculate and interpret capability indices (e.g., Cp, Cpk, Pp, Ppk) and capability ratio (CR) in various situations. (Analyze)

5. Common and special cause variation
   Interpret various control chart patterns (e.g., runs, hugging, trends) and use rules for determining statistical control to distinguish between common cause and special cause variation. (Analyze)

6. Data plotting
   Identify the advantages and limitations of using this method to analyze data visually. (Understand)

III. Metrology and Calibration (18 Questions)

A. Types of Measurement and Test Equipment (M&TE)
Describe, select, and use the following types of M&TE, and evaluate their measurement results to determine conformance to specifications. (Evaluate)

1. Hand tools (e.g., calipers, micrometers, linear scales, analog, digital, vernier scales)

2. Gauges (e.g., pins, thread, custom gauges, gauge blocks)

3. Optical tools (e.g., comparators, profiles, microscopes)

4. Coordinate measuring machines (CMM) (e.g., touch probes, vision, laser)

5. Electronic measuring equipment (e.g., digital displays, output)

6. Weights, balances, and scales

7. Hardness testing equipment (e.g., Brinell, Rockwell)

8. Surface plate methods and equipment

9. Surface analyzers (e.g., profilometers, roughness reference standards)

10. Force measurement tools (e.g., torque wrenches, tensometers)

11. Angle measurement tools (e.g., protractors, sine bars, angle blocks)

12. Color measurement tools (e.g., spectrophotometer, color guides, light boxes)

13. Automated in-line inspection methods (e.g., vision systems, laser inspection systems, pyrometers)

B. Control and Maintenance of M&TE

1. M&TE identification, control, and maintenance
Describe various methodologies for identifying and controlling M&TE to meet traceability requirements, and apply appropriate techniques for maintaining such equipment to obtain optimum performance. (Apply)

2. Customer-supplied M&TE
Describe and apply requirements for validation and control of customer-supplied equipment. (Apply)

C. Calibration of M&TE

1. Calibration intervals
Apply calibration schedules on the basis of M&TE usage history and risk. (Apply)

2. Calibration results
Interpret calibration results and the potential impact of using out-of-calibration tools or failing to calibrate equipment on a regular basis. (Analyze)

3. Calibration error
Identify the causes of calibration error and its effect on processes and products. (Understand)

4. Hierarchy of standards
Explain the levels of standards (e.g., reference, primary, transfer) and their relationship to one another. (Apply)

IV. Inspection and Test (23 Questions)

A. Blueprint Reading and Interpretation

1. Blueprint symbols and components
Interpret drawings and apply requirements in various test and inspection activities. (Analyze)

2. Geometric dimensioning and tolerancing (GD&T)
   Define and apply GD&T covered in the ASME Y14.5 standard.
   (Analyze)

3. Classification of product defect characteristics
   Define and distinguish between defect characteristics (e.g., critical,
   major, minor). (Analyze)

B. Inspection Concepts

1. Types of measurements
   Define and select between direct, differential, and transfer
   measurements. (Understand)

2. Gauge selection
   Determine which measurement instrument to use considering
   factors such as resolution, accuracy, tolerance, environment, and
   product features. (Evaluate)

3. Measurement systems analysis (MSA)
   Define and distinguish between measurement terms such as
   correlation, bias, linearity, precision-to-tolerance, and percent
   agreement. Describe how gauge repeatability and reproducibility
   (R&R) studies are performed and how they are applied in support of
   MSA. (Analyze)

4. Rounding rules
   Use truncation and rounding rules on both positive and negative
   numbers. (Apply)

5. Conversion of measurements
   Convert between metric and English units. (Apply)

6. Inspection points
   Define and distinguish between inspection point functions (e.g.,
   receiving, in-process, final, source, first-article), and determine what
   type of inspection is appropriate at different stages of production,
   from raw materials through finished product. (Analyze)

7. Inspection error
   Explain various types of inspection error, including operator error
   (e.g., parallax, fatigue), environment (e.g., vibration, humidity,
   temperature), and equipment (e.g., limitations, capability, setup).
   (Understand)

8. Product traceability
   Explain the requirements for documenting and preserving the
   identity of a product and its origins. (Apply)

9. Certificates of compliance (COC) and analysis (COA)
   Define and compare these two types of certificates. (Understand)

C. Inspection Techniques and Processes

1. Nondestructive testing (NDT) techniques
Explain various NDT techniques (e.g., X-ray, eddy current, ultrasonic, liquid penetrant, magnetic particle). (Understand)

2. Destructive testing techniques
Explain various destructive tests (e.g., tensile, fatigue, flammability). (Understand)

3. Other testing techniques
Describe characteristics of testing techniques used for electrical measurement (e.g., DC, AC, resistance, capacitance, continuity), chemical analysis (e.g., pH, conductivity, chromatography), physical/mechanical measurement (e.g., hardness, pressure tests, vacuum, flow), and other techniques such as gravimetric testing, cleanliness testing, contamination testing, and environmental testing (e.g., bioburden, surface, air, water testing). (Remember)

D. Sampling

1. Sampling characteristics
Identify and define sampling characteristics such as operating characteristic (OC) curve, lot size, sample size, acceptance number, and switching rules. (Apply)

2. Sampling types
Define and distinguish between sampling types such as fixed sampling, single, double, skip lot, 100% inspection, attributes, and variables sampling. (Apply)

3. Selecting samples from lots
Determine sample size (e.g., AQL), selection method and accept/reject criteria used in various situations. (Apply)

E. Nonconforming Material

1. Identifying and segregating
Determine whether products or material meet conformance requirements, and use various methods to label and segregate nonconforming materials. (Evaluate)

2. Material review process
Explain various elements of this process such as the function of the material review board (MRB), the steps in determining fitness-for-use, and product disposition. (Understand)

V. Quality Audits (12 Questions)

A. Audit Types and Terminology
Define basic audit types: **1.** internal, **2.** external, **3.** systems, **4.** product, **5.** process, and **6.** distinguish between first-, second-, and third-party audits. (Understand)

B. Audit Components

Describe and apply various elements of the audit process: 1. audit purpose and scope, 2. audit reference standard, 3. audit plan (preparation), 4. audit performance, 5. opening and closing meetings, 6. final report and verification of corrective action. (Apply)

C. Audit Tools and Techniques

Define and apply various auditing tools: 1. checklists and working papers, 2. data gathering and objective evidence, 3. forward- and backward-tracing, 4. audit sampling plans and procedural guidelines. (Apply)

D. Audit Communication Tools

Identify and use appropriate interviewing techniques and listening skills in various audit situations, and develop and use graphs, charts, diagrams, and other aids in support of written and oral presentations. (Apply)

VI. Risk Management (12 Questions)

A. Risk Assessment and Mitigation

Describe methods of risk assessment and mitigation such as trend analysis (SPC), failure mode and effects analysis (FMEA), root cause analysis (RCA), product and process monitoring reports, and control plans. (Understand)

B. Corrective Action

Explain and apply elements of the corrective action process: identify the problem, contain the problem (interim action), assign responsibility (personnel) to determine the causes of the problem and propose solutions to eliminate it or prevent its recurrence (permanent action), verify that the solutions are implemented, and confirm their effectiveness (validation). (Apply)

C. Preventive Action

Explain and apply elements of a preventive action process: use various data analysis techniques to identify potential failures, defects, or process deficiencies; assign responsibility for improving the process (e.g., develop error- or mistake-proofing devices or methods, initiate procedural changes), and verify the effectiveness of the preventive action. (Apply)

LEVELS OF COGNITION
BASED ON BLOOM'S TAXONOMY—REVISED (2001)

In addition to *content* specifics, the subtext for each topic in this BOK also indicates the intended *complexity level* of the test questions for that topic. These levels are based on "Levels of Cognition" (from Bloom's Taxonomy—Revised, 2001) and are presented below in rank order, from least complex to most complex.

Remember

Recall or recognize terms, definitions, facts, ideas, materials, patterns, sequences, methods, principles, etc.

Understand

Read and understand descriptions, communications, reports, tables, diagrams, directions, regulations, etc.

Apply

Know when and how to use ideas, procedures, methods, formulas, principles, theories, etc.

Analyze

Break down information into its constituent parts and recognize their relationship to one another and how they are organized; identify sublevel factors or salient data from a complex scenario.

Evaluate

Make judgments about the value of proposed ideas, solutions, etc., by comparing the proposal to specific criteria or standards.

Create

Put parts or elements together in such a way as to reveal a pattern or structure not clearly there before; identify which data or information from a complex set is appropriate to examine further or from which supported conclusions can be drawn.

Appendix B
Areas under Standard Normal Curve

z	Area	z	Area	z	Area	z	Area	z	Area	z	Area	z	Area
0.00	0.5000	0.50	0.3085	1.00	0.1587	1.50	0.0668	2.00	0.0228	2.50	0.0062	3.00	1.35E-03
0.01	0.4960	0.51	0.3050	1.01	0.1562	1.51	0.0655	2.01	0.0222	2.51	0.0060	3.01	1.31E-03
0.02	0.4920	0.52	0.3015	1.02	0.1539	1.52	0.0643	2.02	0.0217	2.52	0.0059	3.02	1.26E-03
0.03	0.4880	0.53	0.2981	1.03	0.1515	1.53	0.0630	2.03	0.0212	2.53	0.0057	3.03	1.22E-03
0.04	0.4840	0.54	0.2946	1.04	0.1492	1.54	0.0618	2.04	0.0207	2.54	0.0055	3.04	1.18E-03
0.05	0.4801	0.55	0.2912	1.05	0.1469	1.55	0.0606	2.05	0.0202	2.55	0.0054	3.05	1.14E-03
0.06	0.4761	0.56	0.2877	1.06	0.1446	1.56	0.0594	2.06	0.0197	2.56	0.0052	3.06	1.11E-03
0.07	0.4721	0.57	0.2843	1.07	0.1423	1.57	0.0582	2.07	0.0192	2.57	0.0051	3.07	1.07E-03
0.08	0.4681	0.58	0.2810	1.08	0.1401	1.58	0.0571	2.08	0.0188	2.58	0.0049	3.08	1.04E-03
0.09	0.4641	0.59	0.2776	1.09	0.1379	1.59	0.0559	2.09	0.0183	2.59	0.0048	3.09	1.00E-03
0.10	0.4602	0.60	0.2743	1.10	0.1357	1.60	0.0548	2.10	0.0179	2.60	0.0047	3.10	9.68E-04
0.11	0.4562	0.61	0.2709	1.11	0.1335	1.61	0.0537	2.11	0.0174	2.61	0.0045	3.11	9.36E-04
0.12	0.4522	0.62	0.2676	1.12	0.1314	1.62	0.0526	2.12	0.0170	2.62	0.0044	3.12	9.04E-04
0.13	0.4483	0.63	0.2643	1.13	0.1292	1.63	0.0516	2.13	0.0166	2.63	0.0043	3.13	8.74E-04
0.14	0.4443	0.64	0.2611	1.14	0.1271	1.64	0.0505	2.14	0.0162	2.64	0.0041	3.14	8.45E-04
0.15	0.4404	0.65	0.2578	1.15	0.1251	1.65	0.0495	2.15	0.0158	2.65	0.0040	3.15	8.16E-04
0.16	0.4364	0.66	0.2546	1.16	0.1230	1.66	0.0485	2.16	0.0154	2.66	0.0039	3.16	7.89E-04
0.17	0.4325	0.67	0.2514	1.17	0.1210	1.67	0.0475	2.17	0.0150	2.67	0.0038	3.17	7.62E-04
0.18	0.4286	0.68	0.2483	1.18	0.1190	1.68	0.0465	2.18	0.0146	2.68	0.0037	3.18	7.36E-04
0.19	0.4247	0.69	0.2451	1.19	0.1170	1.69	0.0455	2.19	0.0143	2.69	0.0036	3.19	7.11E-04
0.20	0.4207	0.70	0.2420	1.20	0.1151	1.70	0.0446	2.20	0.0139	2.70	0.0035	3.20	6.87E-04
0.21	0.4168	0.71	0.2389	1.21	0.1131	1.71	0.0436	2.21	0.0136	2.71	0.0034	3.21	6.64E-04
0.22	0.4129	0.72	0.2358	1.22	0.1112	1.72	0.0427	2.22	0.0132	2.72	0.0033	3.22	6.41E-04
0.23	0.4090	0.73	0.2327	1.23	0.1093	1.73	0.0418	2.23	0.0129	2.73	0.0032	3.23	6.19E-04
0.24	0.4052	0.74	0.2296	1.24	0.1075	1.74	0.0409	2.24	0.0125	2.74	0.0031	3.24	5.98E-04
0.25	0.4013	0.75	0.2266	1.25	0.1056	1.75	0.0401	2.25	0.0122	2.75	0.0030	3.25	5.77E-04
0.26	0.3974	0.76	0.2236	1.26	0.1038	1.76	0.0392	2.26	0.0119	2.76	0.0029	3.26	5.57E-04
0.27	0.3936	0.77	0.2206	1.27	0.1020	1.77	0.0384	2.27	0.0116	2.77	0.0028	3.27	5.38E-04

Continued

Continued

z	Area	z	Area	z	Area	z	Area	z	Area	z	Area	z	Area
0.28	0.3897	0.78	0.2177	1.28	0.1003	1.78	0.0375	2.28	0.0113	2.78	0.0027	3.28	5.19E-04
0.29	0.3859	0.79	0.2148	1.29	0.0985	1.79	0.0367	2.29	0.0110	2.79	0.0026	3.29	5.01E-04
0.30	0.3821	0.80	0.2119	1.30	0.0968	1.80	0.0359	2.30	0.0107	2.80	0.0026	3.30	4.83E-04
0.31	0.3783	0.81	0.2090	1.31	0.0951	1.81	0.0351	2.31	0.0104	2.81	0.0025	3.31	4.67E-04
0.32	0.3745	0.82	0.2061	1.32	0.0934	1.82	0.0344	2.32	0.0102	2.82	0.0024	3.32	4.50E-04
0.33	0.3707	0.83	0.2033	1.33	0.0918	1.83	0.0336	2.33	0.0099	2.83	0.0023	3.33	4.34E-04
0.34	0.3669	0.84	0.2005	1.34	0.0901	1.84	0.0329	2.34	0.0096	2.84	0.0023	3.34	4.19E-04
0.35	0.3632	0.85	0.1977	1.35	0.0885	1.85	0.0322	2.35	0.0094	2.85	0.0022	3.35	4.04E-04
0.36	0.3594	0.86	0.1949	1.36	0.0869	1.86	0.0314	2.36	0.0091	2.86	0.0021	3.36	3.90E-04
0.37	0.3557	0.87	0.1922	1.37	0.0853	1.87	0.0307	2.37	0.0089	2.87	0.0021	3.37	3.76E-04
0.38	0.3520	0.88	0.1894	1.38	0.0838	1.88	0.0301	2.38	0.0087	2.88	0.0020	3.38	3.62E-04
0.39	0.3483	0.89	0.1867	1.39	0.0823	1.89	0.0294	2.39	0.0084	2.89	0.0019	3.39	3.50E-04
0.40	0.3446	0.90	0.1841	1.40	0.0808	1.90	0.0287	2.40	0.0082	2.90	0.0019	3.40	3.37E-04
0.41	0.3409	0.91	0.1814	1.41	0.0793	1.91	0.0281	2.41	0.0080	2.91	0.0018	3.41	3.25E-04
0.42	0.3372	0.92	0.1788	1.42	0.0778	1.92	0.0274	2.42	0.0078	2.92	0.0018	3.42	3.13E-04
0.43	0.3336	0.93	0.1762	1.43	0.0764	1.93	0.0268	2.43	0.0075	2.93	0.0017	3.43	3.02E-04
0.44	0.3300	0.94	0.1736	1.44	0.0749	1.94	0.0262	2.44	0.0073	2.94	0.0016	3.44	2.91E-04
0.45	0.3264	0.95	0.1711	1.45	0.0735	1.95	0.0256	2.45	0.0071	2.95	0.0016	3.45	2.80E-04
0.46	0.3228	0.96	0.1685	1.46	0.0721	1.96	0.0250	2.46	0.0069	2.96	0.0015	3.46	2.70E-04
0.47	0.3192	0.97	0.1660	1.47	0.0708	1.97	0.0244	2.47	0.0068	2.97	0.0015	3.47	2.60E-04
0.48	0.3156	0.98	0.1635	1.48	0.0694	1.98	0.0239	2.48	0.0066	2.98	0.0014	3.48	2.51E-04
0.49	0.3121	0.99	0.1611	1.49	0.0681	1.99	0.0233	2.49	0.0064	2.99	0.0014	3.49	2.42E-04

Appendix C
Control Limit Formulas

VARIABLES CHARTS

$\bar{X}$ and R chart: Averages chart: $\bar{\bar{x}} \pm A_2\bar{R}$ Range chart: LCL $= D_3\bar{R}$ UCL $= D_4\bar{R}$

$\bar{X}$ and S chart: Averages chart: $\bar{\bar{x}} \pm A_3\bar{S}$ Std. dev. chart: LCL $= B_3\bar{S}$ UCL $= B_4\bar{S}$

Individuals and moving range chart:

Individuals chart: $\bar{x} \pm E_2\bar{R}$

Moving range: UCL $= D_4\bar{R}$ LCL $= D_3\bar{R}$

Median chart: $\bar{\bar{x}} \pm \tilde{A}_2\bar{R}$

ATTRIBUTE CHARTS

p-chart: $\bar{p} \pm 3\sqrt{\dfrac{\bar{p}(1-\bar{p})}{\bar{n}}}$

np-chart: $n\bar{p} \pm 3\sqrt{n\bar{p}(1-\bar{p})}$

c-chart: $\bar{c} \pm 3\sqrt{\bar{c}}$

u-chart: $\bar{u} \pm 3\sqrt{\dfrac{\bar{u}}{n}}$

Appendix D

Constants for Control Charts

Subgroup size n	A_2	d_2	D_3	D_4	A_3	c_4	B_3	B_4	E_2	$\tilde{A}_2$
2	1.880	1.128	–	3.267	2.659	0.798	–	3.267	2.660	1.880
3	1.023	1.693	–	2.574	1.954	0.886	–	2.568	1.772	1.187
4	0.729	2.059	–	2.282	1.628	0.921	–	2.266	1.457	0.796
5	0.577	2.326	–	2.114	1.427	0.940	–	2.089	1.290	0.691
6	0.483	2.534	–	2.004	1.287	0.952	0.030	1.970	1.184	0.548
7	0.419	2.704	0.076	1.924	1.182	0.959	0.118	1.882	1.109	0.508
8	0.373	2.847	0.136	1.864	1.099	0.965	0.185	1.815	1.054	0.433
9	0.337	2.970	0.184	1.816	1.032	0.969	0.239	1.761	1.010	0.412
10	0.308	3.078	0.223	1.777	0.975	0.973	0.284	1.716	0.975	0.362

Appendix E

Standard Normal Distribution for Select Values of Z

Z	Area to left of Z	Area to right of Z	Parts per million right of Z
0	0.5000000	0.5000000	500000.0002
0.1	0.5398279	0.4601721	460172.1045
0.2	0.5792597	0.4207403	420740.3128
0.3	0.6179114	0.3820886	382088.6425
0.4	0.6554217	0.3445783	344578.3034
0.5	0.6914625	0.3085375	308537.5326
0.6	0.7257469	0.2742531	274253.0649
0.7	0.7580364	0.2419636	241963.5785
0.8	0.7881447	0.2118553	211855.3339
0.9	0.8159399	0.1840601	184060.0917
1	0.8413447	0.1586553	158655.2598
1.1	0.8643339	0.1356661	135666.1015
1.2	0.8849303	0.1150697	115069.7317
1.3	0.9031995	0.0968005	96800.5495
1.4	0.9192433	0.0807567	80756.71126
1.5	0.9331928	0.0668072	66807.22879
1.6	0.9452007	0.0547993	54799.28945
1.7	0.9554346	0.0445654	44565.43178
1.8	0.9640697	0.0359303	35930.26551
1.9	0.9712835	0.0287165	28716.49286
2	0.9772499	0.0227501	22750.06204
2.1	0.9821356	0.0178644	17864.35742
2.2	0.9860966	0.0139034	13903.39891
2.3	0.9892759	0.0107241	10724.08106
2.4	0.9918025	8.1975289×10^{-3}	8197.528869
2.5	0.9937903	6.2096799×10^{-3}	6209.679859
2.6	0.9953388	4.6612218×10^{-3}	4661.221783

Continued

Continued

Z	Area to left of Z	Area to right of Z	Parts per million right of Z
2.7	0.9965330	3.4670231E-03	3467.023053
2.8	0.9974448	2.5551906E-03	2555.190642
2.9	0.9981341	1.8658801E-03	1865.88014
3	0.9986500	1.3499672E-03	1349.967223
3.1	0.9990323	9.6767124E-04	967.6712356
3.2	0.9993128	6.8720208E-04	687.2020808
3.3	0.9995165	4.8348254E-04	483.4825366
3.4	0.9996630	3.3698082E-04	336.9808229
3.5	0.9997673	2.3267337E-04	232.6733737
3.6	0.9998409	1.5914571E-04	159.1457138
3.7	0.9998922	1.0783015E-04	107.8301454
3.8	0.9999276	7.2372434E-05	72.37243427
3.9	0.9999519	4.8115519E-05	48.11551887
4	0.9999683	3.1686035E-05	31.68603461
4.1	0.9999793	2.0668716E-05	20.66871577
4.2	0.9999866	1.3354097E-05	13.35409733
4.3	0.9999915	8.5460212E-06	8.546021191
4.4	0.9999946	5.4169531E-06	5.416953054
4.5	0.9999966	3.4008031E-06	3.400803062
4.6	0.9999979	2.1146434E-06	2.114643376
4.7	0.9999987	1.3023157E-06	1.302315654
4.8	0.9999992	7.9435267E-07	0.794352669
4.9	0.9999995	4.7986955E-07	0.479869547
5	0.9999997	2.8710500E-07	0.287105
5.1	0.9999998	1.7012231E-07	0.170122314
5.2	0.9999999	9.9834400E-08	0.0998344
5.3	0.9999999	5.8022066E-08	0.058022066
5.4	1.0000000	3.3396123E-08	0.033396123
5.5	1.0000000	1.9036399E-08	0.019036399
5.6	1.0000000	1.0746217E-08	0.010746217
5.7	1.0000000	6.0076532E-09	0.006007653
5.8	1.0000000	3.3260517E-09	0.003326052
5.9	1.0000000	1.8235793E-09	0.001823579
6	1.0000000	9.9012187E-10	0.000990122

Glossary

acceptable quality level (AQL)—The maximum percentage or proportion of variant units in a lot or batch that, for purposes of acceptance sampling, can be considered satisfactory as a process average.

acceptance sampling—Sampling inspection in which decisions are made to accept or not accept product or service; also, the methodology that deals with procedures by which decisions to accept or not accept are based on the results of the inspection of samples.

accuracy—The closeness of alignment between an observed value and an accepted reference value.

action plan—The detailed plan to implement the actions needed to achieve strategic goals and objectives.

activity—An action of some type that requires a time duration for accomplishment.

activity network diagram (AND) (arrow diagram)—A management and planning tool used to develop the best possible schedule and appropriate controls to accomplish the schedule; the critical path method (CPM) and the program evaluation review technique (PERT) make use of arrow diagrams.

advanced product quality planning and control plan (APQP)—APQP is a comprehensive quality planning and control system specifying protocols for product and process design and development, validation, assessment, and corrective action.

advanced quality planning (AQP)—A comprehensive system of applying quality disciplines during a product or process development effort; sometimes also called advanced product quality planning (APQP).

analytical study—A study that uses theory and a model in order to predict future outcomes or to lead to a change in outcomes.

assignable cause—A factor that contributes to variation and that is feasible to detect and identify.

assumptions—Conditions that must be true in order for a statistical procedure to be valid.

attributes data—Data that are categorized for analysis or evaluation. (Attribute data may involve measurements as long as the measurements are used only to place a given piece of data in a category for further analysis or evaluation. Contrasted to *variables data*.)

auditee—The individual or organization being audited.

availability—A measure of the degree to which an item is in the operable and committable state at the start of the mission, when the mission is called for at an unknown (random) time.

average outgoing quality (AOQ)—The expected quality of outgoing product following the use of an acceptance sampling plan for a given value of incoming product quality.

average outgoing quality limit (AOQL)—For a given acceptance sampling plan, the maximum AOQ over all possible levels of incoming quality.

average sample number—The average number of sample units per lot used for making decisions (acceptance or nonacceptance).

B

benchmark—An organization, part of an organization, or measurement that serves as a reference point or point of comparison.

benefit–cost analysis—A collection of the dollar value of benefits derived from an initiative divided by the associated costs incurred.

block diagram—A diagram that describes the operation, interrelationships, and interdependencies of components in a system. Boxes, or blocks (hence the name), represent the components; connecting lines between the blocks represent interfaces. There are two types of block diagrams—a functional block diagram, which shows a system's subsystems and lower-level products, their interrelationships, and interfaces with other systems, and a reliability block diagram, which is similar to the functional block diagram except that it is modified to emphasize those aspects influencing reliability.

brainstorming—A problem-solving tool that teams use to generate as many ideas as possible related to a particular subject. Team members begin by offering all their ideas; the ideas are not discussed or reviewed until after the brainstorming session.

C

calibration—The comparison of a measurement instrument or system of unverified accuracy to a measurement instrument or system of known accuracy to detect any variation from the true value.

causal factor—A variable that when changed or manipulated in some manner serves to influence a given effect or result.

chance cause variation—Variation due to chance causes. Also known as *common cause* or *random* variation.

change agent—The person who takes the lead in transforming a company into a quality organization by providing guidance during the planning phase, facilitating implementation, and supporting those who pioneer the changes.

characteristic—A property that helps to differentiate between items of a given sample or population.

client—A person or organization requesting the audit.

conflict resolution—A process for resolving disagreements in a manner acceptable to all parties.

consensus—Finding a proposal acceptable enough that all team members can support the decision and no member opposes it.

consumer's risk (β)—For a sampling plan, refers to the probability of acceptance of a lot, the quality of which has a designated numerical value representing a level that is seldom desirable. Usually, the value will be the lot tolerance percent defective (LTPD). Also called *beta risk* or *type II error.*

continuous variable—A variable whose possible values form an interval set of numbers such that between each two values in the set another member of the set occurs.

control plan—A document that may include the characteristics for quality of a product or service, measurements, and methods of control.

coordinate measuring machine (CMM)—Coordinate measuring machines (CMM) can most easily be defined as physical representations of a three-dimensional rectilinear coordinate system. Coordinate measuring machines now represent a significant fraction of the measuring equipment used for defining the geometry of different-shaped workpieces.

corrective action—Action taken to eliminate the root cause(s) and symptom(s) of an existing deviation or nonconformity to prevent recurrence.

Crawford slip method—A method of gathering and presenting anonymous data from a group.

critical defect—A critical defect is a defect that judgment and experience indicate is likely to result in hazardous or unsafe conditions for the individuals using, maintaining, or depending on the product, or a defect that judgment and experience indicate is likely to prevent performance of the unit.

critical path—The sequence of tasks that takes the longest time and determines a project's completion date.

critical path method (CPM)—An activity-oriented project management technique that uses arrow-diagramming techniques to demonstrate both the time and cost required to complete a project. It provides one time estimate—normal time.

criticality—An indication of the consequences that are expected to result from a failure.

cross-functional team—A group consisting of members from more than one department that is organized to accomplish a project.

cycle time—The time that it takes to complete a process from beginning to end.

D

defect—A departure of a quality characteristic from its intended level or state that occurs with a severity sufficient to cause an associated product or service not to satisfy intended normal or reasonably foreseeable usage requirements.

dependent events—Two events A and B are dependent if the probability of one event occurring is higher given the occurrence of the other event.

deployment—To spread around. Used in strategic planning to describe the process of cascading plans throughout the organization.

descriptive statistics—Techniques for displaying and summarizing data.

design of experiments (DOE), designed experiment—The arrangement in which an experimental program is to be conducted, and the selection of the versions (levels) of one or more factors or factor combinations to be included in the experiment.

design review—Documented, comprehensive, and systematic examination of a design to evaluate its capability to fulfill the requirements for quality.

detection—The likelihood of detecting a failure once it has occurred. Detection is evaluated based on a 10-point scale. In the lowest end of the scale (1) it is assumed a design control will detect a failure with certainty. In the highest end of the scale (10) it is assumed a design control will not detect a failure if a failure occurs.

discrete variable—A variable whose possible values form a finite or at most countably infinite set.

DMAIC—An acronym denoting a sequence used in the methodology associated with Six Sigma—define, measure, analyze, improve, control.

E

empowerment—A condition whereby employees have the authority to make decisions and take action in their work areas, within stated bounds, without prior approval.

entity—Item that can be individually described and considered.

error—1. Error in measurement is the difference between the indicated value and the true value of a measured quantity. 2. A fault resulting from defective judgment, deficient knowledge, or carelessness. It is not to be confused with measurement error, which is the difference between a computed or measured value and the true or theoretical value.

expected value—The mean of a variable.

external failure costs—Costs associated with defects found during or after delivery of the product or service.

F

facilitator—An individual who is responsible for creating favorable conditions that will enable a team to reach its purpose or achieve its goals by bringing together the necessary tools, information, and resources to get the job done.

factor—An assignable cause that may affect the responses (test results) and of which different versions (levels) are included in the experiment.

failure—The termination, due to one or more defects, of the ability of an item, product, or service to perform its required function when called on to do so. A failure may be partial, complete, or intermittent.

failure mode and effects analysis (FMEA)—A procedure in which each potential failure mode in every sub-item of an item is analyzed to determine its effect on other sub-items and on the required function of the item.

filters—Relative to human-to-human communication, those perceptions (based on culture, language, demographics, experience, and so on) that affect how a message is transmitted by the sender and how a message is interpreted by the receiver.

flowchart—A graphical representation of the steps in a process. Flowcharts are drawn to better understand processes. The flowchart is one of the seven tools of quality.

foolproofing—A process of making a product or process immune to foolish errors on the part of a user or operator. Is synonymous with error-proofing.

G

Gantt chart—A type of bar chart used in process/project planning and control to display planned work and finished work in relation to time. Also called a *milestone chart*.

gatekeeping—The role of an individual (often a facilitator) in a group meeting in helping ensure effective interpersonal interactions (for example, someone's ideas are not ignored due to the team moving on to the next topic too quickly).

gauging—A procedure that determines product conformance with specifications, with the aid of measuring instruments such as calipers, micrometers, templates, and other mechanical, optical, and electronic devices.

goal—A statement of general intent, aim, or desire; it is the point toward which the organization (or individual) directs its efforts; goals are often nonquantitative.

H

hierarchical relationship—A set of relationships that can be ordered or arranged from general to specific.

hold point—A point, defined in an appropriate document, beyond which an activity must not proceed without the approval of a designated organization or authority.

I

independent events—Two events A and B are called independent if the probability that they both occur is the product of the probabilities of their individual occurrence. That is, $P(A\&B) = P(A)P(B)$.

inferential statistics—Techniques for reaching conclusions about a population based on analysis of data from a sample.

information system—Technology-based systems used to support operations, aid day-to-day decision making, and support strategic analysis (other names often used include—*management information system, decision system, information technology (IT), data processing*).

inspection—The process of measuring, examining, testing, gauging, or otherwise comparing the unit with the applicable requirements.

internal failure costs—Costs associated with defects found before the product or service is delivered.

intervention—An action taken by a leader or a facilitator to support the effective functioning of a team or work group.

K

kaizen blitz/event—An intense, short time frame, team approach to employ the concepts and techniques of continuous improvement (for example, to reduce cycle time, increase throughput).

L

leader—An individual recognized by others as the person to lead an effort. One can not be a "leader" without one or more "followers." The term is often used interchangeably with "manager." A "leader" may or may not hold an officially designated management-type position.

leadership—An essential part of a quality improvement effort. Organization leaders must establish a vision, communicate that vision to those in the organization, and provide the tools, knowledge, and motivation necessary to accomplish the vision.

levels—In experimental design, the possible values of a factor.

lot tolerance percent defective (LTPD)—The poorest quality in an individual lot that should be accepted, expressed in percent defective.

M

maintainability—The measure of the ability of an item to be retained or restored to specified condition when maintenance is performed by personnel having specified skill levels, using prescribed procedures and resources, at each prescribed level of maintenance and repair.

major defect—A defect that will interfere with normal or reasonable foreseeable use, but will not cause a risk of damage or injury.

material control—A broad collection of tools for managing the items and lots in a production process.

materials review board—A quality control committee or team, usually employed in manufacturing or other materials-processing installations, that has the responsibility and authority to deal with items or materials that do not conform to fitness-for-use specifications.

mean time between failures (MTBF)—A basic measure of reliability for repairable items—the mean number of life units during which all parts of an item perform within their specified limits, during a particular measurement interval under stated conditions.

mean time to failure (MTTF)—A basic measure of system reliability for nonrepairable items—the total number of life units for an item divided by the total number of failures within that population, during a particular measurement interval under stated conditions.

mean time to repair (MTTR)—A basic measure of maintainability—the sum of corrective maintenance times at any specific level of repair, divided by the total number of failures within an item repaired at that level, during a particular interval under stated conditions.

measurement—1. The process of evaluating a property or characteristic of an object and describing it with a numerical or nominal value. 2. A series of manipulations of physical objects or systems according to a defined protocol that results in a number.

measurement process—Repeated application of a test method using a measuring system.

measuring system—In general, the elements of a measuring system include the instrumentation, calibration standards, environmental influences, human operator limitations, and features of the workpiece or object being measured.

milestone—A point in time when a critical event is to occur; a symbol placed on a milestone chart to locate the point when a critical event is to occur.

milestone chart—Another name for a Gantt chart.

minor defect—A defect that may cause difficulty in assembly or use of the product, but will not prevent the product from being properly used, nor pose any hazard to users.

mistake—Similar to an error, but with the implication that it could be prevented by better training or attention.

multi-voting—A decision-making tool that enables a group to sort through a long list of ideas to identify priorities.

Myers-Briggs Type Indicator—A method and instrument for assessing personality type based on Carl Jung's theory of personality preferences.

N

nominal group technique—A technique similar to brainstorming used by teams to generate and make a selection from ideas on a particular subject. Team members are asked to silently come up with as many ideas as possible, writing them down. Each member is then asked to share one idea, which is recorded. After all the ideas are recorded, they are discussed and prioritized by the group.

nonconformity—A departure of a quality characteristic from its intended level or state that occurs with a severity sufficient to cause an associated product or service not to meet a specification requirement.

O

objective—A quantitative statement of future expectations, and an indication of when the expectations should be achieved; it flows from goal(s) and clarifies what people must accomplish.

objective evidence—Verifiable qualitative or quantitative observations, information, records, or statements of fact pertaining to the quality of an item or service or to the existence and implementation of a quality system element.

observation—The process of determining the presence or absence of attributes or making measurements of a variable. Also, the result of the process of determining the presence or absence of attributes or making a measurement of a variable.

observational study—Analysis of data collected from a process without imposing changes on the process.

occurrence—The likelihood of a failure occurring. Occurrence is evaluated based on a 10-point scale. In the lowest end of the scale (1) it is assumed the probability of a failure is unlikely. In the highest end of the scale (10) it is assumed the probability of a failure is nearly inevitable.

operating characteristic (OC) curve—For a sampling plan, the OC curve indicates the probability of accepting a lot based on the sample size to be taken and the fraction defective in the batch.

organization—Company, corporation, firm, enterprise, or institution, or part thereof, whether incorporated or not, public or private, that has its own functions and administration.

P

parameter—A constant or coefficient that describes some characteristic of a population.

payback period—The number of years it will take the results of a project or capital investment to recover the investment from net cash flows.

poka-yoke—A term that means to mistake-proof a process by building safeguards into the system that avoid or immediately find errors. The term comes from the Japanese terms *poka*, which means "error," and *yokeru*, which means "to avoid."

policy—A high-level overall plan embracing the general goals and acceptable practices of a group.

population—The totality of items or units of material under consideration.

precision—The closeness of agreement between randomly selected individual measurements or test results.

process—An activity or group of activities that takes an input, adds value to it, and provides an output to an internal or external customer; a planned and repetitive sequence of steps by which a defined product or service is delivered.

process improvement team (PIT)—A natural work group or cross-functional team whose responsibility is to achieve needed improvements in existing processes. The lifespan of the team is based on the completion of the team purpose and specific tasks.

process mapping—The flowcharting of a work process in detail, including key measurements.

producer's risk (`)—For a sampling plan, refers to the probability of not accepting a lot, the quality of which has a designated numerical value representing a level that is generally desirable. Usually, the designated value will be the acceptable quality level. Also called *alpha risk* or *type I error*.

product identification—A means of marking parts with labels, etching, engraving, ink, or other means so that different part numbers and other key attributes can be identified.

program evaluation and review technique (PERT)—An event-oriented project management planning and measurement technique that utilizes an arrow diagram or road map to identify all major project events and demonstrates the amount of time (critical path) needed to complete a project. It provides three time estimates: optimistic, most likely, and pessimistic.

project lifecycle—A typical project lifecycle consists of five sequential phases in project management—concept, planning, design, implementation, and evaluation.

project management—The entire process of managing activities and events involved throughout a project's lifecycle.

project plan—All the documents that comprise the details of why the project is to be initiated, what the project is to accomplish, when and where it is to be implemented, who will have responsibility, how implementation will be carried out, how much it will cost, what resources are required, and how the project's progress and results will be measured.

Q

quality assurance—All the planned or systematic actions necessary to provide adequate confidence that a product or service will satisfy given needs.

quality audit—A systematic, independent examination and review to determine whether quality activities and related results comply with planned arrangements and whether these arrangements are implemented effectively and are suitable to achieve the objectives.

quality audit observation—Statement of fact made during a quality audit and substantiated by objective evidence.

quality auditor—Person qualified to perform quality audits.

quality control—The operational techniques and the activities that sustain a quality of product or service that will satisfy given needs; also, the use of such techniques and activities.

quality council—Sometimes referred to as a *quality steering committee.* The group driving the quality improvement effort and usually having oversight responsibility for the implementation and maintenance of the quality management system; operated in parallel with the normal operation of the business.

quality function deployment (QFD)—A structured method in which customer requirements are translated into appropriate technical requirements for each stage of product development and production. The QFD process is often referred to as "listening to the voice of the customer."

quality improvement—Actions taken throughout the organization to increase the effectiveness and efficiency of activities and processes in order to provide added benefits to both the organization and its customers.

quality management—The totality of functions involved in organizing and leading the effort to determine and achieve quality.

quality manual—A document stating the quality policy and describing the quality system of an organization.

quality planning—The activity of establishing quality objectives and quality requirements.

quality policy—Top management's formally stated intentions and direction for the organization pertaining to quality.

quality surveillance—Continual monitoring and verification of the status of an entity and analysis of records to ensure that specified requirements are being fulfilled.

quality system—The organizational structure, procedures, processes, and resources needed to implement quality management.

R

random sampling—The process of selecting units for a sample in such a manner that all combinations of units under consideration have an equal or ascertainable chance of being selected as the sample.

random variable—A variable whose value depends on chance.

readability—The ease of reading the instrument scale when a dimension is being measured.

record—A document or electronic medium that furnishes objective evidence of activities performed or results achieved.

reinforcement—The process of providing positive consequences when an individual is applying the correct knowledge and skills to the job. It has been described as "catching people doing things right and recognizing their behavior." Caution—less than desired behavior can also be reinforced unintentionally.

reliability—The probability that an item can perform its intended function for a specified interval under stated conditions.

repeatability—How close the measurements of an instrument are to each other if such measurements are repeated on a part under the same measuring conditions.

replication—The repetition of the set of all the treatment combinations to be compared in an experiment. Each of the repetitions is called a *replicate*.

reproducibility—A measure of the degree of agreement between two single test results made on the same object in two different, randomly selected measuring locations or laboratories.

resource requirements matrix—A tool to relate the resources required to the project tasks requiring them (used to indicate types of individuals needed, material needed, subcontractors, and so on).

response variable—The variable that shows the observed results of an experimental treatment.

return on investment (ROI)—An umbrella term for a variety of ratios measuring an organization's business performance and calculated by dividing some measure of return by a measure of investment and then multiplying by 100 to provide a percentage. In its most basic form, ROI indicates what remains from all money taken in after all expenses are paid.

robust designs—Products or processes that continue to perform as intended in spite of manufacturing variation and extreme environmental conditions during use.

robustness—The condition of a product or process design that remains relatively stable with a minimum of variation even though factors that influence operations or usage, such as environment and wear, are constantly changing.

S

sample—A group of units, portions of material, or observations taken from a larger collection of units, quantity of material, or observations that serves to provide information that may be used as a basis for making a decision concerning the larger quantity.

sample integrity—Samples are maintained in a unique manner to avoid corruption or confusion with others.

scribe—The member of a team assigned the responsibility for recording minutes of meetings.

self-directed work team (SDWT)—A team that requires little supervision and manages itself and the day-to-day work it does; self-directed teams are responsible for whole work processes and schedules, with each individual performing multiple tasks.

sensitivity—The least perceptible change in dimension detected by the measuring tip and shown by the indicator.

severity—An indicator of the severity of a failure should a failure occur. Severity can be evaluated based on a 10-point scale. In the lowest end of the scale (1) it is assumed a failure will have no noticeable effect. In the highest end of the scale (10) it is assumed a failure will impact safe operation or violate compliance with regulatory mandate.

Six Sigma approach—A quality philosophy; a collection of techniques and tools for use in reducing variation; a program of improvement that focuses on strong leadership tools and an emphasis on bottom-line financial results.

special causes—Causes of variation that arise because of special circumstances. They are not an inherent part of a process. Special causes are also referred to as *assignable causes*.

sponsor—A member of management who oversees, supports, and implements the efforts of a team or initiative.

stable process—A process for which no special causes of variation are present.

stages of team growth—The four development stages through which groups typically progress—forming, storming, norming, and performing. Knowledge of the stages helps team members accept the normal problems that occur on the path from forming a group to becoming a team.

stakeholders—People, departments, and organizations that have an investment or interest in the success or actions taken by the organization.

standard—A statement, specification, or quantity of material against which measured outputs from a process may be judged as acceptable or unacceptable.

statement of work (SOW)—A description of the actual work to be accomplished. It is derived from the work breakdown structure and, when combined with the project specifications, becomes the basis for the contractual agreement on the project (also referred to as *scope of work*).

statistic—A quantity calculated from a sample of observations, most often to form an estimate of some population parameter.

statistical control—A process is considered to be in a state of statistical control if variations between the observed sampling results from it can be attributed to a constant system of chance causes.

statistical process control (SPC)—The application of statistical techniques to control a process.

steering committee—A group responsible for overall selection of continuous improvement projects.

strategic planning—A process to set an organization's long-range goals and identify the actions needed to reach the goals.

substitute quality characteristic—A producer's view/expression of what constitutes quality in a product or service.

subsystem—A combination of sets, groups, and so on, that performs an operational function within a system and its major subdivision of the system.

supply chain—The series of processes and/or organizations that are involved in producing and delivering a product to the final user.

surface metrology—May be broadly defined as the measurement of the difference between what the surface actually is and what it is intended to be. It may involve other terms such as *surface roughness* and *surface finish*.

SWOT analysis—An assessment of an organization's key strengths, weaknesses, opportunities, and threats. It considers factors such as the organization's industry, competitive position, functional areas, and management.

system—A composite of equipment and skills, and techniques capable of performing or supporting an operational role, or both. A complete system includes all equipment, related facilities, material, software, services, and personnel required for its operation and support to the degree that it can be considered self-sufficient in its intended operating environment.

T

team—A group of two or more people who are equally accountable for the accomplishment of a purpose and specific performance goals; also defined as a small number of people with complementary skills who are committed to a common purpose.

team building—The process of transforming a group of people into a team and developing the team to achieve its purpose.

testing—A means of determining the capability of an item to meet specified requirements by subjecting the item to a set of physical, chemical, environmental, or operating actions and conditions.

timekeeper—A member of a team who monitors progress against a predefined schedule during meetings.

traceability, gauge—A process intended to quantify measurement uncertainty in relation to national standards. Evidence of gauge traceability typically consists of certificates and reports on calibration.

traceability, product—The ability to trace the history, application, or location of an item or activity and like items or activities by means of recorded identification.

traceability system, product—A formal set of procedures, usually implemented in a computerized database, that allows the manufacturer of a unit to trace it and its components back to the source.

treatment—A combination of the versions (levels) of each of the factors assigned to an experimental unit.

true quality characteristic—A customer's view/expression of what constitutes quality in a product or service.

type I error—The incorrect decision that a process is unacceptable when, in fact, perfect information would reveal that it is located within the zone of acceptable processes.

type II error—The incorrect decision that a process is acceptable when, in fact, perfect information would reveal that it is located within the zone of rejectable processes.

V

value—The net difference between customer-perceived benefits and burdens, sometimes expressed as a ratio of benefits to burdens or a ratio of worth to cost.

variables data—Data resulting from the measurement of a parameter or a variable. The resulting measurements may be recorded on a continuous scale. (Contrasted to *attributes data*.)

W

work breakdown structure (WBS)—A project management technique by which a project is divided into tasks, subtasks, and units of work to be performed.

work group—A group composed of people from one functional area who work together on a daily basis and whose goal is to manage and improve the processes of their function.

References

AIAG (Automotive Industry Action Group). 2010. *Measurement Systems Analysis Reference Manual*, 4th ed. Detroit, MI: AIAG.

Andersen, B., and T. Fagerhaug. 2006. *Root Cause Analysis*, 2nd ed. Milwaukee: ASQ Quality Press.

ANSI (American National Standards Institute). 2002. ANSI Z540-1-1994 (Revised 2002), *American National Standard for Calibration: Calibration Laboratories and Measuring and Test Equipment (General Requirements)*. Boulder, CO: ANSI.

———. 2009. ANSI Y14.5M-2009, *Dimensioning and Tolerancing*. New York: ASME.

ANSI/ASME (American National Standards Institute/American Society of Mechanical Engineers). 1985. ANSI/ASME B89.1.12M-1985, *Methods for Performance Evaluation of Coordinate Measuring Machines*. New York: ASME.

ANSI/ASME (American National Standards Institute/American Society of Mechanical Engineers). 1997. ANSI/ASME B89.4.1-1997, *Methods for Performance Evaluation of Coordinate Measuring Machines*. New York: ASME.

———. 2004. ANSI/ASME B89.4.22-2004, *Methods for Performance Evaluation of Articulated Arm Coordinate Measuring Machines (CMM)*. New York: ASME.

———. 2008. B89.4.10360.2-2008, *Acceptance Test and Reverification Test for Coordinate Measuring Machines (CMMs) Part 2: CMMs Used for Measuring Linear Dimensions* (Technical Report).

———. 2009. ANSI/ASME B46.1-2009, *Surface Texture (Surface Roughness, Waviness, and Lay)*. New York: ASME.

ANSI/ISO/ASQ (American National Standards Institute/International Organization for Standardization/American Society for Quality). 2005. ANSI/ISO/ASQ Q9000-2005, *Quality management systems—Fundamentals and vocabulary*. Milwaukee: ASQ Quality Press.

———. 2008. ANSI/ISO/ASQ QE19011S-2008, *Guidelines for Management Systems Auditing*. Milwaukee: ASQ Quality Press.

ANSI/NCSL (American National Standards Institute/National Conference of Standards Laboratories). 2006. ANSI/NCSL Z540.3-2006, *Requirements for the Calibration of Measuring and Test Equipment*. Boulder, CO: NCSLI.

Arter, D. 2003. *Quality Audits for Improved Performance*, 3rd ed. Milwaukee: ASQ Quality Press.

ASQ and the Automotive Industry Action Group (Chrysler, Ford, and General Motors Corporations), (February, 1995). "Potential Failure Modes and Effects Analysis," Automotive Industry Action Group; Milwaukee, WI.

ASQ Quality Audit Division. 20145. J.P. Russell, ed. *The ASQ Auditing Handbook*, 4th ed. Milwaukee: ASQ Quality Press.

ASQ Statistics Division. 1996. *Glossary and Tables for Statistical Quality Control*, 3rd ed. Milwaukee: ASQ Quality Press.

———. 2004. *Glossary and Tables for Statistical Quality Control*, 4th ed. Milwaukee: ASQ Quality Press.

ASQ (August, 2018) "What is Root Cause Analysis (RCA). Retrieved fro: http://asq.org/learn-about-quality.

ASQC (American Society for Quality Control). 1996. *Specification of General Requirements for a Quality Program.* American national standard. Milwaukee: ASQ Quality Press.

ASTM (American Society for Testing and Materials). 1977. *ASTM Standards on Precision and Accuracy for Various Applications,* 1st ed. Philadelphia: ASTM.

Barrentine, L. 2003. *Concepts for R&R Studies.* 2nd ed. Milwaukee, WI: ASQ Quality Press.

Bennett, K., and H. Zion. 2005. *Metrology Concepts: Understanding Test Uncertainty Ratio (TUR).* Transwcat white paper. Transcat Calibration & Repair, May.

Berger, R., D. Benbow, A. Elshennawy, and H. F. Walker, eds. 2002. *The Certified Quality Engineer Handbook.* Milwaukee: ASQ Quality Press.

Bosch, J. A. 1984. *66 Centuries of Measurement.* Dayton, Ohio: Sheffield Measurement Division.

Bosch, J. A. 1995. *Coordinate Measuring Machines and Systems.* New York: Marcel Dekker.

Brassard, M., and D. Ritter. 1994. *The Memory Jogger II.* Methuen, MA: Goal/QPC.

Breyfogle, F., (1999). *Implementing Six Sigma: Smarter Solutions Using Six Sigma,* John Wiley & Sons Publisher, New York.

Bucher, J. 2012. *The Metrology Handbook,* 2nd ed. Milwaukee: ASQ Quality Press.

———. 2006. *The Quality Calibration Handbook: Developing and Managing a Calibration Program.* Milwaukee: ASQ Quality Press.

Burke, S. and R. Silvestrini, eds. 202017. *The Certified Quality Engineer Handbook.* Milwaukee: ASQ Quality Press.

Busch, T., Harlow, R. and Thompson, R. 1989. *Fundamentals of Dimensional Metrology,* 2nd ed. Albany, New York: Delmar Publishers

Curtis, M. 2010. *Handbook of Dimensional Measurement*, 5th ed. New York: Industrial Press.

Darmody, W. J. 1967. "Elements of a Generalized Measuring System." In *Handbook of Industrial Metrology.* Englewood Cliffs, NJ: Prentice-Hall (ASTME).

de Silva, G. M. S. 2002. *Basic Metrology for ISO 9000 Certification.* Woburn, MA: Butterworth-Heinemann.

Deming, W. E. 1986. *Out of the Crisis.* Cambridge, MA: MIT Center for Advanced Engineering.

Department of Defense, (November, 1980). Procedures For Performing A Failure Mode, Effects, And Criticality Analysis, @ General Accounting Office Technical Library; Washington, DC.

Devor, R. E., T. Chang, and J. W. Sutherland. 2006. *Statistical Quality Design and Control,* 2nd ed. Upper Saddle River, NJ: Prentice Hall.

Dorris, A. L., and B. L. Foote. 1978. "Inspection Errors and Statistical Quality Control: A Survey." *AIIE Transactions* 10, no. 2: 184–92.

Dotson, C. 2006. *Fundamentals of Dimensional Metrology.* Albany, NY: Delmar.

Dotson, C., R. Harlow, and R. Thompson. 2003. *Fundamentals of Dimensional Metrology,* 3rd ed. New York: Delmar.

Dovich, R. 1992. "Acceptance Sampling." In *Quality Engineering Handbook.* T. Pyzdek and R. Berger, eds. Milwaukee: ASQC Quality Press and New York: Marcel-Dekker.

Elshennawy, A. K., I. Ham, and P. H. Cohen. 1988. "Evaluating the Performance of Coordinate Measuring Machines." *ASQ Quality Progress* 21, no. 1: 59–65.

Elshennawy, A. K. and Weheba, G. S. 2015. *Manufacturing Processes and Materials,* 5th ed. Dearborn, MI: Society of Manufacturing Engineers.

Farrago, F. T. 1994. *Handbook of Dimensional Measurement*, 3rd ed. New York: Industrial Press.

Frankhauser, D. 2003. *Spectrophotometer Use*. Batavia, OH: University of Cincinnati.

Galyer, J. F. W., and C. R. Shotbolt. 1964. *Metrology for Engineers*. London: Cassell & Company.

Hocken, R. J., and P. H. Pereira, eds. 2011. *Coordinate Measuring Machines and Systems*. Boca Raton: FL: CRC Press.

Hull, B. and John, V. 1988. *Non-Destructive Testing*. New York: Springer-Verlag.

IBM (International Business Machines Corporation). 1986. *Process Control, Capability and Improvement*. Thornwood, NY: The Quality Institute.

ISO (International Organization for Standardization). 1993. *International vocabulary of basic and general terms in metrology*, 2nd ed. Geneva: ISO.

———. 2003.10012:2003, *Measurement management systems—Requirements for measurement processes and measuring equipment*. Geneva: ISO.

———. 2005. ISO 17025:2005, *General requirements for the competence of testing and calibration laboratories*. Geneva: ISO.

———. 2007. ISO Guide 99: *International vocabulary of metrology—Basic and general concepts and associated terms* (VIM). Geneva: ISO.

ISO TC 135/SC 2. 1984. ISO 3453: Non-destructive Testing—Liquid Penetrant Inspection. Geneva: ISO.

ISO TC 135/SC 2. 1984. ISO 3452: Non-destructive Testing—Penetrant Inspection— General Principles. Geneva: ISO.

ISO TC 135/SC 3. 2002. ISO 12710: Non-destructive Testing—Ultrasonic Inspection. Geneva: ISO.

Defeo, J., 2017. *Juran's Quality Handbook: The Complete Guide to Performance Excellence*, 7th ed.. New York: McGraw-Hill.

Ketola, J., and K. Roberts. 2009. *Correct! Prevent! Improve!: Driving Improvement Through Problem Solving and Preventive Action*. Milwaukee: ASQ Quality Press.

Kimothi, S. K. 2002. *The Uncertainty of Measurements: Physical and Chemical Metrology Impact and Analysis*. Milwaukee: ASQ Quality Press.

Kolarik, W. 1995. *Creating Quality: Concepts, Systems, Strategies, and Tools*. New York: McGraw-Hill.

Konz, S., G. Peterson, and A. Joshi. 1982. "Reducing Inspection Errors." *Quality Progress* 14, no. 7: 24–26.

Machinability Data Center. 1980. *Machining Data Handbook*. Cincinnati, OH: TechSolve.

Mack, D. A. 1976. "Instrumentation Calibration." Workshop conference on the management of laboratory instruments. Cairo, Egypt, November 7–11. (Conference proceedings collected in a work titled *Management Systems for Laboratory Instrument Services*. Research Triangle Park, NC: Instrument Society of America.)

McNish, A. 1967. "The Nature of Measurement." In *Handbook of Industrial Metrology*. Englewood Cliffs, NJ: Prentice Hall.

NASA (National Aeronautics and Space Administration). 2010. *Measurement Uncertainty Analysis: Principles and Methods*. NASA Measurement Quality Assurance Handbook. Washington, D.C.: NASA.

———. 2010. *Measuring and Test Equipment Specifications*. NASA Measurement Quality Assurance Handbook. Washington, D.C.: NASA.

NIST (National Institute of Standards and Technology). 1981. Special Publication 304A. Gaithersburg, MD: U.S. Department of Commerce.

Okes, D. 2009. *Root Cause Analysis: The Core of Problem Solving and Corrective Action*. Milwaukee: ASQ Quality Press.

Palady, P., (1997). *Failure Modes And Effects Analysis: Practical Applications*, Library of Congress; Ann Arbor, MI.

Patterson, K., J. Grenny, R. McMillan, and A. Switzler. 2011. *Crucial Conversations: Tools for Talking When Stakes Are High.* New York: McGraw-Hill.

Paxton, K., (May, 1996). Corrective Action In The Real World, *Quality Progress*, 29, 5, p184.

Pennella, R. 2004. *Managing the Metrology System.* Milwaukee: ASQ Quality Press.

Pronovost, D. 2000. *Internal Quality Auditing.* Milwaukee: ASQ Quality Press.

Puncochar, D. 2010. *Interpretation of Geometric Dimensioning and Tolerancing,* 3rd ed. New York: Industrial Press.

Raz, T. 1992. "Inspection." In *Quality Engineering Handbook.* T. Pyzdek and R. Berger, eds. Milwaukee: ASQC Quality Press and New York: Marcel Dekker.

Reason, R. E. 1960. *The Measurement of Surface Texture.* London: CleaverHume Press.

Rice, G. O. 1976. "Measurement Systems and the Standards Laboratory." Conference on the management of laboratory instruments. Cairo, Egypt, November 7–11.

———. 1986. "Metrology." In *Quality Management Handbook.* L. Walsh, R. Wurster, and R. J. Kimber, eds. Milwaukee: ASQC Quality Press and New York: Marcel Dekker.

Robinson, J., (March, 1997). Integrate Quality Cost Concepts Into Teams Problem Solving Efforts, *Quality Progress*, 30, 3, p25.

Rodríguez-Pérez, J. 2011. *CAPA for the FDA-Regulated Industry.* Milwaukee: ASQ Quality Press.

Russell, J.P. 2010. *The Process Auditing and Techniques Guide,* 2nd ed. Milwaukee: ASQ Quality Press.

Schrader, G. F., and A. K. Elshennawy. 2000. *Manufacturing Processes and Materials,* 4th ed. Dearborn, MI: Society of Manufacturing Engineers.

Simpson, J. A. 1981. "Foundations of Metrology." *Journal of Research of the National Bureau of Standards* 86, no. 3 (May/June): 36–42.

Spragg, R. C. 1976. "Advanced System for the Measurement of Errors of Form." SME Paper No. IQ 76-807.

Stematis, D., (1995). *Failure Mode And Effect Analysis: FMEA Theory To Execution,* ASQ Press; Milwaukee, WI.

Stephens, K. 2000. *The Handbook of Applied Acceptance Sampling: Plans, Procedures, and Principles.* Milwaukee: ASQ Quality Press.

Surface Engineering Forum. "Hardness Testing." Accessed February 2008. http://www.gordonengland.co.uk/hardness/.

Taylor, C., (March, 1998). Preventive Vs. Corrective Action: The Horse, The Barn, And The Apple, *Quality Progress*, 31, 3, p66.

Taylor, M., (February, 1998). A Systematic Approach To Quality Improvement: The Interactions Between The Technical, Human, snd Quality Systems, *Total Quality Management*, 9, 1, p79.

United States Food and Drug Administration (August, 2018) Corrective and Preventive Action (CAPA). Retrieved from: https://www.fda.gov/icei/inspectionguides.

Vogt, T. 1980. *Optimizing Calibration Recall Intervals and Algorithms.* Gaithersburg, MD: National Institute of Standards and Technology Press.

Walker, F., D. Benbow, A. Elshennawy, M. M. Vaughn and B. Gupta. 2018. *The Certified Quality Inspector Handbook,* 3rd ed. Milwaukee: ASQ Quality Press.

Wilson, P., L. Dell, and G. Anderson. 1993. *Root Cause Analysis: A Tool for Total Quality Management.* Milwaukee: ASQ Quality Press.

Wunchell, W. 1996. *Inspection and Measurement in Manufacturing.* Dearborn, MI: Society of Manufacturing Engineers.

Zipin, R. B. 1971. "Dimensional Measurements and Standards in Manufacturing." *Bendix Technical Journal* 1, no. 4: 15–19.

Index

A

acceptable quality level (AQL), 187
acceptance sampling, 186, 187–189
accuracy, 104
affinity diagramming, 55
air gauge principles, *136f*
air gauges, 135
air instruments, 102
air or pneumatic metrology, 102
American Society for Testing and Materials (ASTM), 137
analysis of variance (ANOVA), 43
Andersen, Bjorn, 196, 217
angle measurement tools, 146
ANSI/ASQ Z1.4-2008 standard, 191
ANSI/ASQ Z1.9-2008 standard, 193
appraisal costs, 7
ASQ code of ethics, 57–58
assignable cause variability, 152–153
attributes charts, 88–91
attributes sampling plans, 190–192
auditors, sources of, 201–202
audits
    communication tools, 213–215
    components, 202–207
    sampling plans, 211–212
    tools and techniques, 207–213
    types and terminology, 199–202
authorization source, identification of, 203–204
automated in-line inspection methods, 148
average, defined, 61
average outgoing quality (AOQ), 188
average outgoing quality limit (AOQL), 188
average quality protection sampling, 184
averages chart, 17–19

B

back-pressure gauges, 135
backward tracing, 211
balances and scales, 137
batch-and-queue process flow, 53
benchmarking, 57
Berger, R. D., 247
between-treatment variation, 42
bevel protractors, 147
bimodal histograms, 70–71
binomial distribution, 67
binomial formula, 68
black belts, 46
blueprint, defined, 161
blueprints
    geometric dimensioning and tolerancing, 162–166
    product defect characteristics, 166–167
    symbols and components, 161
brainstorming, 56
Brassard, M., 196
bridge-type configuration, 126
Brinell hardness test, 138, 183

C

calibration (M&TE), 152–155
calibration error, 156–157
calibration hierarchy of standards, 157–159
calibration intervals, 153–155
calibration results, 155–156
calipers, 105–106
cantilever CMM, 129
cantilever configuration, 126
capability ratio, 92, 94
cause-and-effects diagrams, 8–9, *34f*

c-charts, 90
central tendency, measures of, 20, 69–71
Certified Quality Tech (CTQ) Body of
    Knowledge, 249
certificates of compliance and analysis,
    179–180
checklists, audit, 208–209, *210f, 213f*
check sheets, 11–12
closure, audit, 207
color guides, 148
color measurement tools, 148
column-type configuration, 127
combinations, 79–80
combination sets, 147
common-cause variation, 94–96
common gauges, 113
comparators, 119, 121
complementation rule, 76
composite gauges, 115
computer-assisted CMM, 127
conditional probability, 77–78
confidence coefficient, 73–74
confidence intervals, 74
confidence levels, 73–74
confidence limits, 74–75
conformance status, determination of, 194
consumer's risk, 156, 187
contacting probes, 130
contact instruments, 102
contingency tables, 76–77
continuation of inspection, 191
continuous improvement techniques
    benchmarking, 57
    brainstorming, 56
    plan-do-check-act (PDCA) cycle, 55–56
control charts, 16–20
    attributes charts, 87–92
    constants for, 260
common variation, 94–97
control limits
    data plotting, 97–99
    formulas, 259
    process capability measures, 92–94
    special-cause variation, 94–97
    variables charts, 83–87
    vs. specification limits, 82–83
conversion measurements, 175–176
coordinate measuring machines (CMM),
    124–126, 126–132
COQ (cost of quality), 6–8
corrective and preventive action (CAPA),
    217, 233

correlation, statistical, 87
cost of quality (COQ), 6–8
C_{pk} and C_p, calculation, 92–94
crash testing, 182
critical-to-quality (CTQ) flow-down, 49, *50f*
customers, defined, 1
customer satisfaction, 1–2
customer-supplied M&TE, 151–152

D

data analysis, audit, 206
data collection, audit, 206
data plotting, 97–99
datuming process, 129
defect, defined, 66
defective, defined, 66, 67
defectives, charting, 88
degrees, 146–147
Deming cycle, 55
design FMEA, 225, *230f, 231f, 232f*
design for manufacture and assembly
    (DFMA), 3
design of experiments (DOE), 3, 39–42
destructive testing techniques, 182
dial indicators, 121
differential gauges, 135
digital calipers, 108
digital micrometers, 110
digital readout (DRO), 124
dimensional metrology, 102
direct computer-controlled CMM, 127
discrete distributions, 66, 67
dispersion, measures of, 71–72
disposition, of nonconforming material, 247
dividing heads, 147
DMAIC, 46–49
documentation, audit, 207
DOE (design of experiments), 3
double-end gauges, 113
double sampling plans, 190

E

eddy current testing, 181
8D (eight disciplines)
    final reports, *32f*
    interim actions, 26
    permanent corrective actions, 27
    planning and, 25
    preventive measures, 27

problem definition and description, 26
problem-solving process, 24–25
root causes and escape points, 26–27, 35
team congratulations, 27–28
teams for, 25–26
working documents, *28f, 29f, 31f, 34f*
electrical metrology, 102
electric limit gauges, 133
electron beam metrology, 102
electronic gauges, 133–135
episcopic projection, 123
equipment limitations, 104
equipment traceability, 150
error, main classifications of, 104
ethical dilemmas, 58–59
exit meetings, audit, 206
expected value, 61
external audits, 201
external customers, 1
external failure costs, 7
external measuring snap gauges, 115

F

Fagerhaug, Tom, 196, 217
failure mode or cause, 224
failure modes and effects analysis (FMEA), 3
action based on RPN, 223–224
basic steps, 222
design and process examples, 234,
    235f, 236f
inputs TO, 221
mode or cause, 224
other quality tools, 221
outputs, 221–222
planning, 219–220
potential failure risks, 223
risk components, 223
RPN components, 223
single-point responsibility, 220
standard selection, 219
team members, 220
types, 225–226
fatigue testing, 182
federal accuracy grade 1 blocks, 122
first-party audits, 202
fishbone diagrams, 8
5S tool, 52–53
Five Whys analysis, 22–24
fixed bridge configuration, 126
fixed gauges, 113
flammability testing, 182

flaws, defined, 140
flow, 53
flowcharts (process maps), 10–11
flow gauges, 135
flow processes, 53
flush pin gauges, 118
force field analysis, 55
force measurement tools, 146
forward tracing, 211
fractional factorial designs, 44–46
frequency distribution, 20–21
frequency histograms, 21
functional gauges, 118
functionality testing, 183

G

gauge allowance, 119
gauge blocks, 122–123
gauges
    classes, 112–113
    classes of, 112–113
    common, 113–114
    and comparators, 119–121
    flush pin, 118
    functional, 118
    go/no-go, 113
    indicating, 119–121
    inspection, 113
    maintenance, handling, and storage, 151
    mechanical indicating, 121
    reference, 113
    repeatability and reproducibility, 153
    ring, 114–115
    screw pitch, 116
    sizes of, 118
    snap, 115
    special, 116
    spline, 115
    templates, 115
    tolerances, 119
    uses and applications, 148, 148–*150f*
    working, 112–113
gantry-type configuration, 127
gauging, defined, 180
general addition rule, 76
general multiplication rule, 78
geometric dimensioning and tolerancing,
    162–166
grade 1 blocks, 122
green belts, 46

H

hand tools, 105
hardness testing, 183
hardness testing equipment, 138
helium, 144
hierarchy of standards, 157–159
histograms, 20–21, 62–63
horizontal-arm configuration, 127

I-J

impact testing, 182
I-MR (individuals and moving range)
    charts, 87
indicating gauges, 119, 121
individuals and moving range (I-MR)
    charts, 87
inductance-bridge transducers, 133
initiation of inspection, 191
in-line inspection methods, 148
inspection, defined, 167
inspection concepts
    certificates of compliance and analysis,
        179–180
    conversion measurements, 175–176
    gauge selection, 169–170
inspection error, 178–179
inspection gauges, 113
inspection points, 176–178
    measurement systems analysis, 171–174
    measurement types, 168–169
    product traceability, 179
    rounding rules, 174
    uses of, 167–168
inspection techniques and processes,
        180–183, 180–184
interactions, 43–44
internal audits, 201
internal customers, 1
internal failure costs, 7
International Organization of Legal
    Metrology (OIML), 138
interviewing techniques, 213–214
in-treatment variation, 42
Ishikawa diagrams, 8
ISO (International Organization for
    Standardization), 138

K

kanban systems, 51
Kolarik, W., 196

L

laboratory master blocks, 122
laser scanning probes, 132
lay, defined, 140
layout instruments, 147
Lean
    5S tool, 52–53
    CTQ flow-down diagram, *50f*
    flow, 53
    kanban systems, 51
    pull systems, 52
    value stream maps, 54
legal measurement, 103
levels of inspection, 191
light-wave interference principle, 144, *145f*
light wave metrology, 102
limit gauges, 113
linear measuring devices, 112
linear variable displacement transformer
    transducers, 133
liquid penetration testing, 181
listening skills, 214
locating devices, 147
lot-by-lot sampling, 184
lot tolerance percent defective (LTPD), 187
L-shaped bridge configuration, 127

M

magnetic particle testing, 181
margin of error, 74–75
mass, measuring, 137
master black belts, 46
master blocks, 122
master gauges, 113
match gauging, 135
material review process, 195–196
mean, defined, 61, 69–70
measurement, concepts in, 103
measurement, defined, 103
measurement and test equipment (M&TE)
    accuracy, 104
    angle measurement tools, 146
    automated in-line inspection
        methods, 148
    calibration error, 156
    calibration of, 152–155
    color measurement tools, 148
    concepts in measurement, 103
    coordinate measuring machines, 124
    customer-supplied, 151–152
    electronic measuring equipment, 133–136

force measurement tools, 146
gauge repeatability and reproducibility, 153
gauge uses and applications, 148
gauges, 112
hand tools, 105
hardness testing equipment, 138
hierarchy of standards, 157
identification, control, and maintenance of, 150–151
measurement error, 103–104
optical tools, 123
overview, 101
precision, 104
repeatability and reproducibility, 104–105
roughness reference standards, 143
surface analyzers, 142
surface plate methods and equipment, 139
weights, balances, and scales, 137
measurement classes, 103
measurement error, 103–104
measurement systems analysis, 171–174
mechanical dividing heads, 147
mechanical indicating gauges, 121
mechanical measurement, 183
mechanical metrology, 102
median, defined, 70
median chart, 86
metrology, defined, 102
microhardness testing, 184
micrometer calipers, 111–112
micrometers, 108–110
mode, defined, 70
moving bridge CMM, 129
multidimension gauge, 135
multiple sampling plans, 191
multiplication rule, 78
multisensor coordinate measuring machines, 131–132

N

National Institute of Standards and Technology (NIST), 137
Newton's law, 137
nonconforming materials
defined, 194
identifying and segregating, 194–195
material review process, 195–197
nonconforming product, 66
nonconforming unit, defined, 194
nonconformity, 66
noncontacting sensors, 131
nondestructive testing, 180, 181
nonlimit gauges, 113
normal distribution, 64, 65, 82, 261
np-charts, 90

O

objective evidence, 211
OC (operating characteristic) curve, 185
100% inspection, 186–187
one-piece flow, 53
opening meetings, audit, 206
operator error, 104
optical comparators, 123
optical dividing heads, 147
optical flats, 144
optical tools, 123
out-of-calibration effects, 156

P

parameters, 62
Pareto charts, 13–14
p-charts, 88–90
PDCA (plan-do-check-act-) cycle, 55–56
permutations, 81
physical measurement, 183
plot analysis, visual, 98
plug gauges, 113
pneumatic metrology, 102
Poisson distribution, 69
population mean, 61–62
populations, defined, 61
precision, 104
prevention costs, 6–7
probability, 61, 75–80
problem-solving techniques
8D (eight disciplines), 24–36
Five Whys analysis, 22–24
Six Sigma, 36
procedural guidelines, audit, 212, *213f*
process audits, 200
process capability measures, 92–93
process environment error, 104
process FMEA, 225, *230f, 233f*
process maps (flowcharts), 10–11
process variation, 4–5
producer's risk, 156, 187
product audits, 200

product defect characteristics, 166–167
product design, 3–4
product traceability, 179
profile, defined, 140
progressive gauges, 113
progressive plug gauges, 113
pull systems, 52

Q

QFD (quality function deployment)
    matrix, 36–39, *37f, 38f*
quality audits
    communication tools, 213–215
    components, 202–207
    tools and techniques, 207–213
    types and terminology, 199–202
quality concepts
    cost of quality (COQ), 6–8
    customers and suppliers, 1–2
    principles for products and processes,
        2–5
    standards, requirements, and
        specifications, 5–6
quality principles for products and
    processes, 2–5
quality standards, requirements, and
    specifications, 5–6
quality tools
    cause-and-effects diagrams, 8–9
    check sheets, 11–12
    control charts, 16–20
    flowcharts (process maps), 10–11
    histograms, 20–21
    Pareto charts, 13–14
    quantitative, 210–211
    scatter diagrams, 15–16

R

random errors, 103
rectifying inspection, 186
reference gauges, 113
repeatability and reproducibility, 104–105
ring gauges, 114–115
risk assessment and management
    action based on RPN, 223–224
    basic FMEA steps, 222
    corrective action, 233–234
    design and process FMEA, 226–233

design and process FMEA examples,
    234, *235f, 236f*
    FMEA and other quality tools, 221
    FMEA caution, 234
    FMEA inputs, 221
    FMEA outputs, 221–222
    FMEA planning, 219–220
    FMEA standard selection, 219
    FMEA team, 220
    FMEA types, 225–226
    mode or cause, 224
    potential failure, 223
    risk components, 223
    single-point responsibility, 220
risk priority numbers (RPN), 223, 233–234
Ritter, D., 196
Rockwell hardness test, 138, 183
root cause analysis
    8D protocol and, 36
    CAPA and, 217
    corrective action, 238–242
    defined, 237
    investigation of, 196
    nonconforming material identification,
        245–246
    nonconforming material review process,
        246–247
    preventive action, 242–245
Root Cause Analysis (Andersen and
    Fagerhaug), 217
roughness, *141f,* 143–148
rounding rules, 174
run charts, 16–17

S

sample, defined, 61
sampling
    characteristics, 184–185
    selection from lots, 190–193
    types, 186–189
scatter diagrams, 15–16
scientific measurement, 103
screw pitch gauges, 116
screw thread micrometers, 115
second-party audits, 202
service delivery FMEA, 225
Shewhart, Walter, 55
simple tools, 147
sine bars, 147
single sampling plans, 190

Six Sigma
   design of experiments, 39–42
   DMAIC, 46–49
   fractional factorial designs, 44–46
   interactions, 43–44
   main effects, 42–43
   overview, 36–38
   projects, 46
   QFD matrix, 36–39
   quality function deployment (QFD)
      matrix, 36–38
skid/skidless gauges, 142, *143f*
snap gauges, 115
software testing and verification, 183
sorting, 186
SPC (statistical process control), 62
special addition rule, 76
special-cause variability, 94–96, 152–153
special gauges, 116
specification limits, 82–83
spectrophotometers, 148
spline gauges, 115
spread, defined, 71
standard deviation, 71–73
standard normal curve, 64–65, 257
standards, requirements, and
      specifications, 5–6
statistical correlation, 87
statistical process control (SPC), 62
statistical techniques
   attributes charts, 88
   calculations, 69–81
   common and special cause variation, 94
   confidence levels, 73–74
   confidence limits, 74–75
   control charts, 82–99
   control limits vs. specification limits, 82
   data plotting, 97
   frequency distributions, 62–69
   general concepts, 61–68
   measures of central tendency, 69–71
   measures of dispersion, 71–73
   probability, 75–82
   process capability measures, 92
   terminology, 61
statistics, defined, 61
steel rules, 105
supplier–customer relationships, 1–2
suppliers, defined, 1
surface analyzers, 142
surface characteristics, 140

surface finish, measurement of, 142
surface gauge, 140
surface metrology, 140
surface plate methods and equipment, 139
surface quality specifications, 140
switching rules, for sampling, 191–192
systematic errors, 103
system audits, 200
system FMEA, 225

T

technical measurement, 103
templates, 115
tensile testing, 182
tensiometers, 146
tension testing, 182
testing, defined, 180
third-party audits, 202
thread plug gauges, 115
thread snap gauges, 115
time-related graphs, 98
tolerances, gauge, 119
torque wrenches, 146
total failure cost, 7
total quality costs, 7–8
touch trigger probes, 130
traceability, equipment, 150–151
transfer-type linear measuring devices, 112

U

u-charts, 90
ultrasonic testing, 181

V

value stream maps, 54
variable inductance, 133
variables charts, 83–87
variables sampling plans, 189, 193
variable transformers, 133
variation, defined, 71
venturi gauges, 135
vernier calipers, 105–107
vernier height gauge, 108
vernier micrometer caliper, 110
Vickers hardness test, 184
Vickers pyramid number, 184
voice of the customer (VOC), 36

W

waste categories, 50–51
wear allowance, 119
weights, balances, and scales, 137–138
working papers, audit, 206, 209

X-Y

X and R chart, 19
x-ray techniques, 181

Z

z, standard normal distribution for
       select values of, 261

WHY ASQ?

ASQ is a global community of people passionate about quality, who use the tools, their ideas and expertise to make our world work better. ASQ: The Global Voice of Quality.

FOR INDIVIDUALS

Advance your career to the next level of excellence.

ASQ offers you access to the tools, techniques and insights that can help distinguish an ordinary career from an extraordinary one.

FOR ORGANIZATIONS

Your culture of quality begins here.

ASQ organizational membership provides the invaluable resources you need to concentrate on product, service and experiential quality and continuous improvement for powerful top-line and bottom-line results.

www.asq.org/why-asq

ASQ
The Global Voice of Quality

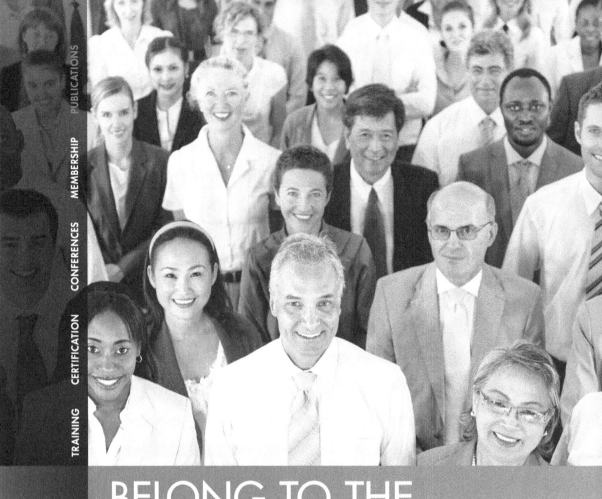

PUBLICATIONS

MEMBERSHIP

CONFERENCES

CERTIFICATION

TRAINING

BELONG TO THE
QUALITY COMMUNITY

JOINING THE ASQ GLOBAL QUALITY COMMUNITY
GIVES YOU A STRONG COMPETITIVE ADVANTAGE.

For people passionate about improvement, ASQ is the global knowledge
network that links the best ideas, tools, and experts — because ASQ has the
reputation and reach to bring together the diverse quality and continuous
improvement champions who are transforming our world.

• 75,000 individual and organizational members in 150 countries

• 250 sections and local member communities

• 25 forums and divisions covering industries and topics

• 30,000+ Quality Resources items, including articles, case studies, research
  and more

• 19 certifications

• 200+ training courses

ASQ
The Global Voice of Qu

For more information, **visit asq.org/communities-networking.**

ASK A LIBRARIAN

Did you know?

Quality Resource contains a wealth of knowledge and information available to ASQ members and non-members.

A librarian is available to answer research requests using ASQ's ever-expanding library of relevant, credible quality resources, including journals, conference proceedings, case studies and Quality Press publications.

ASQ members receive free internal information searches and reduced rates for article purchases.

You can also contact the Quality Information Center to request permission to reuse or reprint ASQ copyrighted material, including journal articles and book excerpts.

For more information or to submit a question, visit asq.org/quality-resources.

ASQ
The Global Voice of Quality